"THE BEST, MOST COMPLETE LOW-SODIUM COOK-BOOK that is on the market today. Because it gives the complete analysis of all the food listed, it is of great value to anyone requiring that information when they are on a strict low sodium diet." —*Ruth Dickie, Chief Dietitian, Wisconsin General Hospital*

"Practical help for thousands of men and women . . . the problem of how to make foods taste good without salt is a very real one, and this book is exceedingly helpful." —*Chicago Tribune*

"Unique . . . the recipes and menus can be used for the whole family." —*The Independent Woman*

ABOUT THE AUTHORS: Alma Smith Payne, a gourmet cook, has for many years been engaged in Heart Association activities. *Dorothy Callahan* is a former research dietitian in the hypertension clinic of Massachusetts General Hospital.

Eating is the first business of a man. If his food is unpleasant to him, his health suffers, his labour is not so productive, his genius deteriorates, and his progeny dwindles and sickens. A healthy digestion, on the other hand, produces a healthy mind, a clear intellect, a vigorous family, and a series of inestimable benefits to generations yet unborn: and how can you have a good digestion, I ask, without a good dinner? and how have a good dinner, without knowing how to cook it?

WILLIAM MAKEPEACE THACKERAY in *Punch*

THE LOW SODIUM, FAT-CONTROLLED COOKBOOK

BY ALMA SMITH PAYNE, M.A.

Former Supervisor, Berkeley (California) Public Schools

and DOROTHY CALLAHAN, B.S.

Former Research Dietitian, Massachusetts General Hospital

with an Introduction by

FRANCIS L. CHAMBERLAIN, M.D., M.SC.D.

Clinical Professor of Medicine, University of California Medical School

A DELL BOOK

Published by DELL PUBLISHING CO., INC.
750 Third Avenue, New York 17, N.Y.

Copyright, © 1953, 1960, by Alma Smith Payne
and Dorothy Callahan

Dell ® TM 681510, Dell Publishing Co., Inc.

Reprinted by arrangement with Little, Brown and
Company, Boston, Mass.

DEDICATION: We dedicate this book to the memory
of Buff, who started it all—and to the
countless other dieters, who inspired us to finish it.

First Dell printing—July, 1963

Printed in U.S.A.

ACKNOWLEDGMENTS

For their help and encouragement in the development and writing of this book, we wish to thank:

FRANCIS L. CHAMBERLAIN, M.D., M.SC.D., Clinical Professor of Medicine, University of California Medical School

DIETARY STAFF AND DIET KITCHEN OF THE MASSACHUSETTS GENERAL HOSPITAL

SUNKIST GROWERS, and especially DR. EDNA SOUTHMAYD and MRS. GERTRUDE AUSTIN, Consumer Service Division and Nutrition Research

CORN PRODUCTS COMPANY, especially HELEN C. HAMILTON, Home Service Department, and NEAL E. ARTZ, PH.D., Assistant to the Director of Research

WILLIAM H. THOMAS, M.D., Assistant Clinical Professor of Medicine, University of California Medical School

HAROLD I. GRIFFEATH, M.D., Assistant Clinical Professor of Medicine, University of California Medical School

RALEIGH H. LAGE, M.D., Assistant Clinical Professor of Medicine, University of California Medical School

BENJAMIN LIEBERMAN, M.D., President, Alameda County Heart Association

MAURICE SOKOLOW, M.D., Chairman of Committee on Low Sodium Diets, San Francisco Heart Association

JOHN LUETSCHER, M.D., for allowing use of facilities of Stanford Medical School laboratories for some of the sodium analyses

JOHN W. FERREE, M.D., Former Associate Medical Director, American Heart Association

MARY ROURKE, Nutrition Consultant, California State Department of Public Health

BETH HEAP, Nutrition Consultant, Heart Disease Control Program, Division of Special Health Services, Department of Health, Education, and Welfare

CALLIE MAE COONS, PH.D., Director, Human Nutrition Research Division, Institute of Home Economics, United States Department of Agriculture

LIDA A. JAMISON, Dietitian, the Chicago Dietetic Supply House, Inc.

MARG, KAY, AND DICK, without whose help this manuscript could not have been completed

MRS. JEAN OLLIKKALA, Typist

MISS EDNA BLACKLEDGE, Typist

UNITED STATES DEPARTMENT OF AGRICULTURE, for the use of its material, especially the following:

> *Composition of Foods,* by Bernice K. Watts, Annabel L. Merrill, and others
>
> *Composition of American Foods Materials,* by C. Chatfield and G. Adams
>
> *Fatty Acid Content of Food Fats,* Home Economics Research Report No. 7, United States Department of Agriculture

AMERICAN HEART ASSOCIATION, for material and reports

CALIFORNIA HEART ASSOCIATION, for various research data and invaluable assistance

ALAMEDA COUNTY HEART ASSOCIATION, for material and reports

LOS ANGELES HEART ASSOCIATION, for material and reports

SAN FRANCISCO HEART ASSOCIATION, for material and reports

SAN JOAQUIN HEART ASSOCIATION, especially GRACE FOWLER, Nutritionist, for material and reports

COUNCIL ON FOODS AND NUTRITION OF THE AMERICAN MEDICAL ASSOCIATION, for information on sodium-restricted products

AGRICULTURAL EXTENSION SERVICE, UNIVERSITY OF CALIFORNIA, for material and assistance, especially for use of the circular *Frozen Desserts,* by Hilda Faust

DAIRY INDUSTRY ADVISORY BOARD, San Francisco, for sodium and fat information for dairy products

NATIONAL CANNERS ASSOCIATION, for suggestions about listing of sodium-restricted foods and permission to use material regarding quick test of water for sodium content

CAMPBELL SOUP COMPANY, for fat content of their products

H. J. HEINZ COMPANY, for fat content of their products

FISHER FLOURING MILLS, for information and analysis of "Ala" and other products

OROWEAT BAKING COMPANY

HOME ADVISORY SERVICE, WINE INSTITUTE, San Francisco, and especially JESSICA MCLACHLIN, for suggestions about use of wine in low sodium cookery and tested recipes

RESEARCH DIVISION, ABBOTT LABORATORIES, for information and research on Calcium Sucaryl

TERMINOLOGY COMMITTEE OF THE FOOD AND NUTRITION DIVISION, AMERICAN HOME ECONOMICS ASSOCIATION, for material from the *Handbook of Food Preparation*, especially the reproduction of the *Baking Chart* and *Oven Temperatures*

SMITHWICK FOUNDATION, for the baking powder formula from the Smithwick Foundation recipe book

TODAY'S HEALTH, for permission to reprint (in Chapter 17) part of an article, "How to Travel with a Bad Heart," by Alma Smith Payne.

Authors and Journals, for permission to use material or tables from the following articles and booklets:

BILLS ET AL, "Sodium and Potassium in Foods and Waters," *J.A.D.A.*, 25:304, April, 1949

PAGE, IRVINE H., and BROWN, HELEN H., *Vegetable Oil Food Pattern and Recipes*, Cleveland Clinic Foundation, Research Division

LUCIA, SALVATORE P., and HUNT, MARJORIE L., "Dietary Sodium and Potassium in California Wines," *American Journal of Digestive Diseases*, 2:26, January, 1957

SOKOLOW, ET AL, "Practical Aspects of the Low Sodium Diet," *California Medicine*, 74:1, January, 1951

The sodium, fat, and caloric values were calculated from the following sources:

Composition of American Foods Materials, by C. CHATFIELD and G. ADAMS

Composition of Foods, by BERNICE K. WATTS, ANNABEL L. MERRILL, and others

Food Values of Portions Commonly Used, by ANNA BOWES and CHARLES CHURCH

The Nutritive Value of Cooked Meat, by RUTH M. LEVERTON and GEORGE V. ODELL

"Sodium and Potassium in Foods and Waters," by CHARLES BILLS and others, *J.A.D.A.*, 25:304, April, 1949

Sodium Restricted Diets, the Rationale, Complications, and Practical Aspects of Their Use, A Report of the Food and Nutrition Board, Publication 325, by C. S. DAVISON and others. Division of Biology and Agriculture, National Research Council

"Dietary Sodium and Potassium in California Wines," by SALVATORE P. LUCIA and MARJORIE L. HUNT, *American Journal of Digestive Diseases*, 2:16, January, 1957

Nutritional Value of Fish in Reference to Atherosclerosis and Current Dietary Research, by CHARLES BUTLER, Commercial Fisheries Review, July, 1958

"Vitamin, Mineral, and Proximate Composition of Frozen Fruits, Juices, and Vegetables," by MARIE BURGER, L. W. HEIN and others, *Agricultural and Food Chemistry*, 4:418, May, 1956

Analyses, by NICOLAS ZENKER, CD.SC.CH., Université de Louvain, Belgium

Analyses, as supplied by commercial firms

CONTENTS

*restrictions at home and crave a little variety—with spe-
cific suggestions on trip-planning, meal-ordering, and getting a doctor away from home.*

*And that's exactly what it is. Some products came to our
attention belatedly and others warranted mention if not
full chapter treatment. We refer to the egg and what to
do with it on this diet—dietetic cheese—Casec, the protein
supplement—Calcium Sucaryl—and other foods. Here are
also some menus for special occasions.*

*Practical hints for the homemaker on how to prepare tasty
meals yet control fat in the diet. Suggestions for all food
classifications with chapters of the main section "in miniature" for your special needs.*

*Here are all the working tools you will need to plan the
sodium- or fat-restricted diet, including the all-important
table for the mathematics-minded reader who must count
those special milligrams of sodium—or grams of total or
saturated fat—every day. Here, too, is a list of some of the
available low sodium products with the names of the con-
cerns manufacturing or handling them—to lighten your
task in the kitchen and to make for more pleasurable eating in the dining room. Sections on foods low and high in
saturated fats, fatty acid content of foods, and other perti-
nent matters.*

INTRODUCTION

By Francis L. Chamberlain, M.D., M.Sc.D., Clinical Professor of Medicine, University of California Medical School; President, American Heart Association, 1958-1959.

SALT CONTROL

Salt (sodium chloride) is one of the most important elements of the human body. Man cannot live without salt in his body fluids and tissues.

Although the value of salt restriction in the treatment of heart disease was commented on more than six hundred years ago (John of Gaddesden), it was not until the turn of the last century that comments began to appear in the medical literature to the effect that salt restriction could be helpful in heart failure. Nevertheless, most physicians relied primarily on restrictions of fluids, rather than of salt, for treatment of heart failure and certain types of kidney disease associated with retention of abnormal amounts of fluid (dropsy) in the body tissues. It wasn't appreciated by most physicians until quite recently that salt restriction was the key to the prevention of dropsy, and that salt (sodium chloride) and, specifically, the sodium part of the sodium chloride, if wisely restricted, would give maximum relief from dropsy and at the same time avoid the distressful thirst which dominated the earlier day treatment.

It is now appreciated that in most types of heart failure the kidneys become unable adequately to excrete sodium from the body, so that it is sometimes accumulated in very large amounts. Sodium in the body, just like salt in the pantry, tends to attract water to it, and holds the water, thus becoming the building stone for the excess fluid which produces the "waterlogging" in dropsical conditions.

It has only become recognized by most physicians in the past fifteen years that the logical way to keep potentially dropsical patients free of excessive accumulations of salt and water is to restrict the sodium intake in the diet to the point where they will have sufficient sodium for their body needs, yet in an amount restricted to the point where it will not accumulate in the body.

Drugs have been developed which contain organic types of mercury (mercurial diuretics) the injection of which temporarily corrects the above mentioned inadequacy of the kidneys and may result in the excretion from the body of large amounts of various salts and water.

More recently, drugs have been developed which can be given orally and which are even more effective than the mercurial diuretics in ridding the body of excess sodium and water. The most valuable of these are the benzothiadiazines (examples—chlorothiazide, flumethiazide, hydrodiuril, esidrix). These drugs have an added advantage of helping to lower excessive blood pressure. The blood pressure lowering effect appears to be only in part due to sodium elimination. Though they may bring dramatic relief from the dropsical condition or from excessive blood pressure, these drugs cannot be administered without some dangers. In some instances sudden lowering of blood pressure may precipitate strokes or coronary heart attacks (coronary thrombosis). Furthermore, in removing excessive sodium from the body, they often remove too much sodium, or they remove needed potassium and chloride from the body, sometimes with grave danger.

The average unrestricted diet contains about 4000 milligrams of sodium. Since salt is about 40 per cent sodium, this means the average unrestricted diet may contain about 10,000 milligrams of sodium chloride. Elimination of salt at the table and elimination of salt-preserved foods and the most highly salted foods will decrease the sodium intake to about 2000 milligrams. The additional help from some of the above mentioned diuretic drugs could decrease the total sodium intake to some figure between 500 and 1500 milligrams—an amount which would be helpful in some conditions requiring only "mild sodium restriction," provided the kidneys were not diseased. We must remember that the daily body needs for sodium vary from 80 to over 2000 milligrams as a very minimum, depending primarily on the integrity of the kidneys. It becomes obvious that diuretics must be used very carefully, if at all, in individuals who have severe kidney disease or who need a dietary restriction to as low as 200 milligrams (as required by some of the diets used in the treatment of hypertension or resistant heart failure). The amount of sodium, then, to be advised in a sodium-restricted diet for a given individual and the question of diuretic supplementation must be decided by the physician.

Dropsical conditions may occur in some types of kidney disease (as in chronic glomerulonephritis) wherein the blood becomes deficient in protein, primarily due to the excretion of protein in the urine (due to kidney damage) in very large amounts. Judicious sodium restriction can be very helpful in minimizing this type of dropsy. However, it is important to understand that diseased kidneys are often unable to hold a proper amount of salt within the body, so that very large quantities of salt may be excreted in urine. Some of these patients may excrete many grams of sodium a day. Obviously, if sodium restriction in any patient is carried out to the point where less sodium is given in the diet than the amount excreted in the urine, the patient will develop abnormally low body sodium which may become irreversible and even lead to death. Early symptoms (weakness, muscle cramps, dry tongue, lethargy) usually act as warnings; but they may be absent, so that blood sodium, potassium, chloride or blood N.P.N. (test for waste products in the blood) may, become necessary for safe continuation of the dietary regimen.

In summary, diuretics continue to improve, but as yet they do not provide a safe universal substitute for sodium restriction in the diet.

Advanced liver disease (cirrhosis) may result in deficiency in blood proteins due to inability of the diseased liver to help with their manufacture in the body, and this may lead to dropsy. Wise restriction of sodium may in these cases help to overcome the inadequacy of the blood proteins so that dropsical conditions may be improved.

Premenstrual swelling, with its associated discomfort, may be minimized or eliminated by restriction of sodum intake the last six or seven days before onset of the menstrual period.

Certain complications of pregnancy, known as toxemia or pre-eclampsia, may also be benefited by sodium restriction. However, in these conditions, the kidneys are usually temporarily damaged (with attendant dangers of heavy sodium excretion) so that caution must again be taken to be sure that too marked a restriction of sodium does not occur.

In 1946, Grollman and Harrison, and later, Kempner, showed that diets *very drastically restricted* in sodium could be very helpful to some patients with severe hypertension. Considerable research is still in progress on this important subject. Ten years' experience with these diets has convinced me that from 30 to 50 per cent of patients with hypertension can be helped markedly by drastic sodium curtailment.

Newly developed drugs such as Rauwolfia derivatives or the previously mentioned benzothiadiazines, especially in combination, control hypertension in most instances. Occasionally they must be supplemented by sodium restriction or by less satisfactory drugs such as hydralizine and "ganglion blockers." Inability to tolerate any of these drugs may make a trial of a very rigid low sodium diet mandatory for blood pressure control.

Low sodium diets should meet the following requirements:

(1) The approximate sodium content should be known and understood by patient and physician. If used in the presence of severe kidney disease, the *exact* sodium content must be known and understood.

(2) The diet *must be palatable* so that the patient will not become discouraged (since it is usually difficult to get a patient to change lifelong habits of eating his favorite foods, unless reasonable substitutes can be found).

(3) The diet *must not be harmful* to the patient. It must not contain a smaller amount of sodium than necessary for the body demands, plus the daily amount of sodium excreted in the urine (because of the resultant dangers of sodium depletion).

(4) It *must not be deficient in protein* (a real danger, since most sources of protein contain relatively large amounts of sodium).

(5) It *must contain sufficient vitamins and minerals* (all of which are apt to become deficient on low sodium diet). It is recommended that diets be supplemented by a concentrated vitamin preparation low in sodium. Your physician should be called on to make the specific recommendation, since there are many satisfactory preparations on the market.

The authors have met these criteria in a very satisfactory manner. They have made an exhaustive search for reliable analyses of sodium in various foods, and they have conducted sodium analyses to cover essential foods whose previous sodium content had not been determined. They have provided practical information about the handling of various foods necessary in this diet, along with numerous easy-to-follow recipes. They have provided figures as to the sodium content of the various menus so that these can be used easily for patients whose physicians have advised them to use the "count method." They have repeatedly insisted that *these diets cannot be used with benefit and safety except through a physician who understands the patient's diagnosis*—the status of the patient's heart, blood vessels, and kidneys—and whose observations will protect his patient from the dangers of abnormally low body sodium.

So used, this book would become a *manual for home use*—with space provided for *additions and deletions to be inserted by the physician.*

FAT CONTROL

It is now well recognized that blood cholesterol levels in man can be satisfactorily lowered by controlling the fat content of the diet.

Evidence showing a relationship between elevated blood cholesterol and atherosclerosis continues to accumulate rapidly.

Atherosclerosis (hardening of the arteries) interferes with the blood supply of the major arteries. It causes, especially, coronary heart disease and strokes, and thus is responsible for about three-fourths of all heart·disease deaths. Heart diseases now cause about 54 per cent of all deaths in the United States.

While pointing out that all the facts about the causes of atherosclerosis are not known, let us review some of the evidence suggesting a relationship between elevated blood cholesterol and atherosclerosis. Most patients with coronary diseases have blood cholesterol levels between 240 and 280 mgm./100 cc. Men in the first four years of the Framingham, Massachusetts, study are four times as likely to develop coronary heart disease if their blood cholesterol level is above 260. All diseases characterized by high blood cholesterol (diabetes, nephrosis, xanthomatosis and hyperthyroidism) show high predisposition to atherosclerosis. Populations with low blood cholesterol averages have much less tendency to atherosclerosis and vice versa. Migratory changes resulting in increased average cholesterol levels (for example, Japanese to Hawaii and to Los Angeles) are associated with increased susceptibility to atherosclerosis.

Of course the cholesterol concentration in the blood is not the sole factor in the production of atherosclerosis. Fat in the body is transported in large protein molecules which also contain phosphorus and cholesterol. In order to find out about our blood fats, one can determine the relative amount of *alpha* and *beta* lipoproteins in the blood or the amount of blood cholesterol. The latter is so much simpler to determine and so much less expensive that most physicians use the cholesterol determination as an index of fats in the blood.

Moreover, atherosclerosis cannot be produced experimentally in animals without elevating blood cholesterol levels. Reduction of these elevated blood cholesterol levels in animals results in reversal of the atherosclerosis.

Evidence continues to accumulate suggesting that population groups whose diet is high in fat and especially animal fat (such as ours in the United States) have high blood cholesterol levels and high incidence of atherosclerosis. Decreased fat content of the diet in some of the European countries in World War II was followed by decreased incidence of reported atherosclerosis.

While the exact cause of atherosclerosis is unknown, three main predisposing factors are known. These are high blood pressure, obesity, and high blood cholesterol. In most instances, all three of these factors are reversible. Life-saving and life-prolonging effect of correction of high blood pressure and correction of obesity are now established facts. It must be emphasized that dietary control of blood cholesterol levels, though effective, is new. It will take several more years before we have absolute evidence of its effectiveness in prolonging life and preventing atherosclerosis. Until we have this proof, it is not wise to advise drastic changes in the diet of all Americans. The minimum amount of fats for growing children has not been determined. Women, apparently due to their female sex hormones, have lower blood cholesterols until after the menopause and enjoy special protection from atherosclerosis during these years. Furthermore, some men tolerate diets high in saturated fats without elevation of blood cholesterol.

Who, then, should be advised to change dietary fats in light of our as yet incomplete knowledge? I believe any one with known coronary or other arterial atherosclerosis in himself or his immediate family whose blood cholesterol level exceeds 200. Furthermore, I advise all other individuals to keep their blood cholesterol level below 225 as a prophylactic measure, appreciating that this arbitrary level will probably be revised downward after a longer "test of time."

The indifferent results in the past with dietary attempts to lower blood cholesterol levels with "low cholesterol diets" or with ordinary "low fat diets" are now *at long last* understood. Cholesterol-free fats which are hydrogenated actually cause our bodies to produce cholesterol and raise our blood cholesterol levels. Furthermore, some fats (highly unsaturated liquid oils) will make our blood cholesterol levels drop. Thus we now appreciate that dietary reduction of blood cholesterol levels demands selective manipulation of fats. About two-thirds of the blood cholesterol level reduction is accomplished by restricting the intake of fats which are composed largely of *saturated* fatty acids. These are the fats in meat, dairy products, and hydrogenated vegetable fats. These are crudely identified by being solid at room temperature. Diets high in meat are usually high in saturated fat, since our processing of meat (stall feeding) causes some meats, such as sirloin or ham, which may look quite lean, to contain as much as 30 per cent solid fat. About one-third of our blood cholesterol lowering is done by adding oils rich in polyunsaturated fatty acids (liquid at room temperature). The main sources of these are fish, shellfish, nontropical nuts, and most of the common liquid vegetable oils with the exception of coconut and olive oil.

The authors have provided not only recipes which make this type of fat control pleasant and easy, but they have also provided tables which make it possible at a glance to know which fats should be excluded and which foods, because of high polyunsaturated fatty acid content, should be included.

Fat control diets then should meet the following requirements:

(1) The amount of fat control must be understood by patient and physician.

(2) Fish, shellfish, and nuts should be served often in amounts as prescribed; meat, solid shortenings, margarines, and the fats in dairy products should be eliminated or curtailed to specified allowances, depending upon the necessity in the individual to lower blood fats.

(3) The diet must respect the standards of adequate nutrition insofar as protein, minerals, and vitamins are concerned. It should be supplemented with Vitamins A and B unless patients are eating a high fish diet. Your physician should be called upon to make the specific recommendations in this connection.

1. THE EXPERTS TELL US

. . . Just how important you are to be in the daily preparation of the sodium- or fat-restricted dietary.

You must learn to cook without many of the usual food "indispensables."

You must be able to satisfy highly cultivated taste buds, and at the same time meet the numerous and trying requirements of the specialized dietary.

At first glance, it may appear to you that the task is just too much to undertake on top of all of your other household chores. Actually, with a little thought and imagination, it's no trick at all to serve attractive and well-balanced meals for the whole family, meet the requirements of the restricted dietary, and spend very little extra time and effort in the kitchen.

A thorough understanding of the whys and wherefores behind the restricted sodium and fat dietaries is the best starting point toward success in your new program. Often, your first and only introduction to the diet is a "Do and Don't" list handed to you by some other member of the family. Or, even if you were present when the diet was instructed, there may be many unanswered questions now that you are back in your own kitchen with only a sheet of mimeographed directions as a guide. And the answers to those questions are important. They may mean the difference between the success and failure of the specialized diet.

THE SODIUM-RESTRICTED DIET

Perhaps even the term "low sodium" or "sodium-restricted" is new to you. Perhaps your diet is called "low salt" or "salt-free." "Low sodium" and "low salt" have been used so commonly, in the past few years, to express the same diet that many people believe them to be synonymous.

Actually, "sodium-restricted" is the more correct term, as it is the sodium content of your diet that is significant. Salt is restricted only because it is approximately 40 per cent sodium.

All low sodium diets are not identical. They may vary in the *amount* of sodium that they contain. The diet that you must prepare may be mildly, moderately, or severely restricted in sodium content—ranging anywhere from 200 to 4500 milligrams of sodium daily. Possibly, 1000 milligrams sounds like a lot of sodium to you. Perhaps even 200 milligrams seems like an ample amount. But when you consider that the average "salt lover" (and how many of us fall into this class!) may consume as much as 6000 or more milligrams of sodium each day, radical changes in both cooking and eating habits are necessary to cut down to a 200 milligram level. That pinch of salt (150 milligrams of sodium) that you may be tempted to use, or that one slice of regular bread (138-200 milligrams of sodium), does make a difference.

No doubt, you will be discussing your diet with some friend or relative "who has been on the low sodium diet for years" or knows someone who has been on it. You may be surprised or confused by the many differences in the two diets. These differences are generally due to the degree of sodium restriction necessary, so don't be tempted to make any changes in your own diet. Your physician is the only person who can decide what is the right amount of sodium for the dieter in your family. Remember, each person is an individual with his own special needs and requirements. Follow your physician's directions explicitly. The recipes in this book were planned mainly for the strict sodium-restricted diet (500 milligrams sodium)—but, as you will see in Chapter 3, they may be readily adapted for any level of restriction.

There are two methods commonly used for instructing low sodium diets. For simplicity, we will call them the *list* or *exchange method* and the *count method*.

If your diet is the *list method*, your physician has given you a list of foods that you may use in any amount; a list of foods that you may use in limited amounts; and a list of foods that you must avoid. Substitutions should be made only as outlined. When you follow this plan you will have a balanced diet considerate of your special needs.

If your diet is the *count method*, you must get out your pencil and paper each day and add up the exact amount of sodium that your dieter consumes.

Both methods are good, and either may be used with this book. Possibly, you may be able to include more variety in your menus with the count method. If your diet is the list diet method, and still you would like to try counting, the physician or dietitian can tell you how many milligrams of sodium you may use each day.

For ready reference, you will find the sodium content of many common foods listed in the Appendix. However, a more general background of the sodium content of foods and how it is affected in processing or cooking is both helpful and necessary in planning your low sodium meals. Why must you be especially careful when you use meat stock? Why can't you use all kinds of frozen foods? What must you look for on the labels of canned foods?

We are ready with the answers to most of these questions, because of studies reported by the Food and Nutrition Board of the National Research Council, the Council on Food and Nutrition of the American Medical Association and the American Heart Association. Their work has done much to lighten your job in the kitchen.

Unfortunately, most of the hearty, substantial foods that form the backbone of your menus are high in sodium content: meat, fish, eggs, milk, cheese—in fact, *most foods from an animal source are high in sodium,* and must either be eliminated or used in restricted amounts. You must learn to make a little of these go a long way. Meat-stretching recipes, and the like, which provide satisfying portions with a limited sodium content, will become your old stand-bys.

You are restricted, not only in the *amount* of meat or fish you may use, but also in the *kinds* of meat and fish that you may use. Take your meat market list. You may include fresh meats—some of those lifelong favorites, such as rump roast, leg of lamb, or fresh shoulder of pork. You may also include frozen meats—those tender sandwich steaks, or plump turkeys. But cross off from your market list those processed meats, such as cold cuts, smoked shoulder, bacon, and innumerable others. You will also have to cross off koshered meat.

Much sodium is added during the processing of these products—most often in the form of salt. Take beef, for example. As a sirloin steak or a boneless chuck pot roast, one ounce of beef contains approximately 20 milligrams of sodium. After it goes through the brining process and emerges as corned brisket, one ounce contains 369 milligrams of sodium. If it has been koshered, one ounce of beef contains 454 milligrams of sodium. It is plainly evident that such items would work havoc to a low sodium diet.

On your fish market list, you may include all fresh fish

except shellfish on the 500 milligram diet. Strangely enough, in general, a salt-water fish contains no more sodium than its fresh-water cousin.

Unfortunately for most of you inland housewives, *frozen fish is taboo, unless it is frozen whole.* Most of those handy frozen fillets and steaks are chock-full of sodium because brine is used in the processing. One ounce of halibut steak jumps from 15 milligrams of sodium when it is fresh to 130 milligrams of sodium when it is frozen. Look before you buy and make sure that your fish fillets are fresh.

Perhaps the greatest change in your market habits will be in the amounts of milk, eggs, butter, and cheese you may buy. Analyses for the sodium content of these foods show that they are, in many instances, even higher than meats. Milk, for example, contains nearly 500 milligrams of sodium per quart. If you are on the severely restricted allowance of 200-400 milligrams of sodium a day, it is obvious that you will have to use a commercial low sodium milk (fresh, frozen or powdered, whole or non-fat) or dialyzed milk (p. 23) rather than the familiar whole or non-fat milk.

With one egg consuming more than an eighth of your daily allowance on the 500 milligram diet, you will have to watch that sodium count when planning menus about soufflés, omelets, or the like. It is well to remember, too, that most of the sodium is concentrated in the egg white. Although you may be able to include some of those delicious fruit whips or meringues, try to favor the egg yolk most often in your cooking or baking, unless otherwise instructed. Just the opposite for saturated fat restriction— you pay court to the white of egg.

With cheese and butter, it is the salt added for flavor which puts them in the taboo class. One Swiss cheese and rye sandwich packed in the lunch box or taken as an evening snack will raise your sodium count as much as 600 milligrams—and that is a lot.

Fortunately, *most foods from a vegetable source are low in sodium content.* Fruits, vegetables, nuts, grains, and legumes—fresh from the garden or unprocessed— have just a trace of sodium. These foods must make up the bulk of your meals and can often be used in abundance. Your job will be to serve them in many and tempting ways, so that your menus will be appetizing and satisfying.

There are, however, a few exceptions to this rule regarding the low sodium content of foods of vegetable origin. *Some vegetables are so high that they must be entirely eliminated.* Artichokes, beets, carrots, celery, many of the greens—such as beet greens, chard, dandelion greens, kale, mustard greens, and spinach—frozen Lima beans and peas, sauerkraut, white turnips, and most canned vegetables (except low sodium dietetic ones canned without added salt) are on the taboo list.

If you scan down the list of vegetables that you are allowed to use, you will find that even a few of these must be used with discretion. If your diet is the count method, your daily allowance will suggest just how many you may include. But when using the list method, use vegetables only as listed.

Fruits, bless them, *are as a group consistently low in sodium content* and can be used to your heart's desire in your menus. Even canned fruits offer little problem. Read the label, of course, to be sure that no artificial color, flavor, or corn sirup has been added. Actually, very few have such additions. There are some limitations, we'll admit. You won't be able to top your dessert with a maraschino cherry, but a sprig of mint or a canned Bing cherry is just as decorative.

The pure fruit jellies (without added preservatives), jams, and conserves, whether from your own shelf or favorite store brand, fall within fruit classification and can add much to your meals. But do remember to read jelly labels and use nothing but pure fruit jelly and preserve.

Let's get back to salt again—that much overworked seasoning. Salt is our major dietary source of sodium, and it is easy to understand why so many low sodium diets are called "low salt" diets. As a seasoning, it adds milligrams of sodium a day to our diets, depending upon our use of it.

"Salting to taste" in home cooking may add as much as 800 milligrams of sodium to half a cup of food, and "salting to taste" in manufactured foods has the same result. Regular dressings, sauces, pickles, processed meat and fish, canned vegetables and soups, and innumerable other products are all on your "Don't" list because of their added salt content.

Consider the effect of salt with grains. As grains enter the factories, their sodium content is insignificant, but by the time they reach the store counters, many of their products are on your "Don't" list. Most ready-to-eat cereals (200 milligrams of sodium or more per dish), crackers (one soda cracker contains 62 milligrams of sodium), breads, cookies, cakes, and other bakery goods are all banned because of salt added as a seasoning.

Some bakery items are double offenders—in using both

salt and the leavening agent. One teaspoon of baking powder (378 milligrams of sodium) or one teaspoon of baking soda (1232 milligrams of sodium) can do untold damage to even the moderately restricted sodium diet.

Fortunately, *most of our flours* (except the self-rising varieties), *some of the ready-to-eat cereals,* and *many of our cooked cereals* are *low in sodium content,* so that they will not be wanting in our menus.

Many manufactured foods are not intentionally salted for seasoning, but use salt in processing. Brine is used to sort peas before freezing them, to prevent toughening of vegetables before canning, and to prevent the discoloration of fruits.

As if this were not enough, sodium is often added to foods in forms other than salt. Sodium bicarbonate (baking soda) is used in ready mixes and self-rising flour. Sodium benzoate is used as a preservative. Other sodium compounds are used in water-softening, preventing mold, drying fruits—to name just a few from a lengthy list.

You can easily see that manufactured foods must be used with extreme care. Read and reread labels for the addition of salt itself or any of the sodium compounds. See the list of Available Products on page 346 for those that have been laboratory-tested for your use.

Your physician has probably told you that your method of preparing foods is important, too.

High sodium foods, such as meat or salty foods, lose some sodium when boiled. The amount of this sodium or salt that is lost will depend partly upon the amount of water used—more salt being lost in a larger quantity of water. Thus, stewed or boiled meats will contain less sodium if the cooking water is discarded.

On the other hand, low sodium foods may gain some sodium from the tap water in which they are cooked. This makes the sodium content of the water supply important, too. Most water softeners leave a large amount of sodium in the water and therefore may not be used with this diet.

You may consume, you know, as much as 2½ quarts of fluid a day in your food and drink. If your water supply contains under 2.5 milligrams of sodium per cup, this amount is not too significant. But if it contains as much as 5, 10, 15 milligrams, or more, as it does in some cities, then water, as a source of sodium in the diet, is important.

For local information, consult your water purveyor, Heart Association, or Public Health Department. If you must depend upon well water for water, perhaps your doctor will want to run this simple color test made available to us by the Western Branch of the National Canners Association Research Laboratories:

Reagents
  1. Potassium chromate 10 per cent
  2. Silver nitrate 0.74 per cent

Procedure
  Measure out 40 drops of water in a small test tube. Add 1 drop of reagent 1 and 1 drop of reagent 2 and mix with water.
  A reddish precipitate will form. If this does not disappear on mixing, water is satisfactory. If red color disappears leaving a bluish white precipitate, water contains more than 3 milligrams sodium per ½ cup.

Medications are often another overlooked source of sodium. Use only the medicine prescribed by your doctor. Some medicines that may contain sodium are: "alkalizers," antibiotics, cough medicines, laxatives, pain relievers, and sedatives. Toothpastes and powders, as well as mouth washes, may also contain harmful amounts of sodium. If you don't swallow the toothpaste, you don't have to worry. But be sure to rinse your mouth thoroughly with water after brushing your teeth.

Perhaps, by this time, you are getting discouraged and are wondering how anyone can possibly cook an appetizing meal with so many Don't's.

Well, all is not as black as it would appear. Whereas some manufacturers have added to your Don't list, others have stepped in to lighten your task.

If your diet is severely restricted in sodium content, ordinary milk probably heads your list of Don't's. There are several good sodium-restricted substitutes on the market, such as Lo-Sodium milk, "Trim," (a low sodium modified non-fat milk), and Cellu Low Sodium Non-Fat Dry Milk Solids (which can be used as an instant milk powder). You may also dialyze milk (remove the sodium content) at home, but this is a tedious process.

Many of the chain stores and independent grocers now stock sodium-restricted bread. But be sure when you buy this and all diet items to read the label for the amount of sodium in 1 slice or 1 serving. Not long ago, we were shopping in a big health store where so-called low sodium bread contained 55 milligrams of sodium per slice. Sure enough, the analysis was stamped on the jacket, but the sales force was urging this product on its consumers as a low sodium item.

Low sodium crackers, like "Venus" bread sticks, like Stella D'Oro Low Sodium Genuine Italian Bread Sticks, and the Jewish Passover matzoth (made with flour and water), are now on the market. Check with your doctor or local Heart Association for a list of grocery and health food stores in your community which have sodium-restricted bakery items.

Sodium-free baking powder is available commercially (Cellu brand) for homemade low sodium baked goods. It may also be ordered by prescription at your neighborhood druggist's.

The formula for your druggist is as follows:

Postassium Bicarbonate	79.5	grams
Cornstarch	56.0	grams
Tartaric Acid	15.0	grams
Potassium Bitartrate	112.25	grams

The powders are mixed thoroughly and sifted several times. These baking powder substitutes make it possible for you to add many delicacies and old favorites to your menus.

Some permissible canned goods and other processed items may now be found on your grocer's shelf. Low sodium dietetic canned salmon, shrimps, chicken, and tuna are available, as is a low sodium peanut butter—cashew butter, too. Low sodium cottage cheese, several low sodium dietetic cheddar-type cheeses and the popular Cellu Low Sodium Dietetic Cheese Spread may be found locally or ordered direct from mail order supply houses.

A few low sodium soups are available, such as Anderson's Split Pea and Tomato Vegetable, Cellu Tomato Rice and Bouillon Cubes (although they are not allowed unless they contain less than 5 milligrams of sodium if you are on the list method and 500 milligrams of sodium is your restriction).

One of the newest and most delectable low sodium items is Cellu's Unsalted Dietetic Cooked Ham. Produced in Holland, it contains only 56 milligrams sodium in a 4-ounce serving and 8 grams fat. Imagination went into this product along with good flavor, for it is even packed in a 1-pound tin shaped like a regular ham. And you can do anything with it that you would do with regular ham.

Recently specialties have been flooding the market. You may now season your sodium-restricted dishes with such additions as Plantation Very Low Sodium Mustard

and Worcestershire Sauce, Tomato Paste,* packed without added salt, Cucumber Pickles,* Catsup,* Chili Sauce,*
and Vegetable Relish.*

A selection of dietetic vegetables is generally available,
packed without added salt or other seasonings.

There is at least one commercially-made Low Sodium
Ice Cream.†

Melba toast, cookies, low sodium cake mix, a low sodium
type of pound cake, and special desserts, like Cellu Gelatin Dessert, are among a few of the other specialties that
broaden your eating even with sodium restriction.

It will take a while for you to become familiar with the
material presented in this section. At first, it may be necessary to read and reread it, as you plan your menus or do
your shopping and cooking. Do not become discouraged
if the task seems endless the first few weeks. In a short
time it will become a familiar reference.

The following summary may prove helpful:

1. Whether your diet is called "sodium-restricted," "low
sodium" or "low salt," it is the sodium content of the
diet that is significant. Only the doctor can determine
how much sodium your dieter should be allowed.

2. There are no foods, not even ordinary drinking water,
completely free of sodium. Consequently, distilled water
for drinking, cooking, and preparation of soups and beverages must be used in some areas to keep the sodium intake within the allowable level.

3. Most animal foods are high in sodium content. Use
them carefully.

4. Most foods from a vegetable source are low in sodium
content. Plan your meals around them.

5. Most canned or processed foods contain more sodium
than the fresh product. Know your product before you
buy.

6. Many special low sodium products are available on
the market, but buy manufactured products only with
your doctor's approval.

*The Chicago Dietetic Supply House, Inc., Chicago 12, Illinois.

†Lady Lois Custom Tailored Ice Creams, 1550 Taraval Street, San Francisco 16, California.

2. WHEN FAT IS CONTROLLED

For many of you, the preparation of tasty meals controlled in fat may be the major problem—an even greater challenge in the kitchen. Restricting sodium means a change in the familiar flavor of our food, and re-education to new flavors. But restricting fat not only affects the ordinary accepted flavors, but also necessitates changes in usual cooking methods.

As with anything new, it will seem difficult at first. When you become familiar with your diet, you will learn short cuts and discover ways to minimize kitchen effort —and with surprisingly good results.

The success of your new program depends upon a thorough understanding of your diet sheet. You should know what foods are allowed, and in what amounts. You should also know what substitutions can be made. Sometimes, knowing why the diet has been ordered makes it easier to put the doctor's instructions to work.

The purpose of many controlled-fat diets is to lower the *cholesterol* content of the blood. *Cholesterol* may be a new term to you. One of the adjectives describing this substance is *fatty*. This is a clue to one reason for restricting fat in the diet. All of us have some cholesterol in our bodies and in the blood. But in some, the amount is higher than average. It may accumulate along the walls of the blood vessels. This, of course, narrows the opening of the blood vessel and puts an extra burden on the heart. Sometimes the blood vessel closes completely.

All would be relatively easy if we could just restrict the foods which contain cholesterol. However, the body can make cholesterol from the fats that we eat. Here, then, is one reason for limiting the *amount* of fat.

On most diets, not only the *amount* of fat but also the *kind* of fat is controlled. What we are concerned with here is the degree of *saturation*. All of the fats and oils that you are familiar with contain *hydrogen* (a chemical element) in varying amounts. *If the fat or oil has all of the hydrogen it can contain, it is called a saturated fat: if it can take on more hydrogen, it is called an unsaturated fat*— the more hydrogen it can absorb, the higher the degree of unsaturation.

Usually the hardness of the fat is a clue to its saturation. Fats that are solid at normal room temperature are generally highly saturated. These include meat fats, butterfat, margarine, lard, and most vegetable shortenings. Fats that are liquid at normal room temperature (vegetable and marine oils) are highly unsaturated. Coconut oil is an exception to this rule—it is liquid at room temperature, yet is highly saturated.

Research indicates that when *saturated fats are restricted,* the cholesterol content of the blood may decrease. This means that in certain people, if animal fat, butterfat, margarine, lard, and vegetable shortenings are either limited or eliminated, the cholesterol content of the blood will decrease.

Other studies have indicated that in some people, if the *saturated fats are limited and a specified amount of unsaturated fat is added,* the level of cholesterol in the blood may drop even lower. In other words, in this diet, the amount of animal fat, butterfat, margarine, and other high saturated foods is decreased, and specified amounts of vegetable oil, such as corn or cottonseed oil, are added.

It is plain then that no two fat-restricted diets may be exactly alike. Some may restrict the total fat yet allow the use of limited amounts of all kinds of fat. Others may restrict only the amount of saturated fats. Still others may restrict saturated fats and add vegetable oil. Only the doctor can decide which diet meets your special health needs. Follow his directions explicitly.

It is easy to see how the restriction of fat, and particularly saturated fat, is going to affect your eating habits. When you consider the sources of fat in your daily foods, you will have little difficulty in naming the *visible* fats— meat fats, butterfat, margarine, lard, vegetable shortenings, and oils. And of these fats, all are highly saturated, except the vegetable oils, and so are usually restricted or eliminated from the diet.

Perhaps you are wondering why vegetable shortenings are saturated, whereas vegetable oils are unsaturated. After all, vegetable shortenings are made from vegetable oil. Vegetable shortenings are high in saturation because they have been *hydrogenated.* In *hydrogenation,* hydrogen is forced into a liquid oil to make it a solid, thus changing it from an unsaturated oil to a saturated fat.

Many brands of peanut butter are now hydrogenated. This changes them from an unsaturated to a saturated fat. If you are restricted in saturated fat, read the peanut butter label for *hydrogenation,* or *hardening,* as it is sometimes called.

You are more likely to miss the *invisible* fats. Fat is actually hidden even in lean meats—and in fish, poultry, and egg yolk, too. Even when all of the visible fat is trimmed from, say, a rib steak, when the meat is cooked, the drippings in the broiler will contain additional fat.

For this reason, although we have already advocated *lean* meat in Chapter 1, we doubly emphasize *lean* meats to you homemakers with saturated fat restrictions. This usually means avoiding the use of choice grades of meat with their fat marbling, and selecting instead the leaner *good* or *commercial grades*. It sometimes means selecting the leaner cuts of meat—top round of beef for roasts, stews, and ground meat rather than rib or chuck or some of the other fatter cuts. For example, one ounce of lean roasted top of round contains about 2 grams of fat, whereas one ounce of lean roasted ribs of beef contains about 6 grams of fat. Similarly with other meats—leg of lamb is lower than chops, and pork loin is the best pork choice. But whatever your selection, always trim meat of all visible fat before using.

One bright spot for homemakers with saturated fat restriction is the use of fish. Marine oils are usually unsaturated and are classed with vegetable oils rather than animal fats. You may find that the use of fish often (perhaps even once a day) is highly recommended on your diet list.

The restriction of butterfat affects not only the use of butter, with its saturated fat content of about 4 grams per teaspoon, but also whole milk, cream (including sour cream), and cheese. This restriction also means that commercial foods made of whole milk, such as ice cream, milk shakes, chocolate milk, malted milk, milk mixes, and bakery products, too, are taboo.

Whole milk, either homogenized or family (with the cream at the top of the bottle), contains a required amount of butterfat. When you buy skim or non-fat milk, the butterfat content has been removed. (We might state here that pouring the cream off the top of the bottle is not a satisfactory method of removing the butterfat. If you have not already done so, observe the ring of cream remaining even when you pour one to two cups from the top.) Therefore, skim or non-fat milk must be your choice. Fortunately, it is readily available either in dried or fresh milk form (low sodium variety, of course, if you have sodium restrictions, too).

As stated before, the butterfat content of cheese puts it on your restricted list. Cottage cheese (specially prepared, low in sodium, if you have sodium restrictions) and Sapsago, a Swiss green grating-type cheese (if you have no sodium restrictions), are your best choices. But even with cottage cheese, make certain that no milk or cream has been added by buying the dry form and "creaming" it with non-fat milk.

At the present time, egg yolk, too, with its high saturated fat content, must be either restricted or eliminated for those of you with saturated fat controls. One medium egg yolk contains 5 grams of fat—about the same amount as in one teaspoon of butter or salad oil. Of course, you will follow the dictates of your diet. In general, favor recipes using just the egg white and use the whole egg (if allowed) as your protein in the meal. (But you must use care here if you are on sodium restrictions, as one medium egg white contains about 47 milligrams of sodium.)

Now for the vegetable fats—ordinary shortenings and margarine (see page 30 for low saturated fat margarine) are taboo because of their saturated fat content. Vegetable oils, such as corn, cottonseed or soybean, will become your standbys for baking and other cooking purposes. And you will have to turn out your own baked products and other goodies—perhaps even bread—because the ready-mixes and commercial baked goods contain whole milk, whole egg, shortenings, and other highly saturated fats. In fact, you will have to become a label reader, whether it be bread, regular bakery items, or canned goods. Always be on guard against the use of saturated fats in the ingredients.

Many of the vegetable fats, too, are invisible fats—such as those found in olives, nuts, avocados, coconut, chocolate, and peanut butter. Coconut, chocolate, and *hydrogenated* peanut butter are high in saturated fats and are on your Don't list; *regular* peanut butter, olives (if no sodium restriction), nuts, and avocados are low in saturated fats and rich in unsaturated fats and may be allowed in specified amounts if a ratio between saturated and unsaturated fats is required and if total fat is not restricted.

And now for a look at some of the commercially prepared foods insofar as fat is concerned. Many foods, that are normally low in fat, are on your Don't list because of the fat added during processing. (*Remember that most of these foods are high in sodium content and may not be used if sodium is restricted.*)

Many canned soups contain less than 2 grams of fat per average serving (3 servings per can) when prepared with water or non-fat milk. (See listing on page 67, and check with your diet list to see if allowed.) Often, this two grams of fat is saturated fat—added chicken fat, for example. If you are severely restricted in total or saturated fat, a wiser expenditure of your precious fat allowance might prove more beneficial.

Most of the familiar canned meats—luncheon meat, sausage, spiced ham, et cetera—are too high in fat content to be used. It is possible to purchase canned chicken, roast beef, and turkey, in which the visible fat can be removed fairly easily, and the resulting product made satisfactory insofar as fat is concerned. They are more expensive than the fresh product, and in general not as flavorsome, but are good to have on the shelf for emergency use. You will, of course, avoid the selection of creamed meats, meats packed in gravy, and products containing other items not on your diet list.

Canned fish, such as crabmeat, lobster, salmon, shrimp, and tuna, will hold a high spot in your menu-planning if you are on the low saturated (moderately) high unsaturated fat regime. If you are restricted in total fat, you will have to use waterpack and not oil-pack tuna. And as with meats, you should avoid creamed fish or other combinations that include restricted items.

Most homemakers like to have a hurry-up meal on the shelf for emergency use in the form of a canned casserole, paste, or stew. Fat restriction does offer a problem here. All canned products of this sort do contain fat, and it is difficult to determine just how much of this fat is saturated. And as with soups, some of the fat is in the form of an added fat, such as beef suet and chicken fat, rather than from the meat itself. Check with your diet list, doctor, or dietitian to see if you may use any of the commercial products. If they are not allowed, put your freezer to work with some of your homemade specialties.

At your drugstore or supermarket you may be able to buy at least one margarine containing less saturated fat than regular margarine or butter—Pitman-Moore's Emdee Margarine or Fleishmann's Corn Oil Margarine. The Best Foods division of Corn Products is now test-marketing its tasty Cornette. Other brands will follow.

Cereal grains are low in fat, so your worries are few insofar as breakfast cereals or flours are concerned. However, baked and processed items such as breads, crackers, cookies, cakes, pastries, and so forth have added saturated fats in the form of lard, hydrogenated shortenings, butter, and margarine. Many also include whole milk and whole egg or egg yolk. Some dessert items also use chocolate and coconut.

Your diet may allow the use of regular yeast breads. (Rye and Italian breads contain negligible amounts of fat per slice; other yeast breads contain about 1 gram of fat per slice.) Some of you may be allowed moderate use of crackers. (Ry-Krisp and plain matzoth contain negligible amounts of fat per cracker; most other crackers contain about 1 gram of fat per cracker.)

You will have to depend upon homemade products with vegetable oil, egg white, and non-fat milk for hot breads, cakes, cookies, and pastries. Homemade products is the answer for other dessert items, too, such as puddings and frozen desserts.

To sum up the use of commercial products on a fat-restricted program—read labels for the food content before you buy, check against your allowables, and if you have any question about its use, do not buy.

Remember, fat-restricted diets do differ. Follow your physician's recommendations explicitly. Use this book only as a guide, and adapt it to meet the requirements of your diet. With each recipe, we have included the grams of total and saturated fat per serving for those who must count. Whenever possible or necessary, we have offered a low saturated fat variation for the basic recipe. The teaspoons of oil per serving have also been calculated for those who must include vegetable oil in their meals.

We suggest, now, that you reread Chapter 1 (if you are on sodium restrictions) and then read Chapters 3, 4, 5, and 19 to become acquainted with the general information given, and to get started with herb and wine cookery. Seasoning is very important in low fat cookery. Herbs, lemon, wine, et cetera, help take the place of seasoning without butter or margarine just as they do of seasoning without salt.

Keep the following points in mind as you read for your fat restrictions:

1. Most fruits and vegetables are low in fat so may be used generously on fat-controlled diets.

2. Favor fish in your menus restricted in saturated fat because of its high unsaturated fat content.

3. Among the fats to be used with discretion and only as your diet allows are butterfat (including milk, cream,

and cheese), beef, lamb, pork, veal, and poultry. Trim all meats and poultry of visible fats. (See suggestions for Special Gravies, pages 105, 114.)

4. Hydrogenated shortenings are taboo on diets restricted in saturated fats. Whenever our recipes include unsalted butter or margarine, or vegetable shortening, use vegetable oil or oil spread.

5. Do not use chocolate, coconut, or hyrogenated peanut butter. But you may use non-hydrogenated peanut butter and nuts, such as almonds, cashews, peanuts, pecans, or walnuts, if total fat is not restricted.

6. In general, use only egg white in cooking. Use whole egg or egg yolk only in amounts allowed on your diet.

7. Avoid special preparations being offered as "protection against heart and artery disease." Use only medications, preparations, and diet recommended by your doctor.

8. In adapting bakery recipes for diets restricted in saturated fat, you cannot substitute oil on a one-to-one basis—usually a little less oil is needed than solid fat. Heating times and processes must also be adjusted. So until you have had time to experiment, choose tested recipes from manufacturers of vegetable oils, or from our suggestions.

9. Read labels of commercial products for additions of saturated fats. And for consumer aids, consult your local Heart Association.

10. If you have no sodium restrictions, whenever the recipe lists low sodium dietary products such as baking powder, milk, canned goods, and so on, you may substitute regular or salted products; you may also add salt to taste.

3. GETTING TO WORK

One should eat to live, not live to eat.
—BENJAMIN FRANKLIN

Now you are ready to begin your work.

The visits to the physician, the tests, and the diagnosis are in back of you.

The mimeographed instructions on the sodium- or fat-restricted diet are in front of you—but only you can make them work.

Gone from the list, as we have shown, are most of the familiar labor-saving food preparations used in the modern kitchen; but the laboratory has stepped in to give you help in your task of cooking meals without benefit of such aids.

First of all, it has given you research findings on the sodium and fat content of many unprocessed foods, as presented on pages 328-346. You will come to see just how important this material is as you do your daily planning of diet meals.

Then there are the synthetic products of the laboratory —the substitutes you may use, such as salt and baking powder substitutes, low sodium milk, and such other items as may be prescribed by your physician.

Various state and local Heart Associations affiliated with the American Heart Association, as well as health departments, the Council on Foods and Nutrition of the American Medical Association, the National Canners Association, and various governmental agencies—all of these agencies are carrying on studies and putting out materials or products to improve the quality and variety of your daily fare. For the most part, these materials are available only to physicians, but where distribution is general you will perhaps find them included with your instructions.

For general use, try checking your meals against the guide drawn up by the United States Department of Agriculture (Leaflet 424). Foods are classified according to their contribution of several nutrients, although the emphasis is placed on key foods as important sources of these nutrients. The daily food plan gives a basis for an adequate diet for the entire family but permits the individual wide choice in his food selections. Adjust the dieter's requirements to meet his medical needs and ensure adequate nutrition for other family members by frequent checking against the following:

MILK GROUP. Some milk daily:
    Children—3 to 4 cups
    Teen-agers—4 or more cups
    Adults—2 or more cups
    Cheese and ice cream can replace part of the milk

MEAT GROUP. Two or more servings (2 to 3 ounces of lean cooked meat)—beef, veal, pork, lamb, poultry, fish, eggs, with dry beans and peas and nuts as alternates

VEGETABLE-FRUIT GROUP. Four or more servings, including:
    A dark green or deep yellow vegetable important for vitamin A, at least every other day
    A citrus fruit or other fruit or vegetable important for vitamin C, daily
    Other fruits and vegetables including potatoes

BREAD-CEREALS GROUP. Four or more servings—whole grain, enriched, restored

This fundamental plan will provide the adult with one-half to two-thirds of his caloric requirements, four-fifths of the iron, four-fifths of the thiamine, nine-tenths of the niacin, and all of the riboflavin allowances. These nutrients and others not mentioned will be raised to adequate amounts by the other foods included in the day's food but not specially noted in the basic plan. Such foods as butter, margarine, other fats and oils, sugars, desserts, jams and jellies, plus additional servings of food from the basic groups, if desired, serve to fulfill the caloric and nutrient allowances. Proper selection and preparation of foods go hand in hand in providing the family an adequate diet.

It is obvious that the person on a restricted diet will not be able to have all of the foods listed in this guide nor in the amounts listed, in many cases. In order to plan adequate nutrition for all of the family, why not post a copy of the U.S.D.A. Leaflet 424, *Food for Fitness,* on the inside door of your food cupboard? You could make notations in each of the food sections to indicate special requirements. By so doing, your planning would be considerate of the needs of *all* family members.

Unfortunately, there is no time to review your nutrition. You must get on the job and will have to learn as you go— *learn by doing*, they call it in modern education.

You will find that the suggestions and recipes in this book are directed, in the main, to the 500 milligram sodium dietary. However, they should be equally usable for those of you with more generous allowances. It is far easier to add milk, eggs, cheese, size of meat servings, or other high sodium foods in amounts specified to bring your diet up to your requirements than to limit the dietary downward, but the diet patterns on pages 39 to 46 will show you how to do this, too.

Suggestions and recipes are also directed to those of you concerned with planning menus restricted in fat, whether total or saturated. Most of our recipes are constructed with vegetable oil instead of solid shortening because of increasing emphasis on the role of the vegetable oils in certain disease states. We must say here that while there is as yet no conclusive evidence that the quantity and quality of fat in the diet will be clinically useful, the circumstantial evidence relating the level of blood cholesterol to the incidence and severity of atherosclerosis has reached a point where many physicians are ordering specified amounts of saturated and unsaturated dietary fats.

Each diet is necessarily individualized so you will have to make your own substitutions as you go along. Our recipes are developed with low sodium non-fat milk. But you may substitute measure for measure whatever form of milk your particular diet specifies, whether it be whole milk, non-fat, or one of the low sodium milks, fresh or powdered.

Similarly with seasonings—we make a special point of giving you recipes that bring out the natural flavors of foods and food ingredients. We use lemon juice, wines, and herbs to point up natural flavors. We think they improve restricted dishes even more than regular ones. But use these flavor aids only if they appear on your diet list. And use them sparingly in the beginning if they are new to you and your family.

You will, no doubt, find a few recipes which violate some of your special instructions. Perhaps your diet list says "no brown sugar" or "no maple sirup." It is plain to see that no one cookbook can meet all of your individual needs, so why not draw a line through any menu or recipe that you should not use—and so be done with it forever?

You can readily see that this book should be used as *a*

guide rather than a final answer. And as a guide, we hope it will be helpful and stimulating to you, regardless of your sodium or fat allowance.

WORKING AIDS

One of the important things to remember in getting started is how cooking may affect the sodium and fat content of foods.

You know that meat and fish shrink during cooking, due to the loss of moisture and fat. Four ounces of raw hamburger may weigh only 3 ounces after it is cooked. But in these 3 ounces of cooked meat will be found almost all of the sodium that was present in the original weight of 4 ounces. Thus, in counting the milligrams of sodium, or the number of ounces of meat or fish in the portion that you are serving your dieter, you must remember the difference between raw and cooked weight.

When you adapt your own recipes, you will need to allow for shrinkage in cooking. For the average non-fatty meat, 25 per cent will make fairly generous shrinkage allowance. For example, if your diet list allows 4 ounces of meat (raw weight) per day, you will plan to serve 25 per cent less, or 3 ounces, cooked meat—but calculate sodium content in terms of raw weight, unless otherwise instructed.

The recipes in this book have been calculated to give you the approximate milligrams of sodium and grams of fat for individual and total servings. Meat, chicken, and fish have also been calculated in terms of ounces, cooked weight.

The *method of cooking* meat (or chicken or fish) that you choose may also affect the sodium and fat content of foods you prepare. Actually, you may select any method —frying, broiling, baking, roasting, stewing, boiling—but boiled meats contain less sodium if the cooking water is not used. During the boiling, some of the sodium is dissolved in the cooking water. Frying is perhaps the least desirable form of meat and general food cookery where fat is restricted. Better choose broiling or baking meats so that some of the invisible fat can drip to the bottom of the pan.

Some sodium as well as fat also goes into meat drippings. For this reason, you are not allowed to save meat drippings to use promiscuously in other foods, soups, or gravies. Use meat drippings and meat stock only with the consent of your physician—and then only when you can be absolutely certain that the dieter is receiving just his share—and when you can calculate how much sodium and fat his share contains. It is obvious that gravies will play a very small part (if any) in your new dietary regimen.

There is one more point to consider with high sodium or fat foods. This is mainly for those of you using the list method. You must learn to decrease proportionately from the daily food allowance any amount of these foods used in cooking. For instance, if you are limited to 1 egg a day, you cannot plan to serve a poached egg for breakfast and then have a custard pie for dessert at dinner. Or, if you serve 2 ounces of fish in a salad at luncheon, you must count this as part of your meat allowance for the day and content your dieter with his remaining allowance at dinner (a stretcher-type meat dish, perhaps).

You will want to make as few changes as possible in the beginning—to be considerate of the needs and likes of all family members. Alter seasonings, get acquainted with necessary substitutes, and start to work. Most foods will taste flat and different on the special diet for a time. No matter what you offer, the transition from the usual diet to the sodium- or fat-restricted one is a matter of re-education and cannot be accomplished in a day.

Pay extra attention to food selection and preparation. This is particularly true of meats and vegetables, because they will have new flavors without the familiar salt seasoning and rich sauces made with eggs and butter or margarine.

A little lemon juice, combined with other seasonings, will get you through the first days of special meat cookery. *Do not use your salt-substitute* in any of your dishes until you are ready to serve them, and then use only if prescribed by your physician. Some substitutes cook up bitter and ruin the natural flavor of the food. Divide your dish for regular and special needs just before serving, using salt for the "regulars" and substitute for the special diet, if allowed. And remember that a few drops of fresh, tangy lemon juice is a wonderful substitute for the salt shaker. Tasty for the regulars, too.

Similarly with vegetable preparation—buy only fresh, seasonal, frozen vegetables, or canned without added salt for those of you with sodium restrictions. For best flavor, minister to them with care. Read the section on vegetable preparation if you want to review vegetable cookery.

Use fruits in abundance for their fine flavor. And for morale's sake, whip up a dessert or two. Topping the meal with a good dessert can earn raves for an otherwise very simple meal. It need not be overly sweet to be good, but

should complement and round out the rest of the meal.
Fruit in wine is a case in point. Simple to do, it lifts the
usual flavor to the unusual when you want a little variety.

Of course, the big cooking job of the first week is breadmaking, unless you are fortunate enough to be able to buy
a low sodium or low fat loaf that meets your physician's
specifications. If you must make it, decide right now to
turn out a really good loaf of bread. It is easy, once you
have learned the simple processes involved (page 191). In
no time at all, you will be branching out from basic breadmaking to the specialities in breads, rolls, and quick
breads, all of which can give variety to your meals.

Are you impatient to get started? Well, why not do some
planning right now? Read over the suggestions for changing a basic family menu to meet diet limitations, get out
paper and pencil and make the necessary changes in your
menus to meet requirements and taste. Then check your
final results against the U.S.D.A. Leaflet 424 standards
to bring your meals up to the standard of adequacy for
everyone in your family according to individual need.

Begin your arithmetic now, too, whether you are to follow the count or list method. We will not confound you
with the intricacies of the metric system, but will give
the amount of sodium, total fat, saturated fat, and calories of our recipes in terms of household measurement
(such as ½ cup, 6 stalks, 1 teaspoon) for individual and
total servings. The saturated fat content of our recipes is
based on the total grams of fat supplied by foods classified
as highly saturated. For general classification of foods as
to saturated fat content, see Appendix IV, page 351. For
fatty acid content, see Appendix V, page 356.

Our calculations are *approximate*. There are the variables of foods and ingredients used due to climatic and
other differences; the care and preparation of foods; the
varying amounts of water used in cooking, as well as the
sodium content of waters; and cooking time—to mention
just a few of the variables from our kitchens to yours. In
certain areas, you will have to add the sodium content of
your water supply in calculating your recipes, or cook
with distilled water for your dieter, whichever is indicated
by your physician. When you want to adapt your own
recipes, consult the tables in the Appendices.

As you go along in the planning and preparation of this
dietary, you will learn more, just as we have, about the
scientific whys and wherefores of the low sodium and low
fat diet. In fact, you may find that your written instructions may become the most absorbing textbook you have
ever studied.

MENU PATTERNS

To help get you off to a good start, we are listing a basic family menu and indicating how it might be changed to meet diet requirements, whether they be sodium- or fat-restricted, limited or unlimited in calories. Remember, in most instances, it is not necessary to cook dieter's food separately or to prepare two recipes. Vegetables, sauces, and the like can be salted and buttered for the family just before serving, and oil added or served plain, or with a few drops of lemon juice, to dieter. The family can enjoy the low sodium muffins, low fat rolls, low sodium or low fat desserts, and so on, right along with the dieter. One of the basic aims of this book is to present recipes that can be used by the entire family—and thus conserve your kitchen effort.

BASIC FAMILY MENU

BREAKFAST

Grapefruit	½ medium
Shredded wheat	1 biscuit
with whole milk	½ cup
and sugar	1 teaspoon
Boiled egg	one
with butter*	½ teaspoon
Plain muffin	two
with butter	2 teaspoons
Coffee	1 cup
with light cream	2 tablespoons
and sugar	1 teaspoon

LUNCH

Halibut, broiled	3 ounces
with butter	1 teaspoon
served with lemon wedges	
Cheese sauce	¼ cup
Tomato, broiled	½ medium
with butter	½ teaspoon
Frozen green peas	½ cup
with butter	½ teaspoon
Pan roll, commercial	one
with butter	1 teaspoon
Fruit Jell-O	1 serving
with whipped cream	1 rounded tablespoon
Milk, whole	1 cup

*Margarine may be substituted for butter in those menus calling for it.

DINNER

Cranberry nectar	½ cup
Baked veal steaks	3 ounces
with butter	½ teaspoon
Orange candied yams	1 serving
with butter	½ teaspoon
Savory green beans	½ cup
with bacon fat	1 teaspoon
Baking powder biscuit (made with hydro-genated shortening)	one
with butter	1 teaspoon
Lemon ice cream	1 serving
Sugar cookies, commercial	two
Milk, whole	1 cup

SODIUM-RESTRICTED MENUS

500 MILLIGRAM SODIUM
UNLIMITED CALORIES

With unlimited calories, the basic pattern needs but few changes to meet the requirements of the 500 Milligram Sodium Diet. Food will be cooked without salt, and low sodium foods such as breads, butter, or desserts will be substituted. If regular milk allowance is used as a beverage, low sodium milk must be used in cooking.

BREAKFAST

Grapefruit	½ medium
Shredded wheat	1 biscuit
with whole milk	½ cup
and sugar	1 teaspoon
Boiled egg	one
with unsalted butter*	½ teaspoon
Low sodium plain muffin †	two
with unsalted butter	2 teaspoons
Coffee †	1 cup
with light cream	2 tablespoons
and sugar	1 teaspoon

*Unsalted margarine may be substituted for unsalted butter in those menus calling for it.
†Recipe is given in this book. See Index.

LUNCH

Halibut, broiled *	2 ounces
with unsalted butter	½ teaspoon
Low sodium cheese	
sauce *	¼ cup
Tomato, broiled *	½ medium
with unsalted butter	½ teaspoon
Fresh green peas *	½ cup
with unsalted butter	½ teaspoon
Low sodium pan roll *	one
with unsalted butter	I teaspoon
Fruit gelatin *	I serving
with "whipped cream"	
topping *	I rounded tablespoon
Milk, whole	¾ cup

DINNER

Cranberry nectar	½ cup
Baked veal steaks *	2 ounces
with unsalted butter	½ teaspoon
Orange candied yams *	I serving
with unsalted butter	½ teaspoon
Savory green beans	½ cup
and lemon juice	
with olive oil	I teaspoon
Low sodium baking	
powder biscuit *	one
with unsalted butter	I teaspoon
Lemon water ice *	I serving
Low sodium sugar	
cookies *	two
Milk, whole	¾ cup

500 MILLIGRAM SODIUM—
1200 CALORIE MENU

Limiting calories with a sodium-restricted diet presents
the same problem as curtailing calories on a regular diet.
Fats, starches, and sugars are decreased; and with the
lower total food content, careful planning is necessary to
make certain that all of the essential food nutrients are
included. Starred foods indicate that the recipe is given
in this book.

BREAKFAST

Grapefruit	½ medium
Shredded wheat	I biscuit
with non-fat milk	½ cup
and Calcium Sucaryl	as desired

* Recipe is given in this book. See Index.

Boiled egg	one
Low sodium plain	
muffin *	two
with unsalted butter	1 teaspoon
Coffee *	1 cup
with Calcium Sucaryl	as desired

LUNCH

Halibut, broiled *	2 ounces
Tomato, broiled *	½ medium
Fresh green peas *	½ cup
Low sodium pan roll *	one
with unsalted butter	½ teaspoon
Fruit gelatin * made	
with Calcium Sucaryl	
and unsweetened fruit	1 serving
Milk, non-fat	¾ cup

DINNER

Cranberry nectar	½ cup
Baked veal steaks *	2 ounces
Mashed sweet potato *	¼ cup
Green beans *	1 cup
Low sodium baking	
powder biscuit *	one
with unsalted butter	½ teaspoon
Lemon water ice * with	
Calcium Sucaryl	1 serving
Milk, non-fat	¾ cup

500 MILLIGRAM SODIUM— 1800 CALORIE MENU

BREAKFAST

Grapefruit	½ medium
Shredded wheat	1 biscuit
with whole milk	½ cup
and Calcium Sucaryl	as desired
Boiled egg	one
Low sodium plain	
muffin *	two
with unsalted butter	1 teaspoon
Coffee *	1 cup
with light cream	1 tablespoon
and Calcium Sucaryl	as desired

* Recipe is given in this book. See Index.

LUNCH

Halibut, broiled *	2 ounces
Tomato, broiled *	½ medium
Fresh green peas *	½ cup
Low sodium pan roll *	two
with unsalted butter	1 teaspoon
Fruit gelatin * with Calcium Sucaryl and unsweetened fruit	1 serving
Milk, whole	¾ cup

DINNER

Cranberry nectar	½ cup
Baked veal steaks *	2 ounces
Mashed sweet potato *	¼ cup
Green beans *	1 cup
Low sodium baking powder biscuit *	two
with unsalted butter	1 teaspoon
Lemon water ice * with Calcium Sucaryl	1 serving
Low sodium sugar cookie *	one
Milk, whole	¾ cup

FOR 250 MILLIGRAM DIET: Use same meal patterns but substitute low sodium milk for regular milk.

FOR 1000 MILLIGRAM, UNLIMITED CALORIE DIET: Use same meal pattern, except to increase halibut and veal to 3 ounces, increase milk at lunch and dinner to 1 cup, use ½ cup regular canned green beans, and use 2 teaspoons salted butter.

FOR 1000 MILLIGRAM, 1200 CALORIE DIET: Use same meal pattern but substitute ½ cup regular canned peas for fresh peas, 1 commercial pan roll (with salt) for 1 low sodium pan roll, and 2 teaspoons salted butter or margarine for unsalted butter.

FOR 1000 MILLIGRAM, 1800 CALORIE DIET: Use same meal pattern but substitute ½ cup regular canned peas for fresh peas, and ½ cup regular canned green beans for fresh or frozen green beans.

RESTRICTED SATURATED FAT WITH ADDED VEGETABLE OIL MENU

This menu pattern supplies approximately 2000 calories,

* Recipe is given in this book. See Index.

225 grams carbohydrate, 70 grams protein, and 90 grams fat (15 grams saturated fat and 75 grams vegetable oil).

BREAKFAST

Grapefruit	½ medium
Shredded wheat	1 biscuit
with non-fat milk	½ cup
and sugar	1 teaspoon
Low saturated fat	
muffin *	one
with oil spread *	1 teaspoon
Coffee *	1 cup
with non-fat milk	¼ cup
and sugar	1 teaspoon

LUNCH

Halibut, broiled *	3 ounces
with vegetable oil	1 teaspoon
Mock cheese sauce *	
made with vegetable	
oil	¼ cup
Tomato, broiled *	½ medium
with vegetable oil	1 teaspoon
Frozen peas	½ cup
with vegetable oil	1 teaspoon
Low saturated fat pan	
roll *	one
with oil spread *	1 teaspoon
Fruited Jell-O	1 serving
with "whipped cream"	
topping *	1 rounded teaspoon
Milk, non-fat	¾ cup

DINNER

Cranberry nectar	½ cup
Baked veal steaks *	3 ounces
with vegetable oil	1 teaspoon
Orange candied yams *	1 small serving
with vegetable oil	1 teaspoon
Savory green beans	1 serving
with vegetable oil	1 teaspoon
Low saturated fat baking	
powder biscuit with oil	
spread *	one
	1 teaspoon
Chiffon pie with vege-	
table oil pastry *	1 serving
Milk, non-fat	¾ cup

* Recipe is given in this book. See Index.

FOR SODIUM RESTRICTION: Follow same menu pattern, substituting fresh or dietetic canned peas for frozen peas; use fresh, frozen, or dietetic canned green beans; substitute fruit gelatin * for Jell-O; and use low sodium, low saturated fat recipes for starred items.

TOTAL FAT-RESTRICTED MENUS

25 GRAM FAT—
1200 CALORIE MENU

BREAKFAST

Grapefruit	½ medium
Shredded wheat	1 biscuit
with non-fat milk	½ cup
and Calcium Sucaryl	as desired
Boiled egg	one
Toast	1 slice
with jelly	1 teaspoon
Coffee *	1 cup
with non-fat milk	¼ cup
and Calcium Sucaryl	as desired

LUNCH

Halibut, broiled *	2 ounces
Low fat mock cheese sauce *	¼ cup
Tomato, broiled *	½ medium
Frozen peas	½ cup
Low fat pan roll *	one
with jelly	1 teaspoon
Fruit gelatin * with Calcium Sucaryl and unsweetened fruit	1 serving
Milk, non-fat	¾ cup

DINNER

Cranberry nectar	½ cup
Baked veal steaks *	2 ounces
Mashed sweet potato *	¼ cup
Green beans *	1 cup
Low fat baking powder biscuit *	one
with jelly	1 teaspoon
Lemon water ice * sweetened with Calcium Sucaryl	1 serving
Milk, non-fat	¾ cup

* Recipe is given in this book. See Index.

25 GRAM FAT—
1800 CALORIE MENU

BREAKFAST

Grapefruit	½ medium
Shredded wheat	1 biscuit
with non-fat milk	½ cup
and sugar	1 teaspoon
Boiled egg	one
Toast	2 slices
with jelly	1 tablespoon
Coffee *	1 cup
with non-fat milk	¼ cup
and sugar	1 teaspoon

LUNCH

Halibut, broiled *	2 ounces
Low fat mock cheese sauce *	¼ cup
Tomato, broiled *	½ medium
Frozen peas	½ cup
Low fat pan roll *	two
with jelly	2 teaspoons
Fruit Jell-O	1 serving
with "whipped cream" topping *	1 rounded teaspoon
Milk, non-fat	1 cup

DINNER

Cranberry nectar	½ cup
Baked veal steaks *	2 ounces
Orange candied yams *	1 small serving
Green beans *	1 cup
Low fat baking powder biscuit *	one
with jelly	1 teaspoon
Lemon water ice *	1 serving
Meringue kisses *	two
Milk, non-fat	1 cup

FOR SODIUM RESTRICTION: Use basic menu patterns except use low sodium toast; low sodium, low fat recipes for starred items; fresh or canned dietetic peas and fresh, frozen, or dietetic canned beans; fruit gelatin * in place of Jell-O; and do not add salt in cooking.

* Recipe is given in this book. See Index.

4. OF HERBS AND GREENS AND SEASONINGS

Herbs are to restricted cookery what heavy cream is to old-fashioned strawberry shortcake. They should be considered additional seasoning to the familiar sugar and spice, or pepper, oil, vinegar, and mustard treatment. Used with care and understanding, they can bring out the natural flavors of food and lift your restricted recipes out of the prosaic and into the gourmet class.

After all, the only way to be creative, in this field, is to plan and cook by *principles*. One of the best ways to achieve this is to recognize that a recipe can be flavored in many different ways and with different results. One good recipe, then, has the potential of being two, five, or many recipes, with the use of as many different herbs, their combinations and seasonings.

In order to get the most out of your varying flavors for new results, you will want to become oriented to the know-how of herbal cooking. Foreign cookery has given us some wonderful guides in the development of their native dishes with subtle and aromatic flavors. A review of some of these old and many of the newer recipes can give you some marvelous ideas for your own cookery. In all of the literature on the subject, you will find a word of caution: *Don't overdo*. We add it, too, for restricted cookery. When in doubt, remember the pinch flavor method of Grandmother's time.

All herb seasoning should, of course, bring out the natural flavor of foods and never be so strong as to be dominant. The essential oils in each herb give the food its characteristic flavor. Or perhaps it would be more accurate to say that the release of these oils blends with the food to bring out its unique flavor. It takes time for herbs to do their best work for you. Heat reacts more favorably than cold in releasing these pungent oils. The time element is the reason why so many herb-seasoned dishes are more flavorsome the day following first preparation.

Fresh herbs have a truer taste; but except for salads, fresh or dried herbs may be used almost equally well. Salads are definitely improved when garden-fresh herbs are available. If you must depend upon commercially prepared ones, do buy only the leaves or seeds and forget all about the inferior powdered form. Do your own pulverizing with a small home mortar and pestle.

If you are lucky enough to be able to start with fresh herbs, first pick off the leaves and discard all stems. They are apt to be the bitter part of the herb. Make little bunches of the leaves and snip fine with kitchen scissors, or mince with a pestle for most satisfactory results. Seeds and dried varieties can often be pulverized in your hand at time of use. The warmth of the hand works on the essential oils in releasing them to begin their work.

Above all, in restricted cookery, don't become a one-herb cook, no matter how good that herb may be. Think of the flavor of the food itself, and then use your herbs to enhance that flavor. Don't distort it and don't drown it. Think of *relatedness* and *suitability* and do some experimenting. Your use of herbs can make your restricted cookery distinctive and bring you distinction, too.

HERBS

Basil

A native of the Far East, we find that BASIL comes from the Greek word meaning royal. Royal it certainly is—in its contribution to good flavor. It has a faint fragrance of tea and mint, if you smell its subtle odor in garden patch or in dried form.

Use basil in many ways. It will aromate an egg dish so that it is positively delectable—similarly with tomatoes or tomato juice. It is a natural for most Italian dishes, soups, meats (particularly stews, ground beef, and lamb), salads, fruits and vegetable juices, sauces, and duck. It is such a good friend to restricted cookery that it deserves your best ministrations.

Bay

The CALIFORNIA BAY, or PEPPERWOOD as it is often called, is particularly well known in the Far West, where it grows to be a good-sized tree, with its sprawling roots reaching far out into gardens.

Either fresh or dried, its leaves give zest to many meat dishes (especially roasts, stews, and pot roasts), soups, poultry, and a few stuffings. Whatever you do, don't underestimate its potency, for if used uncontrolled, you will taste bay flavor alone—and lose all trace of the flavor you started out to accent. A half leaf will go a *long* way in adding pungency to your dishes.

Caraway

Are you thinking of "CARAWAY seeds for cookies and cakes"? That is their traditional use, to be sure. But have you tried this old-time herb in ground meats and soups, salads, and certain vegetables?

The leaves, which closely resemble carrot foliage, and the seeds can be used in breads, pies (particularly apple), baked apples, German-type cabbage soup, and goulashes. For something different, strew over your pork roast. However you use caraway, use it in moderation. Store seeds in refrigerator to keep from getting rancid, if you plan to keep them for any length of time.

Chives

And what homemaker lacks a little pot of CHIVES on her kitchen window shelf today? Cheap to buy, easy to grow, paying increasingly better dividends in the form of luxuriant growth with each snipping, Chives are a veritable treasure-trove for flavor. They, too, have a time-honored history and have met the taste-test of time.

As for their uses, they are many. They give a great lift to low sodium cottage cheese and yoghurt. They are a must in many salads, particularly potato, are an epicurean addition to many egg dishes, and invite your use in sauces and vegetable cookery.

Dill

In spite of its odor, DILL is grown in real herb gardens almost as frequently as parsley and sage. For good reasons, too, for it is a versatile friend, once you know its characteristic flavor. Both its leaves and seeds can be useful to you, who must get every bit of goodness out of food prepared.

The garden-fresh leaves give tang to fish and its sauces; to "creamed chicken" made with low sodium milk; to low sodium tomato soup; to chops and steaks when broiled with a light sprinkling of it. It adds a special something to hot or cold potato salad. The seeds are spicy in soups, avocados, beans, gravy, and, believe it or not, in apple pie.

Sweet Marjoram

Lovely, fragrant MARJORAM sprigs are often laid among fine linens or woolens to keep them sweet and are no less magical in their contribution to making good food better. The dainty, silver leaves may be used fresh or dried in soups (particularly onion), salads, sauces, mushroom dishes, meats (particularly pot roasts, pork, and veal), strewn over fish to be broiled or baked, or combined with certain vegetables (particularly peas, beans, and tomatoes). It has enjoyed long fame with lamb. An old recipe calls for it combined with onion, summer savory, mushrooms, and lemon, as a "dressing" for lamb.

Its sister-plant, OREGANO, or WILD MARJORAM, is a flavorful addition to many meat, pasta, and vegetable dishes.

Parsley

> Parsley, parsley, everywhere
> On my daily bill of fare.
>
> See that kippered herring staring
> At the silly sprig he's wearing.
>
> Be it steak or creamed potatoes,
> Oyster plant or grilled tomatoes,
>
> Squash or scrambled eggs or scrod—
> Each must wear its little wad;
>
> Each must huddle underneath
> Its accursed parsley wreath.
>
> Parsley, parsley, everywhere,
> D———! I want my victuals bare.
> —MARGARET FISHBACK *

This bit of verse indicates our sentiments about PARSLEY. It certainly is the overworked herb of American cooking. We trim every conceivable dish with it, and only too often cast it aside for eating purposes. It deserves a better life, having contributed good flavor as well as good garnishing through the ages.

* *Out of My Head,* 1933. (Printed by permission of E. P. Dutton & Co.)

Yes, parsley has had a long and honored life, should have its due in food seasonings—as well as in garnishing our palefaced dishes. Whether you use the fern-leafed Italian variety or the curly one, do enrich the flavor of your soups, salads, meats, and vegetables with it. It is good in fish and sauces, too. It can be cooked into the food, or added the last few minutes of cooking. The flavor will be more penetrating, of course, if it is allowed to blend with the main ingredients for a longer period of time.

Parsley is even a pretty addition in the garden. It is charming as a border or in combination with such flowers as violets or spiced pinks, or in patch planting, where space permits. It grows slowly—may not show itself above ground for at least four weeks after planting, and may take a little encouraging in the beginning. After that, you sometimes have to discourage it or it takes over.

Rosemary

Sir Thomas More, in *Utopia,* called ROSEMARY "the herb sacred to remembrance and therefore to friendship." It is a good friend, indeed, to low sodium dishes, for it peps them up and at the same time draws out their natural flavors. It will be one of the hard-working herbs in your new program, we predict, just as soon as you learn its value and many uses.

It does wonders for meat recipes. Just try it and see if you don't like it in chicken dishes, veal stew, meat loaf, or sprinkled over pork or beef roast. If you cultivate a luxurious bush at your back door, it can be used in many other ways for your pleasure.

Mincing it very fine, it adds piquancy to many sauces, stuffings, and poultry. It's a delightful addition to baking powder biscuits (see special recipe), to homemade jams and spices, and to certain vegetables (particularly browned new potatoes). Its aroma is deceptive—so again, you will have to watch your amounts. It's another one of those dominant herbs, if you give it half a chance.

Sage

So popular is this perennial that it is grown in almost every American garden giving any space to herbs. No wonder, because of its all-around usefulness in party dishes, particularly stews and other meats (such as veal and beef), sauces, in some stuffings, with duck and geese. Many people believe FRESH SAGE is more satisfactory to use than the dried variety. You will want to use its gray pointed leaves very sparingly, remembering how penetrating that sage taste is.

Its cousin herbs, WINTER and SUMMER SAVORY, are kinder to most stuffing flavors when blended with any stale low sodium bread. In fact, Mrs. Mazza and other writers on herbs and cookery consider sage too strong for poultry stuffing at any time. They recommend, instead, a blend of savory, thyme, and sweet basil for all-around use.

Savory

You will want to know the two SAVORY varieties. SUMMER SAVORY is the better known and is widely useful in salads, meat dishes, stuffings, scrambled eggs, soups, and certain vegetables (string beans and tomatoes), and poultry.

WINTER SAVORY is harder to find, but it is worth the search. It is delicious in many fish dishes. Its leaves are pungently rewarding in soups, meats, and sauces. Some people call it a man's seasoning, but chefs will tell you that ladies like it, too, when delicately blended with other herbs and seasonings.

Thyme

Kipling speaks of the "blunt, broe-headed, whale-backed Downs covered with the wind-bit thyme that smells of dawn in Paradise." The eloquence was well deserved, for THYME is one of the most satisfactory and usable of the culinary herbs.

There are many thymes in use today for various purposes, and all are true to their name, for thyme means incense. The common garden variety is the most satisfactory for cooking. Its range of usefulness is broad.

The leaves can be pulverized in low sodium milk to "kill" its flavor, if you object to it. Its leaves can be blended with other herbs in making herbal vinegars. It is excellent, also, in sauces and meats (particularly veal and pork), fish, soups and chowders, dressings for meats and poultry, vegetables (particularly onions, peas, and tomatoes in any form), and salads. No other seasoning does quite so much for the lowly egg as does the addition of a little thyme. Taking it all in all, it is a hard-working herb in restricted cooking, as you can see.

Turmeric

This Indian herb is delightfully aromatic. It is an essential of curry powder. TURMERIC will give a dash to beans, sauces, and meats—particularly if you want to give them a Mexican tang.

MORE HERBS AND SEASONINGS

Curry Powder

CURRY POWDER is not truly an herb, but since it is combined with herbs and spices, it deserves mention here. CORIANDER and CUMIN SEEDS, GREEN GINGER and TURMERIC, GARLIC, CHILI, and PEPPERCORNS, all go into its making.

The use of curry dates back to old-time cooking and the Far East. In our time, it is often associated with Army fare rather than geography. It has a very penetrating flavor, so use it subtly in the beginning until you are sure of its reception. It is delicious sprinkled lightly over fish to be broiled or baked—similarly with chicken. It is a natural with many meats (particularly lamb and rice dishes).

Garlic

If there is one thing many husbands can't stand, it is GARLIC. Or, should we say, garlic's after-breath? The secret, of course, is to let it do its work in cooked or uncooked foods and then *remove it before serving*. Actually, it is the eaten garlic that is the breath offender.

There are three ways to avoid L.G. (lingering garlic). For meats, soups, and other cooked foods, wherever you may want to use one or more cloves, do not mince into food, but simply split the clove lengthwise and skewer onto wooden pick. Let the garlic cook for an hour or so with other ingredients. Remove from cooking kettle before it becomes so tenderized that it falls away from the pick.

For a tossed salad, rub your split clove of garlic on a low sodium bread crust, and put into your salad bowl. After you have tossed and dressed your salad, remove the bread and you will have an even garlic flavor with no after-effects.

For some salads, you may want the garlic flavor in the dressing. Split a garlic clove lengthwise and put it into your dressing. Let stand about 30 minutes and remove before using.

One of the new garlic presses will even provide you with an easy way to inject direct garlic into your foods and protect your hands from clinging odor when you elect to use "garlic straight."

Lemon Juice

LEMON JUICE may be worked overtime in restricted cookery. Sprinkled over meats, fish or fowl, it will add both flavor and zest to many of your restricted dishes. For sodium restriction, use just as you would salt for an aromatic flavor to your cookery.

Meat Tenderizers

Don't overlook these "friends" to restricted cookery. For those of you on sodium restriction, get either the low sodium seasoned or unseasoned meat tenderizer and use as you would a regular meat tenderizer. (We have used Adolph's in most of our recipe-building.) Regardless of the kind, cut, or grade of meat, regardless of how you may cook it, it will be more tender, more juicy and delicious if you use a meat tenderizer, according to Jeannette Frank, Director, Consumer Service Department, Adolph's Ltd.

Onion

For the purpose of this book, ONION will appear both as a vegetable and here as a seasoning. It is probably the greatest single boon to the seasoning of dishes you will have at your command. You don't have to go overboard with your use of it any more than you do with garlic. Onion, wisely used, will give "oomph" to many otherwise flat-tasting dishes.

Onion adds a hearty pungency to stews and soups, and makes a real plus contribution to meat roasts and Italian-type sauces.

Onions and salads just seem to go together; as Sydney Smith has said, "Let onion atoms lurk within the bowl and, half suspected, animate the whole." Spring onions, with their light bulbs and green stalks, are best for this purpose. Their very freshness gives a lift to a salad. You will want to use both the bulb and stalk, relying on the bulb when you want a more robust accent, and using the green stalks for piquancy.

Dried red onions are also very useful in tossed salads. Their swirling slices are juicy, rich, and decorative. They do something very nice for string beans when minced fine and blended with vegetable oil, too. Ditto for zucchini squash.

Pepper

PEPPER becomes the more important in the absence of salt, it would seem. For that reason, if for no other, invest in a pepper mill and grind your own peppercorns. Only in this way can you get the best that pepper has to give you as a seasoning.

Vinegar

There's a right kind of vinegar for every use. Acrid and penetrating, you may even want to dilute some of your vinegars with a little water when using in special ways. CIDER VINEGAR, with its low sodium count, will have right-hand use, along with wine and garlic in many of your meats, soups, gravies, and salads.

Get a good clear vinegar and taste-test. Once you've found a brand that gives you the flavor you want, continue with it. But don't depend upon cider vinegars exclusively, for the wine and herb vinegars have much to offer in restricted cookery. WINE VINEGAR is particularly useful in tossed salads and may be used with restraint in meat-base soups. HERB VINEGARS offer you many taste varieties in salad dressings. Once you get a small herb plot started, you may even want to blend your own.

Remember, though, that herb and wine vinegars contain more sodium than cider vinegar. The daily total will tell you "counters" how much you may include; but for the rest of you, refer to your list of allowables or to your physician. If permitted, use with restraint with other higher sodium foods. Cider vinegar may be substituted in all recipes for a lower count. Do not use malt and spirit vinegars as they make no flavor contribution worthy of consideration.

SPICES

Spices can be one of your best kitchen investments and deserve careful selection and care (keep lids screwed on tightly to preserve pungency), if you want them to work well for you.

Get your spices off the shelf and get acquainted with them once again in terms of their basic aromas. Smell, then taste-test, so that you will know the flavors you are going to use. The first job to do is to discard all stale spices. They pay poor dividends.

A pinch of spice, rightly used, will do much to pep up some of your low sodium dishes. Have you tried:

A CINNAMON STICK in low sodium blancmange?
A dash of NUTMEG as a topping for rice pudding or in meat pie crust?
A dash of ALLSPICE in a meat loaf?
A half dozen whole CLOVES in your soup pot?
A spoon of NUTMEG in rhubarb?
One-fourth teaspoon CURRY in "creamed" eggs?
A dash of MACE or CARAWAY in a coffee cake?
A sprinkling of CURRY or DILL on fish before baking or grilling?

When you really know your spices, there are almost limitless combinations possible for flavor enrichment. Don't be afraid to try some new ones in your new cooking.

SALT SUBSTITUTES

Use only as prescribed by your physician. If allowed, season at time of serving unless you are very sure that the salt substitute which you are allowed does not "cook up bitter." If you learn to add salt substitute in this way, it will be no trick at all to add salt for the regulars at time of serving.

Some of the best-known salt substitutes are: Adolph's Salt Substitute, Diasal, Co-Salt, Lawry's Salt Substitute, Neocurtasal, Saltrol and Gustamate.

FATS

Fats are flavors just as much as are spices and herbs. For sodium restriction without low saturated fat requirements, select fats from your diet list, as unsalted butter and unsalted margarine; olive, corn, cottonseed, soybean or peanut oils; or solid shortenings, as Crisco, Spry, or lard, for baking. But use these *only* if they appear on your diet list.

Where saturated fat is limited, use only the fats on your diet list, as corn, cottonseed, or soybean oil. Use unsaturated or liquid fats only in the amounts specified. This will be individualized for your special needs so that it is of paramount importance to know your allowance. Do not use any solid fats, as Crisco, Spry, butter, margarine (see page 30 for special margarine), or lard. Don't feel too sorry for yourself if butter no longer appears on your list; you will be surprised at the excellent flavor you can give to your vegetables, salads, and casseroles with the liquid oils, once you become accustomed to their flavors and ways to use.

Generally speaking, substitution of an oil for a solid fat in baking should not be made one to one; the oils go farther. If you are adapting your own recipe, "one cup of shortening" may be interpreted as three-fourths of a cup of oil, or a little less.

We have tried all of the different oils in our cooking and for flavor we prefer corn oil for salads and vegetables (but soybean and peanut are very usable too) and corn or cottonseed oil for baking bread, muffins, cakes and cookies, and pastry. Talk about flaky piecrust, wait until you have tried an "oil"-crusted pie for tenderness and excellent flavor. Easy to handle, too.

Different oils are not identical in cooking properties, but corn, cottonseed, and peanut oil are very much alike for baking, although they do differ in some ways in frying. Olive oil, if allowed, is a wonderful flavor-aid to salads, vegetables, and meat dishes, and maintains its flavor in baking but loses most of it in frying.

A WORD TO THE WISE

But now a word to the wise before we get on with the recipes.

1. Palatability is what you are striving for in all cooking. Your selection of foods has been made on the basis of nutritional adequacy, so that each part of the meal is important. Herbs and spices can do much to increase the palatability of many of your dishes and bring out their essential flavors.

2. Don't use herbal seasonings in all of your dishes at any one meal. Rather, consider them as you would the accessories of your costume—an accent. An overdose can be as bad as no use.

3. In general, don't combine more than three herbs in any one dish. Have a preponderance of one so that its savor will predominate. When in doubt, let this be parsley, for it will do wonders for so many restricted dishes. As Irma G. Mazza wrote in her *Accent on Seasoning,* "it helps marry the flavors of the other herbs."

4. Dried herbs that are fresh are more concentrated than green ones, so use only half as much of them. In the main, our recipes are constructed and calculated with dried herbs. Not because they are better, because they are not, but because they are more readily available and we have the sodium content for many of them.

We hope the material in this chapter will open new vistas to you in planning taste-wise and health-wise meals for your dieter.

5. HOW TO USE SPIRITS IN DIET COOKERY

If you want to give diet cookery a real gourmet quality, wines and spirits are a must. Knowingly used, they add zest and sparkle to an otherwise simple dish. They enhance the natural flavor of many foods, add flavor to others, and improve the texture of still others. In other words, wine is considered a flavoring here (like salt substitute and pepper); one which, when blended with other ingredients, complements and enriches the natural goodness of foods in various ways.

Unlike the other seasonings, wine is not detectable in and of itself (unless you use too much and so defeat the whole purpose of its use in cooking). As with herbs, a little goes a long way, for it is not used to hide the natural flavor of foods.

The amount and the way you use it depend a good deal upon the effect you want to achieve. A light dribbling of wine over fish or fowl, blended with other seasonings, will bring out the *natural subtle flavors* of these foods and give them added richness. But for a different effect, wine and seasonings may be brewed together and used as a basting sauce. Still another variation is accomplished when wine is added to gravies or sauces before serving them.

Similarly with low sodium or non-fat milk dishes—the addition of wine to your puddings and soups will give them that *added bit of flavor* they so much need and will mask the low sodium milk taste. It will lift them out of the bland and listless class to something delicate and delectable.

Used with meats, wine not only enhances flavor but makes less expensive cuts tender and tasteful.

All in all, wine, used in conjunction with restricted cookery, can increase pleasurable eating, no matter how it is used. And there is really no trick to cooking with wine. All you have to do is master a few simple principles and have an adventuresome spirit about restricted cookery. At first, you may want to follow tested recipes, but in many cases you won't need a recipe. Measure a small amount of wine and add with other seasonings and taste-test to your liking. Wine, so used, acts as a flavoring only, so you can feel free to use it, teetotaler or not. It acts in much the same way as does vanilla. The alcohol evaporates, or passes off, as heat is applied, leaving a lingering flavor that is something pretty special to food lovers.

One of the best ways to get started in the use of wine in cookery is to make room right now on your flavoring shelf for a bottle of sherry; port or muscatel; a white wine such as sauterne or Rhine wine; and a red dinner wine such as claret or Burgundy.

As you cook with these artful flavorings in soups, meats, and desserts, and add them to salad mixings, new aromas will arise in your kitchen—and your reputation as a cook will rise, too. In general, it is easier to introduce wine to your dishes than herbs. Experiment, with wine and without, and let taste and flavor decide your usage.

There are a few simple rules to guide you in your use of wine in restricted cookery. We are indebted to the Home Advisory Service of the Wine Institute in San Francisco for these suggestions, and for some of the special recipes in this book which were worked out specifically for these diets.

1. Wine must be used with an eye to its sodium content for those who must reckon with this restriction. The daily total will dictate the amount for those who count; others should refer to their diet list or physician, and, if permitted, select lower count wines and use in small quantities—particularly when used with higher sodium foods.

2. Use wine as a flavor *accent*. Do not flavor every dish with it at any one meal.

3. Use wine with caution until you know its gentle savors. Use a little *less* rather than a little more to accent, but not dominate, the food prepared.

4. Do not allow any dish containing eggs and wine to boil, or it will curdle.

5. Wine is usually the last ingredient to be added to a dish (with the exception of meat cookery) to protect its fine flavor. Use it in about the same way you use vanilla, unless recipe otherwise specifies.

6. When using wine with fruits, add the wine several hours in advance, so that the wine will have a chance to fully flavor the food.

7. In general, light and delicate dishes invite the use of the light and more delicate wines (the white wines); while the heavier foods, such as red meats, have a natural affinity for the richness of the red wines to bring out their full-bodied flavor.

The kind of wine partly depends upon the kind of grapes used. The red dinner wines are made from the juice of grapes fermented with the skins on, while the white dinner wines are made from the juices alone (no pulp or skins). From time to time, we will list a table or dessert wine in a recipe and leave the specific choice to you. In the fermentation of the grape juice, most of the sweetness disappears, yielding a "dry" wine, such as claret and Burgundy in the red dinner wines—sauterne and Rhine in the white. When you want a delicate, aromatic, and tangy wine you will select from these four wines, or from the varietals.

Wine Type	Examples	Characteristics	Foods They Go with Best
Appetizer	Sherry	Nutty flavor, dry to semisweet	Appetizers and soups Chicken Desserts
Red Dinner	Burgundy Chianti Claret	Dry (not sweet) and slightly tart. Blend with hearty foods.	Meat dishes of all kinds —steaks, roasts,
	Zinfandel Cabernet	Light to ruby red in color	chops, games, spaghetti, low sodium cheese
	Rosé	Gay pink, fruity, light-bodied, dry or slightly sweet	Meat dishes, cheese, wine jellies, punches
White Dinner	Sauterne Rhine Riesling Sylvaner Chablis	Delicate flavor and very dry to semisweet, pale to deep gold in color	Fish, chicken, eggs and light main course dishes (casseroles)

Wine Type	Examples	Characteristics	Foods They Go with Best
Dessert	Port Muscatel	Sweet, full-bodied. Port is red, muscatel is amber in color with pronounced flavor and aroma of muscat grapes	Fruits, cookies, sweet cakes, low sodium cheese, jellies
	Tokay	Pinkish amber	Fruits

On the other hand, when you are adding flavor to a sweet dish, you will turn to the sweeter wines, such as sherry, port, and muscatel. These dessert wines do not have any sugar added to them, so you needn't have any anxieties on that score. They simply are not allowed to finish their fermentation and have a little pure grape brandy added to them to arrest the fermentation and hold the natural sweetness of the grapes.

There are natural affinities between certain foods and wines just as there are among herbs and foods. Some of the most usable ones in restricted cookery are shown in the table above.

We are omitting the sparkling wines, inasmuch as they are not cooking wines.

NOTES

You will note, from the above chart, that in addition to the familiar-sounding table wines we have listed a few of the *varietal* wines, for which sodium analyses are available (page 349). These varietals are named after the grape varieties from which they are made. Some are lower in sodium content than the standard table wines. Riesling is enough lower than sauterne to warrant its use in your high-ranking sodium foods calling for a white dinner wine, such as chicken cookery. Similarly with the red varietals—Chianti has the lowest sodium content of the red wines.

The beautiful part of all this is that to all intents and purposes you may use the white dinner wines interchangeably and you may use the red dinner wines interchangeably without any taste loss. Choose the type of wine that blends with the particular dish you are going to create and choose the lowest-ranking wine within that classification, if you have to work your arithmetic every day on sodium content totals. For saturated fat restriction, you have no worries here.

In our recipes calling for a "white dinner wine" or a "red dinner wine," our calculations are based upon the *lowest-ranking wine* of the class named unless otherwise specified. You may alter the selection to suit your requirements and palate. We have based our calculation of wine in our recipes on the maximum sodium content of the selected wine, as listed in the table (page 349), to protect those of you on most severe restrictions.

Start right now, won't you, to discover how easy it is to improve the flavor of your restricted cookery with wine?

6. START THE MEAL WITH SOUP

The soup tureen of Grandmother's time is reappearing in antique shops and on dining room tables today. Can it be that with its return there will be an upsurge in the fine old art of soup-making, too?

The "ready-mades" are not for you (with a few exceptions) who are concerned with sodium-restricted or low fat cooking. The commercial products, you will remember, are seldom low in sodium. Many are high in fat content too.

But you may as well face it. Man wants his soup, whatever his diet limitations. You will have to tackle the problem in your own kitchen, whether or not you have a tureen to glamorize your efforts.

Suggestions for soup-making:

1. Plan soups in relation to the rest of your meals. The lighter soups combine with a hearty meal; the pottages and chowders as meat substitutes; the chilled soups as lunch or warm-day stand-bys.

2. Be consumer-wise in your choice of ingredients. For sodium restriction, do not buy ready-to-use packets of vegetables, as they often contain celery and other greens not allowed on this diet. Make your selections in terms of the importance of the soup in the meal, the blending quality of the various ingredients, and cost.

3. Save all leftover vegetables and juices from cooked vegetables to use in soup for flavor enrichment.

4. Use herbs in various combinations for a plus-value in flavor. Try:

Bay leaf and parsley in low sodium pea soup and fish chowders

Curry and onion in fish chowders

Summer savory and cloves in minestrone

Thyme and cayenne in low sodium milk base soups

Thyme and marjoram in meat-vegetable combinations

5. Vary the seasonings, too. Try:

A pinch of mustard in bean soups

One fat-trimmed pork chop, cut small, in place of salt pork (if sodium and fat count allows)

A half-dozen cloves in chowders

A dash of allspice in vegetable-base soups

1 teaspoon vinegar to each quart vegetable soup (use cider, tarragon, or wine for variety)

A dash of cayenne

Peppercorns (whole pepper) for chowders and pottages

A little fat, in the form of unsalted butter or margarine, or vegetable oil, to add body and richness of flavor if allowed

6. Experiment with the addition of wine instead of vinegar in some of your cookery. Try a small amount at first to test its flavor. A word to the wise: add wine just before serving soup for best results. Be sure to calculate the sodium content of wine if you are adapting your own recipe. It is included in calculations calling for wine in our recipes.

Herb brandies offer still another savor.

7. Pay special attention to soup accompaniments and garnishings. Eye appeal and taste appeal march side by side. Try:

Thin lemon slices for tomato bouillons

Finely chopped parsley or chives as toppings for "cream" soups

Paprika sprinkling for pale soups

A topping of freshly cooked, unsalted popcorn

Slivers of toasted almonds as floaters

Leftover low sodium pancakes, cut in strips and floated on thick soups

Low sodium croutons

A slice of toasted low sodium bread, lightly coated

with paprika—floated on the top of steaming mine-
strone
Unsalted matzoth
Onion or garlic croutons

FOR SODIUM-RESTRICTED DIETERS

You may use meat and fresh fish in your soups only
when you can calculate the sodium content accurately—
remembering to portion both the meat and broth carefully. You may use vegetable stock and vegetables in
quantities; fresh mushrooms; low sodium milk; herbs;
wines—to mention some of the most important ingredients for your consideration.

You will want your soups to be something more than a
combination of leftovers carelessly tossed into an ever-
present soup kettle on the back of the stove, whose yawn-
ing depths seem to have no other purpose than to re-
ceive the castoffs of the day. This is not to suggest that
there is no place for leftovers. To the contrary, they can
be a lifesaver to you. Planned and creative use of leftovers—vegetable juices drained from vegetables when
served, vegetable peelings, and the outside leaves of lettuce and cabbage—can greatly enrich and so improve the
flavor of many of your soups.

But the real task in soup-making for sodium-restricted
diets is to bring out the *natural flavor* of ingredients used
and to enhance them by every known cooking trick. This
means you will have to think through the prevailing
flavor of the soup you want to make and select ingredients
for their blending qualities. Take, for instance, a fish
chowder. Milk, butter, fish, salt, and pepper are the old
familiars. On this diet, low sodium milk rather than whole
milk might form the base of the soup if you want to conserve your milk allowance for a beverage. The best way to
bring out the prevailing flavor of fish in combination with
low sodium milk is to add a little wine for richness and
for its blending qualities, and a bit of parsley with your
choice of herbs to sharpen flavor. These additions
strengthen the prevailing fish flavor without detracting
from it in any way.

Recipes in this chapter are based upon the restrictions
listed below for the sodium-restricted diet. Check them

against your own list and make such changes as may be necessary.

For sodium restriction, do not use:

Canned soups (except approved sodium-restricted)
Canned vegetables (except approved sodium-restricted)
Cheese (except low sodium dietetic)
Fresh vegetables on your prohibited list
Frozen peas or Lima beans
Meat stocks or gravies
Ready-to-use packets of vegetables, as they often contain celery and other greens not allowed on this diet

FOR FAT-RESTRICTED DIETERS

Consommé and bouillon, which are relatively fat-free, may be used as desired if your diet is not restricted in sodium. They may be canned, made from cubes, or homemade.

To remove fat from homemade soups:

Cut a piece of paper towel the size of saucepan; float on the surface of the soup. When it has absorbed all the grease it will hold, remove the towel.

Chill the soup with a piece of ice, or better still, cool in refrigerator, and remove the solid grease from the cold soup.

Float a large lettuce leaf in the hot soup until grease is absorbed; remove leaf.

Some commercial soups are low in fat and perhaps may be used on this diet if it is not restricted in sodium. Listed below are some canned soups which have 2 grams or less of fat per serving, after suggested dilution with water or non-fat milk (3 servings per can). As in most instances at least a part of this fat is saturated, you will want to check with your diet list, doctor, or dietitian to see if they are allowed on your diet.

Asparagus, Cream of (Campbell's)
Beef; Beef Broth; Beef Noodle (Campbell's)

Beef, Vegetable with Barley (Heinz)
Black Bean (Campbell's)
Chicken Gumbo; Chicken Noodle; Chicken with Rice
   (Campbell's and Heinz)
Chicken Vegetable (Heinz)
Green Pea, Cream of (Heinz)
Gumbo Creole (Heinz)
Turkey Noodle (Campbell's)
Turtle, Genuine (Heinz)
Vegetable; Vegetable Beef; Vegetarian Vegetable
   (Campbell's)
Vegetable with Beef Broth; Vegetable without Meat
   (Heinz)

For saturated fat restriction, do not use:

Butter or margarine (except special margarine if
   allowed)
Cheese (except approved low fat)
Cream
Soup mixes, canned soups, or frozen soups without
   physician's consent, as some of these may contain
   as much as 11 grams of fat per serving
Soups made with fatty cuts of meat
Whole milk

POTTAGES

To our way of thinking, the pottages are the best of our
soup recipes. Their many ingredients, inviting a blend of
savor—their heavy thickness and fragrant earthiness—
contribute goodness in unstinted amounts.

ITALIAN MINESTRONE
8 Servings

There are almost as many ways to make minestrone as
there are cooks. They all have one essential in common
—namely that vegetables form the base of this delicious
soup. If you are looking for something thick, chock-full
of vegetables, and hearty, this is a good recipe to use. It
will give you its best if you cook it one day and serve it
the next.

*Natale Barbieri of San Jose is responsible for our mine-
strone. Omitting the salt pork and Parmesan cheese, and*

*adding more herbs to spice the blend of vegetables, here
is the recipe pretty much as he served it to us:*

2 cups dried beans (cranberry or navy preferred)	½ cup water
	2 tablespoons vinegar
	½ teaspoon sugar
2 quarts water	6 whole cloves
4 dried red peppers, thinly sliced	1 teaspoon summer savory
4 mashed peppercorns	1 teaspoon sweet basil
1 chopped garlic clove	2 cups cut-up tomatoes
1 cup chopped onions	1 cup finely chopped zucchini
3 tablespoons minced parsley	
¼ teaspoon dry mustard	1 cup peeled and cubed potatoes

Soak beans overnight; drain and put into large soup
kettle. Add fresh water, peppers, and peppercorns; cook
slowly until soft (about 1½ hours). Drain 2 cups of
beans; mash or press through coarse sieve or purée in
blender. Return to soup kettle and stir well. Meanwhile,
combine garlic, onions, and parsley in saucepan with ½
cup water; cook over low heat for 10 minutes. Add to
soup kettle. Add seasonings. Bring soup to a boil. Add
vegetables and water to make desired thickness. Cover
and simmer until vegetables are fork-tender. Serve in a
tureen from table, with paprika-coated croutons, or onion
or garlic croutons. A sprinkling of Parmesan cheese may
be added for "regular" family members, and salt for all
except sodium-restricted dieters.

One Serving (1 cup)	Total Recipe	
Without croutons		
6	49	milligrams sodium
1	8	grams total fat
negligible	negligible	grams saturated fat
208	1664	calories

VARIATION

To make this soup really authentic and a whole meal if
served with bread and a tossed salad, add 1 cup cooked
paste (spaghetti or macaroni broken into small pieces).
Prepare and add to soup just before serving.

ONION CROUTONS
8 Servings

Combine 1 tablespoon corn oil and 1 teaspoon onion. Add 1 cup soft ¼" low sodium bread cubes (homemade bread) and stir until each one is coated with the oil mixture. Spread on a cooky sheet and toast under low broiler heat for about 10 minutes or until golden brown. This will give you onion croutons for your soup.

One Serving	Total Recipe	
negligible	2	milligrams sodium
2	16	grams total fat
negligible	negligible	grams saturated fat
40	321	calories

One serving: ¼ teaspoon vegetable oil.

CHOWDERS

We don't have to look to Europe for all of our good thick soups—our pottages—as our own New England has given to us bountifully in this field of cookery. Its wonderful chowders carry us back in our memories to the vigorous days of colonizing and settling—with their demands for a hearty fare. The old chowders were originally made of milk and fish. As vegetables abounded in home garden patches, chowders came to include vegetable-milk combinations, too. Many of the old-time recipes have been handed down from generation to generation. These chowders were so chock-full of good ingredients they were meals in themselves.

For you dieters, the adapted chowders are still fine one-dish meals, if you combine them with low sodium bread sticks, a tossed salad, beverage, and fruit dessert.

NEW ENGLAND VEGETABLE CHOWDER
8 Servings

The New England vegetable chowder, like the minestrone, is a vegetable soup, thick and flavorsome if well prepared. It lacks some of the body of the minestrone, due to the bean base of the Italian soup, but is luscious-good and quite palatable even without salt.

1 teaspoon unsalted butter or margarine	½ teaspoon sugar
	Bouquet of herbs
½ cup sliced fresh mushrooms	½ cup fresh peas
	3 cups low sodium non-fat milk
6 string beans, cut-up	
¼ cup finely cut onions	2 tablespoons chopped parsley
1 cup diced potatoes	¼ cup sauterne
1 cup cream-styled corn, canned without added sodium	1 tablespoon grated low sodium cheese; Parmesan cheese for regulars (optional)
Water to cover (about 2 cups)	Paprika
6 mashed peppercorns	

Melt fat in small skillet; add mushrooms and sauté for 5 minutes. Prepare vegetables and combine with mushrooms and water in saucepan. Heat to boiling; then simmer for 10 minutes. Add seasonings, peas, and milk. Cook for 10 minutes, stirring from time to time. Fork-test vegetables for doneness. Add parsley and wine; heat slightly. Serve at once, with or without cheese, and a dash of paprika on top of each serving. Salt for regulars.

One Serving (1 cup) With cheese	Total Recipe Without cheese	
8	56	milligrams sodium
3	7	grams total fat
3	4	grams saturated fat
121	740	calories

VARIATION

Float a piece of low sodium toast sprinkled with paprika on top of chowder. Or sprinkle with low sodium onion or garlic croutons.

Many substitutions may be made with this basic recipe. It may be made thicker or thinner according to preference, depending upon the amount of liquid used. Many different vegetable combinations may be used.

LOW SATURATED FAT VARIATION

Follow Basic Recipe and Variations except substitute vegetable oil for butter and omit cheese. When not restricted in sodium, use regular canned vegetables and add salt to taste. *One serving: negligible saturated fat (⅛ teaspoon vegetable oil).*

CODFISH CHOWDER
8 Servings

Our original recipe called for salt pork but this must be eliminated for diet purposes. We think the chowder remarkably good in this new form. With bread sticks or low sodium bread, toasted, a tossed salad, and simple fruit in season for dessert, you will have a well-balanced and satisfying meal, and one that is not too hard on the budget. When you are going to use your chowder as a main meal, you may leave fish in chunk size instead of flaking.

2 pounds fresh cod	6 whole cloves
1 quart boiling water	6 peppercorns
1 bay leaf, crumbled	2 cups low sodium non-
¼ cup chopped onion	fat milk
2 cups diced potatoes	½ cup Rhine wine
2 tablespoons chopped	(optional)
parsley	

Place cleaned and washed fish in stewing pan; cover with boiling water. Add bay leaf, cover pan, and simmer fish until fork-tender (about 15 minutes). Drain, saving broth. Flake the fish, removing skin and bones; set aside. Strain broth; measure 3 cups into stewing pan. Add onions, potatoes, 1 tablespoon parsley, and seasonings. Simmer until potatoes are nearly tender (about 10 minutes). Add fish and milk; simmer to heat thoroughly but do not boil. Add wine; garnish each serving with parsley and serve at once. Add salt for those without sodium restrictions.

One Serving (1½ oz. fish, cooked weight)	*Total Recipe*	
With wine		
49	391	milligrams sodium
negligible	3	grams total fat
negligible	negligible	grams saturated fat
105	839	calories

VARIATION

Other fish on your diet list, such as haddock or halibut, may be substituted for the cod. Canned salmon (without added sodium for sodium-restricted dieters) may be used for a hurry-up chowder. Fresh salmon is delicious, too. Vegetable variations may be made to suit individual likes.

SHRIMP-OKRA GUMBO
6 Servings

Like the minestrones, fish-okra gumbos are almost as numerous as there are good cooks in the Deep South. We have taken an old family recipe and have adapted it for sodium and fat restrictions. Rich and luscious, it is really a meal in itself ladled over steaming rice with raw vegetable accompaniments.

6 chicken-flavored low sodium bouillon cubes
6 cups boiling water
3 cups chopped, peeled fresh tomatoes (or 3 cups canned without added sodium)
2 tablespoons chopped parsley
1 cup chopped green pepper
2 cloves garlic, chopped fine
1 cup chopped onions
10-oz. package frozen okra (or 1 pound fresh okra, washed and trimmed)
Pinch of thyme
2 (4½-oz.) cans shrimp, canned without added sodium
½ cup Chablis (optional)
Paprika
¾ cup hot, cooked rice

Dissolve bouillon cubes in boiling water. Add vegetables and thyme (cutting okra into ¾-inch length). Cover and heat to boiling; simmer for 10 minutes. Add shrimp and simmer until gumbo slightly thickens from the vegetables and fish, breaking into pieces and mingling with the liquid. Add wine just before serving. Serve in soup bowls with 2 tablespoons hot rice lining bottoms or dropped into each serving. Garnish with paprika; add salt for those without sodium restrictions. (A dash of cayenne gives a red-hot gumbo.)

One serving With rice and wine	Total Recipe	
52	309	milligrams sodium
1	7	grams total fat
negligible	negligible	grams saturated fat
155	930	calories

LOW SATURATED FAT VARIATION

If not restricted in sodium, use regular bouillon cubes and canned shrimp; add 1 cup sliced celery and 10-oz. package frozen ready-cut Alaska crab or an equal amount of fresh crab meat; add salt to taste. If you like a very hot gumbo, add 6 to 8 drops tabasco sauce just before serving. *One serving: negligible grams saturated fat.*

SOME OTHER SOUPS
HAMBURGER-VEGETABLE SOUP
8 Servings

This is a man's soup, hearty and complete in itself. It is a very thick soup and is so loaded with vegetables and meat that there is little liquid, as such, at time of serving. If you want a thinner soup, simply increase the amount of liquid used.

- 1 tablespoon vegetable oil
- ½ cup minced onion
- 1 minced garlic clove
- 1 pound *lean* ground beef, made into small balls
- 4 whole cloves
- 1 tablespoon vinegar
- ½ teaspoon thyme
- 1 teaspoon marjoram
- Black pepper
- 1 cup shredded cabbage
- 1 cup cut-up fresh tomatoes
- 1 cup fresh, cut string beans
- 1 cup fresh peas

Put oil into warm skillet; heat. Add onion and garlic; lightly brown. Add meat balls; simmer gently for about 10 minutes. Remove to soup pot. Add seasonings, cabbage, and tomatoes. Bring to a boil; add string beans and peas. Cook until soup thickens and vegetables are fork-tender. You may take out a cup of vegetables, mash them and return to kettle if a thick pottage is wanted. Salt for the regulars before serving.

One Serving (1½ oz. meat, cooked weight)	Total Recipe	
45	356	milligrams sodium
6	50	grams total fat
4	34	grams saturated fat
157	1256	calories

LOW SATURATED FAT VARIATION

Use top round steak for ground meat choice, selecting *good* or *commercial* grade of meat; brown meat in ribbed-bottom skillet and discard drippings. Chill soup before serving, and remove hardened fat; then reheat. Add salt to taste if not restricted in sodium. *One serving: 3 grams saturated fat (⅜ teaspoon vegetable oil).*

BASIC CREAM SOUP, SODIUM-RESTRICTED
Base for 4 Servings

1 tablespoon unsalted butter	½ teaspoon onion powder
1 tablespoon flour	1 cup low sodium non-fat milk
⅛ teaspoon white pepper	
½ cup vegetable water	2 tablespoons Riesling
	Paprika

Melt butter, blend in flour and seasonings. Stir in vegetable water, mixing until smooth. Add milk. Cook over low heat until thickened, stirring constantly (about 10 minutes). Add 1 cup vegetables (page 76); blend and heat. Add wine just before serving; sprinkle with paprika and add salt for those without sodium restrictions.

One Serving	Total Recipe	
Without vegetable		
6	24	milligrams sodium
3	12	grams total fat
3	12	grams saturated fat
59	237	calories

BASIC CREAM SOUP, FAT-RESTRICTED
Base for 4 Servings

½ cup vegetable water	1 cup non-fat milk (low sodium if restricted in sodium)
1 tablespoon flour	
⅛ teaspoon white pepper	2 tablespoons Riesling
½ teaspoon onion powder	Paprika

Pour vegetable water into small jar; add flour and seasonings. Cover; shake until smooth and pastelike. Add milk gradually, stirring to avoid lumps. Transfer to saucepan and cook over low heat until thickened, stirring constantly (about 10 minutes). Add salt to taste if not restricted in sodium. Add 1 cup vegetable (see below); blend and heat. Add wine and sprinkle with paprika.

One Serving	Total Recipe	
Without vegetable		
negligible	negligible	grams total fat
34	137	calories

Vegetables to use: add to the Cream Soup Base 1 full cup of any of the following (*check against your allowable*) vegetables, mashed, put through a coarse sieve, or minced very fine: Asparagus, broccoli, cauliflower, corn, onion, or potato (add green and white parts of 1 leek and ¼ cup chopped cooked onion).

If you are lucky enough to have a blender, prepare vegetables and blend according to instructions. Then add all ingredients for Basic Cream Soup and blend according to directions.

SPLIT PEA SOUP
4 Servings

¾ cup dried split peas	3½ cups water
Dash of nutmeg	½ cup sauterne
4 crushed peppercorns	Paprika

Soak peas in water overnight. Drain; put into soup kettle with nutmeg, peppercorns, and 3½ cups water. Cover and bring to boil. Simmer for about 2 hours, or until mixture is soft and thick. Add wine; reheat. Garnish with paprika at time of serving. Salt for those without sodium restrictions.

One Serving (1 cup)	Total Recipe	
13	51	milligram sodium
negligible	2	grams total fat
negligible	negligible	grams saturated fat
155	618	calories

TOMATO SOUP
2 Servings

12-ounce can un-salted tomato juice	¼ teaspoon thyme
	1 teaspoon grated onion
1 teaspoon chopped parsley	1 small bay leaf
	Pepper to taste

Heat unsalted tomato juice (use only approved brand). Add spices. Do not bring to a boil, but simmer gently. Serve at once with a thin slice of lemon in each cup, and add a sprinkling of salt for those without sodium restrictions.

One Serving	Total Recipe	
6	12	milligrams sodium
1	1	grams total fat
negligible	negligible	grams saturated fat
41	81	calories

VARIATIONS

Use cloves with thyme.

Use ½ garlic clove in juice while heating. Remove before serving.

TOMATO CORN SOUP
3 Servings

2 tablespoons unsalted butter
¼ cup finely chopped onion
½ small bay leaf
1 tablespoon flour
Pepper

1 cup chopped fresh tomatoes
1 cup cream-style corn, canned without added sodium
1 cup water
3 parsley sprigs

Melt butter over low heat. Add onions; cook for about 5 minutes. Combine all ingredients in soup kettle. Cover; bring to boil and simmer for 30 minutes. Mash through sieve or purée when thick soup is your choice. Add salt for those without sodium restrictions.

One Serving	Total Recipe	
13	38	milligrams sodium
8	25	grams total fat
8	23	grams saturated fat
153	460	calories

LOW SATURATED FAT VARIATION

Follow Basic Recipe except to substitute vegetable oil for butter. Or omit all fat, combine other ingredients in soup kettle and continue as directed. If not restricted in sodium, use regular canned corn and add salt to taste. *One serving, with vegetable oil: negligible saturated fat (2 teaspoons vegetable oil).*

CHILLED TOMATO MADRILENE
2 *Servings*

Heat a 12-ounce can tomato juice, canned without added sodium.

Meanwhile, soften 1 scant tablespoon gelatin in ½ cup cold water. Add 1 tablespoon lemon juice and 1 teaspoon *minced* parsley. Add hot juice; add dash fine black pepper and cayenne. Blend. Chill until ready to serve. Cube lightly with knife, and pile into bouillon cups. Top with a slice of lemon. Sprinkle with salt for those without sodium restrictions.

One Serving (¾ cup)	*Total Recipe*	
8	15	milligrams sodium
1	1	grams total fat
negligible	negligible	grams saturated fat
60	119	calories

7. MEAT'S SPECIAL ROLE

Some have meat but can not eat;
Some could eat but have no meat;
We have meat and can all eat;
Blest, therefore, be God for our meat.
    —UNKNOWN: the Selkirk Grace
    (from MS. of about 1650)

This old-time grace bespeaks the sentiments of thousands of people who are on restricted diets. Meat is to them one of the bright spots of their "allowables," because of its fine flavor and appetite appeal, with or without salt.

Meat has been the mainstay of man's diet since the beginning of time. "Protein" comes from the Greek verb meaning to take first place, and of all the proteins meat ranks first in flavor and high in nutritive value. Do treat it well in the way you cook it.

Although it is the most expensive food in our diet, it is such a high quality protein, and a good source of vitamins and minerals to boot, that we are usually willing to pay for its fine flavor.

The principal reason meat is limited on the low sodium diet is due to the high sodium content of foods of animal origin. Where servings must be small, it is particularly important that selection and preparation be undertaken with care.

The principal reason meat is restricted on the low saturated fat regimen is to limit the amount of animal fat. As in sodium restriction, with small servings the rule of the day, particular attention should be given to selection and method of preparation. You will have to give up the "choice" grade of meats with their high marbled fat and make your selections from "good" or "commercial" grades.

Whatever your choice, meat should be cooked to bring out its natural flavor. Whatever method is used, it should in no way, spoil, lose, or cover up its characteristic flavor.

The full-bodied flavor of meat makes it possible to serve

it often with very little added seasonings, once you have become accustomed to the flavor of foods without the salt shaker. A little lemon juice and freshly ground pepper dribbled over a sizzling steak or young and juicy chops will suffice. Add a sprinkling of salt if sodium is not restricted.

But for texture improvement, flavor richness, and variety, you will find that the use of wines and herbs will add a gourmet flair to your meat dishes, however simple they may be. If you have never used such aids in your regular cooking, don't rush in with too many new savors all at once. And above all, don't announce in advance all of the secrets of your trade. Be subtle. Accept the compliments, and only then reveal your new kitchen helpers.

The calculations in this chapter are approximate. There are many variables which cannot be controlled from our kitchen to yours. There is the leanness of meat used; the amount of fat trimmed; the shrinkage of about 25 per cent in the cooking process; the variation of sodium content in the different water supplies in the country; the actual amount of water used in meat cookery; the length of time involved in the cooking process and its effect upon the sodium and fat content of the meat itself; the temperature; cooking time; and size of surface of the cooking utensil used in recipes in which dry wines are ingredients; the concentration of sodium and fat in the drippings and juices in prolonged cooking and in repeated boiling of meat—all of these and other factors make it impossible to rule out all of the variables.

Most of the recipes, catering to the very restrictive dietary, are based on 3 ounces of cooked meat or less per serving. If this portion is not satisfying to your "regulars," or if your dietary allowance is more generous, you can plan on 1½ or 2 servings for these members of the family.

For those of you on sodium restriction who find it difficult to stay within your meat allowances, you might like to investigate the interesting article by George Ornstein, M.D., of New York City. He writes in the April 1951 issue of the *Journal of the Medical Society of New Jersey* on the effect of the repeated boiling of meats (and certain vegetables) in terms of their sodium content.

Meats to use:

Beef Lamb Pork Veal

The amount to be used will be determined by your physician, depending upon your particular needs. In general, it will be between 3 and 5 ounces cooked, daily. Three ounces is about 4" x 4" x ½".

For sodium restriction, do not use:

Bacon	Kidneys
Bologna	Koshered meats
Brains	Luncheon meats
Chipped or corned beef	Salt
Frankfurters	Salted or smoked meats
Gravies (unless allowed on your diet list)	Sausage
	Sweetbreads
Ham, except low sodium dietetic	Tongue, smoked

For saturated fat restriction, do not use:

Bacon, except Canadian (if allowed on your diet list)
Butter, hydrogenated shortenings, or margarine (except special margarine if allowed)
Cheese (except *low fat* if allowed on your diet list)
Choice grade meats
Cream, fresh or sour
Gravies (unless allowed on your diet list or specially prepared, pages 114-15)
Sauces, commercial or homemade with whole milk, whole egg or egg yolk, butter, or margarine
Whole milk (dried, condensed, evaporated, or fresh)

Things to remember:

1. Allow approximately 1 pound of meat, without bones, for 3 to 4 servings, or 2 servings with the bone. The amount of fat will alter the number of servings you can get to a pound of raw meat. Meat-stretcher recipes will yield another serving or two to each pound of meat.

You will have to account for the differences in appetites in your family group. Grandma won't need as much meat as your sixteen-year-old footballer.

2. Buy lean "good" or "commercial" grade meat and trim it of all visible fat.

3. Loose-wrap meat and keep in refrigerator until an hour or so before use.

4. Slow-cook for best insurance of full meat flavor and least amount of shrinkage.

5. Use a meat thermometer for guaranteed cooking results.

6. If restricted in fat, avoid frying of meats as this seals in fat. Broil, pan-broil (in cast-iron ribbed-bottom skillet *), bake, braise, pressure-cook, or roast meats. Do not rub meats in flour and pan-brown, as this too seals in fats. Rather broil in oven of ribbed skillet so that fat may drip out, if this is your method choice. Do not baste with pan drippings, plain or combined with other liquids.

7. Use meat tenderizer, seasoned or unseasoned (low sodium for sodium-restricted dieters), on tougher cuts of meat to make fork-tender.

8. Use lemon juice to point up the natural flavor of meats to be broiled.

9. Vinegar added to stews and pot roasts will do the same thing for them and give texture improvement.

10. Or, substitute wine for some of the liquid in your meat recipes when you want extra flavor richness.

11. Don't forget herbs—a marvelous addition to meat cookery.

12. Gravies, if allowed at all, must be used in very limited amounts and must be calculated for sodium and fat content. They must be portioned with same care as you do meat.

AN ADMONITION: Choose your method of meat cookery with the same care you do your meat.

Broil meats when you want their fine, natural flavors.

Pan-broil or pan-fry (as it is sometimes called) the tougher cuts where slow-cooking is indicated.

Braise meats when you use cuts that require special ministrations—such as spareribs, pot roasts, rolled roasts, shoulder cuts, and cutlets, to mention only a few (such cuts invite your ingenuity in seasonings, too).

Pressure cooking is a real timesaver for stews, rolled roasts, and combination dishes, but don't expect quite the same texture fineness as you will get with the slower methods of preparation.

Roasting is an art all itself; it involves much more than proper temperature and time control, although they are important. The selection of the right size

* Axford Broiler, 557 Treat Avenue, San Francisco 10, California.

pan (open and lowsided, of course), preparation, appropriate seasoning for desired results—all must play their part.

For roasting or braising meat, use red or white wine, wine and water, or wine and vegetable oil as your basting sauce. To the sauce, add tomato juice (unsalted for sodium restriction), desired herbal combinations, garlic, or spices. Simmer all together to blend flavors before basting. Keep warm during period of use, but do not boil. Never add a cold sauce to cooking meat.

HERBS AND SEASONINGS TO USE

Although there are no hard-and-fast rules here, there are certain combinations that are traditional in meat cookery and they are good starters. For the nonce, try:

With beef: Basil, bay, caraway, curry, dill, garlic, onion, parsley, rosemary, sage, savory, sweet marjarom, thyme, turmeric, Worcestershire sauce (low sodium dietetic is available)

With pork: Basil, caraway, chives, curry, garlic, ground ginger, lemon peel, nutmeg, onion, rosemary, sage, sweet marjoram, thyme

With lamb: Whole cloves, curry, dill, garlic, onion, oregano, parsley, rosemary, sage, sweet marjoram

With veal: Basil, garlic, nutmeg, onion, parsley, sage, summer savory, tarragon, thyme

ROAST BEEF

So full-flavored is a fine beef roast that you will want to cook it many times "as is" with, perhaps, a little lemon juice and pepper. But with meat so limited in quantity on this diet, even choice roasted beef deserves special preparation and seasoning once in a while to avoid the monotonous. Herbs and wines can be used alone or in combination to give that special savor. Herbs can be brewed in a wine base as suggested before or can be scattered directly over the meat. The results are very different. Wine can be used in basting sauces as suggested, or poured directly over the meat, or used to flavor the gravy only. Where saturated fat is restricted, choose a sirloin of beef or a top of round (using meat tenderizer) for your beef roast as these are ever so much less fat than a prime rib roast.

SIRLOIN OF BEEF

3 Pounds lean *roast*, 9 Servings

Trim meat of all visible fat; wipe thoroughly with a damp cloth. Season with a light sprinkling of freshly-ground pepper and pure garlic powder (not garlic salt for sodium restriction). Place on a rack in a low-sided pan. For robust flavoring, put 3 slices of onion on top of roast, fastening with tooth picks. Put into a preheated 325° (slow) oven and roast according to your temperature chart. For those without sodium restriction, salt after meat is cooked and sliced, as salt penetrates meat when hot.

One Serving
(3 oz. meat, cooked weight)

81	milligrams sodium
6	grams total fat
6	grams saturated fat
161	calories

VARIATIONS

Meat may be marinated (page 120) before cooking. Or you may want to baste for added flavor using a sauce made of:

1 cup claret	1 tablespoon vegetable
½ teaspoon thyme	oil
Dash lemon peel	

Heat sauce and baste at least 4 times during the roasting period.

BEEF JULIENNE
6 Servings

There are many ways to use leftover roast beef. It is good

cold and served with a garnish; it is good in low sodium bread sandwiches spread with unsalted butter and a dash of mustard, or with garlic butter; and it is excellent in a julienne.

½ cup Chianti wine	1 cup water
¼ cup chopped onion	6 slices roasted sirloin
1 tablespoon chopped parsley	of beef (2 oz. per slice)

Simmer wine, onion, parsley, and water over low heat until onion is tenderized (about 5 minutes). Add meat, cover, and let simmer until thoroughly heated (about 30 minutes). Remove meat to platter and thicken liquid with 1 to 2 tablespoons flour. If no sodium restriction, add salt to taste. If dieter is allowed gravy, portion carefully.

One Serving
(2 oz. meat, cooked weight)
With wine gravy

56	milligrams sodium
4	grams total fat
4	grams saturated fat
123	calories

STEAK

LEAN TOP ROUND STEAK

Trim meat of all visible fat; wipe with damp cloth. Sprinkle with seasoned or unseasoned low sodium meat tenderizer; * let stand for 45 minutes. Put into preheated very hot ribbed-bottom skillet. Brown on under side; turn and brown. Remove to warm platter. Season with light sprinkling of freshly ground pepper; salt for those without sodium restrictions.

One Serving
(4 oz. meat, raw trimmed weight)

80	milligrams sodium
6	grams total fat
6	grams saturated fat
195	calories

* Adolph's Low Sodium Meat Tenderizer, Adolph's Ltd., Los Angeles 46, California.

VARIATIONS

Meat may be oven or pan-broiled and braised in ½ cup water or Chianti. Or tomato juice (canned without added sodium for those with sodium restrictions) may be substituted as the liquid. If a more robust flavor is desired, add ½ teaspoon sweet basil or thyme with ¼ cup finely chopped onions to liquid. Simmer gently; then add to browned meat. Cover and let simmer until fork-tender (from 30 to 45 minutes). If gravy is allowed, cool with an ice cube and skim off surface fat; portion carefully.

LOW SATURATED FAT VARIATION

Never dredge steaks in flour and pan-brown, as this seals in fat. Your method must be to prepare meat so that invisible fat drips out as much as possible. Pan-broil in ribbed-bottom skillet, or oven-broil on rack so that fat drips away from meat. If gravy is allowed, chill with ice cube and remove hardened fat, or make according to special recipe (page 105). If no sodium restrictions, salt meat and gravy before serving.

STEWS

Twenty-five minutes in the kitchen and the main part of your meal is prepared—that is if you have a pressure cooker and are not on low saturated fat restriction. We do not like a quick-stew method as well as the slow-simmer method for those who must limit fat.

Pressure cooking is a time-saving way of cooking not only stew, but those cuts of meat which require moist heat cookery. In addition to stews, for sodium restriction try this method for pot roasts, Swiss steaks, short ribs of beef, pork shoulder steaks and hocks, flank steaks, and brisket of beef. The addition of meat tenderizer will cut cooking time, too, and help to assure a tender product from these tougher cuts of meat.

Pressure-cooked meats have a high retention of nutrients, so in addition to being time-savers, they are nutrition-savers, too.

For finest flavor, when pressure cooking is your election, flour and brown meat before adding liquid and seasonings for the final cooking process. *For those of you on fat restriction,* do not dredge meat in flour but sear in ribbed-bottom skillet; drain all fat and then place in pressure cooker, but remember flavor will be finer using the slow-simmer method.

BEEF STEW
8 Servings

2 tablespoons vegetable oil
2 pounds *lean* stew beef
3 tablespoons flour
¼ cup chopped onion
1 minced garlic clove
Pepper
¼ cup water
¼ cup red table wine

¼ teaspoon thyme
1 tablespoon parsley
1 small bay leaf, crumbled
6 medium potatoes, cubed
1 cup cubed rutabaga
2 cups peas, fresh or canned without added sodium

Heat oil in pressure cooker. Meanwhile wipe meat with damp cloth and trim excess fat. Put flour into bag; add cut-up stew meat and shake vigorously to coat. Put meat, onions, and garlic into pressure cooker and lightly brown; turn as needed. Sprinkle lightly with pepper. Heat water, wine, and seasonings in small saucepan; then add to pressure cooker. Cover and cook as directed for your particular cooker (about 15 to 20 minutes). Add vegetables and cook 5 minutes longer. (Canned peas should be heated separately and added just before serving.) Add salt for regulars.

One Serving (3 oz. meat, cooked weight)	Total Recipe	
86	684	milligrams sodium
15	123	grams total fat
12	92	grams saturated fat
377	3017	calories

VARIATIONS

Tomato juice (low sodium dietetic) may be substituted for wine and water.

Sweet basil may be substituted for thyme. Omit bay leaf.

LOW SATURATED FAT VARIATION

Use only top round for stew meat. Trim cut-up meat of all visible fat. Do not dredge in flour but broil or pan-broil in ribbed-bottom skillet. Pour off fat; then proceed as in Basic Recipe. After meat is cooked, swirl ice cube in liquid and remove hardened fat. Add vegetables and cook 5 minutes longer. If desired, thicken gravy with flour mixed with cold water. If no sodium restrictions, regular canned or frozen peas may be used, and add salt to taste. *One serving: 6 grams saturated fat.*

ACCOMPANIMENT
HERB DUMPLINGS

6 Servings

Are you looking for something pungent and different for that pot roast or stew dinner? If so, why not try herb dumplings, keeping the seasoning of your meat on the light side, in so far as herbs are concerned.

1 cup *sifted* all-purpose flour	½ teaspoon powdered savory
2 teaspoons low sodium baking powder	¼ teaspoon thyme
Pinch sugar	½ cup low sodium non-fat milk

Sift dry ingredients together and blend in liquid. Drop by spoonfuls onto your meat. (Not on the liquid of the meat if you would avoid soggy dumplings.) Cook 10 minutes with kettle uncovered; 10 minutes with cover. Serve at once with a light sprinkling of salt for the regulars.

One Serving	Total Recipe	
2	9	milligrams sodium
negligible	1	grams total fat
negligible	negligible	grams saturated fat
75	450	calories

VARIATION

Herbs may be omitted for plain dumplings. Increase sugar to ¼ teaspoon.

GROUND BEEF

The good old "ground round" can be worked overtime on this diet. Moderate in sodium content, it lends itself to any number of combinations when you tire of it plain. It is one of the first to get started with when the rules and regulations all seem a bit confusing. Its good flavor and ease of preparation recommend its use. Of course, ground beef need not be ground top round steak, except for low saturated fat diets. Stew meat, neck, rump, flank and fore-shank, all can be ground for use for general sodium-restricted diets. Have your butcher trim beef before grinding. Be sure to specify the grind you want for your particular meat dish. In addition to the recipes given below, see Tamale Pie in the Veal section.

BEEF PATTIES
4 Patties

1 pound *lean* ground beef	½ teaspoon rosemary
½ teaspoon thyme	1 teaspoon vegetable oil
1 teaspoon minced parsley	½ teaspoon black pepper

Blend ingredients in a mixing bowl. Shape into patties and broil. Turn once. Sprinkle with salt for the regulars; serve. Or you may pan-broil in ribbed-bottom skillet.

One Serving
(3 oz. meat, cooked weight)

80	milligrams sodium
14	grams total fat
13	grams saturated fat
234	calories

VARIATION

Put a slice of Bermuda onion and a slice of tomato on top of shaped beef patties. Lightly season with pepper and broil.

LOW SATURATED FAT VARIATION

Use only top round steak and trim of all visible fat. Oil may be used according to daily allowance. *One serving, without oil: 6 grams saturated fat.*

MEAT BALLS
5 Servings

We are indebted to Mrs. Finn Taaje, of Los Gatos, California, for this old Norwegian recipe, adapted to the purposes of this dietary. The spices give it an unsual flavor.

1 pound *lean* ground beef, ground twice	2 tablespoons minced onion
½ cup low sodium bread crumbs (at least 1 day old)	⅛ teaspoon nutmeg
⅛ teaspoon ginger	½ teaspoon black pepper
	1 tablespoon vegetable oil

Mix all together in a mixing bowl and shape into small, round balls. Brown in heavy skillet, lightly oiled with 1 tablespoon vegetable oil. Cover with water (about 2 cups). Cover pan tightly and let simmer for 1½ hours. Salt for regulars when you serve portions.

One Serving
(2½ oz. meat, cooked
weight)

68	milligrams sodium
14	grams total fat
12	grams saturated fat
239	calories

LOW SATURATED FAT VARIATION

Use top round of beef, trimmed of all visible fat before grinding. Brown under broiler or in ribbed-bottom skillet. Oil may be added to mixture according to daily allowance. If gravy is allowed, swirl ice cube in liquid and remove hardened fat. *One serving, without oil: 5 grams saturated fat.*

HERBAL MEAT LOAF
6 Servings

It is particularly important to make a good meat loaf in restricted cookery, because it is not only good hot when first prepared, but is a welcome addition for a sandwich filling and for cold cuts. There is real herb accent to this meat loaf.

1 pound *lean* ground beef	½ teaspoon sweet basil
1 shredded wheat biscuit, crumbled fine	1 tablespoon vegetable oil
¼ cup minced onion	½ teaspoon black pepper
1 egg (optional)	¼ cup low sodium non-fat milk
¼ teaspoon summer savory	¼ cup red table wine

Put ingredients in a mixing bowl, mix thoroughly and shape into a loaf. Put in a lightly oiled baking pan, or bread pan. Bake in 325° (slow) oven about 60 minutes, depending upon size of loaf and degree of doneness wanted. This makes a fairly moist loaf. Sprinkle salt on portions for the regulars when meat is served.

> One Serving
> (2 oz. meat, cooked weight)

> With egg

67	milligrams sodium
13	grams total fat
11	grams saturated fat
214	calories

VARIATIONS

A tomato-base sauce may be made and served over the meat for variety.

One-half teaspoon allspice may be substituted for savory and basil.

Low sodium dietetic chili sauce may be substituted for milk and wine.

Then there is dill to substitute for the savory, rosemary, thyme combination.

For curry lovers, 1 teaspoonful added to meat and other ingredients will give it a rich and aromatic flavor.

LOW SATURATED FAT VARIATION

Use only ground top round steak when an all-beef meat loaf is your choice. To help the pocketbook as well as the fat content, try the recipe with ½ pound ground top round steak and ½ pound ground veal. Be sure to have butcher trim meat of all visible fat. Use egg white only for binding loaf. For an interesting variation, omit shredded wheat biscuit and use ¼ cup chopped walnuts with an equal amount seedless raisins. Use ½ teaspoon savory and ½ teaspoon allspice in place of seasonings in Basic Recipe. *One serving, all-beef with nuts and raisins: 4 grams saturated fat (½ teaspoon vegetable oil).*

PIN WHEELS
6 Servings

Pin Wheels are sometimes called "porcupine meat balls" because of the rice "bristles." They are ever so pretty and are as tasty as they are attractive. If you have unexpected guests and are a little short on meat, remember Pin Wheels because they do stretch that meat.

For 6 balls you will need:

1 pound *lean* ground beef	¼ teaspoon thyme
¼ cup minced onion	1 teaspoon parsley, minced
¼ cup raw brown rice	¼ teaspoon black pepper
¼ teaspoon vegetable oil	2 tablespoons flour

Mix well and form into balls. Lightly flour with 2 tablespoons flour. Now put into a Dutch oven, or heavy skillet, 2 tablespoons vegetable oil. Brown the meat mixture in it until golden in color. Remove from pan, but do not remove drippings, as they form the sauce base.

You will need:

¼ cup onion, minced	⅛ teaspoon mace
1 garlic clove, split lengthwise and put on wooden pick	4 peppercorns
	2 cups low sodium dietetic tomato juice
¼ teaspoon thyme	¼ cup Chianti

Put onion, garlic, and thyme into drippings and cook slowly for 5 minutes. Add liquids and other seasonings and bring to gentle boil. Now add meat so that sauce is distributed evenly. Cover and let simmer slowly for 40 minutes. Remove garlic and serve with rice. Add salt for the regulars.

> *One Serving*
> (2 oz. meat,
> cooked weight)

60	milligrams sodium
15	grams total fat
10	grams saturated fat
262	calories

LOW SATURATED FAT VARIATION

Omit flouring of meat balls. Oven or pan-broil in ribbed-bottom skillet until brown. Place in Dutch oven or other heavy-duty pan and cover with sauce as outlined. Oil may be added to meat ball mixture according to daily allowance. *One serving, without oil: 4 grams saturated fat.*

HAMBURGER-CORN LOAF
6 Servings

This is a change from the good old meat loaf, and as good cold as it is hot.

1 pound ground *lean* beef	1 tablespoon olive oil
1 cup cream style corn, canned without added salt	1 tablespoon parsley
	½ shredded wheat biscuit
1 teaspoon minced onion	¼ teaspoon rosemary
1 egg	¼ teaspoon black pepper
	½ cup sauterne

Put ingredients in mixing bowl and mix together well. Put into an oiled loaf pan and bake in a 325° (slow) oven about 60 minutes. This makes a solid loaf. It may be served plain or with a tomato sauce. Add salt for the regulars.

> *One Serving*
> (2 oz. meat,
> cooked weight)
> *Without sauce*

70	milligrams sodium
13	grams total fat
11	grams saturated fat
238	calories

LOW SATURATED FAT VARIATION

Follow Basic Recipe except substitute 1 egg white for whole egg. If no sodium restriction, use regular canned corn and add salt to taste. *One serving: 4 grams saturated fat (½ teaspoon vegetable oil).*

LAMB

So good in almost any form, but higher in sodium count than beef. Plan to serve lower count vegetables when lamb is on the menu. Those of you with saturated fat restrictions will want to choose leg of lamb for your recipes because of its lower fat content. Allow 2 servings per pound of uncooked *lean* meat with bone or 4 servings per pound if boned.

LEG OF LAMB
5-pound lean leg, 10 Servings

Wipe meat with damp cloth and cook in open baking pan, fat side up. Cut a few slices of onion over top to give color to your drippings for gravy (these can be removed before making). Roast in 325° (slow) oven, following the directions for your range for cooking time per pound. For gravy, skim off fat and allow 3 tablespoons flour to 1 pint liquid. One tenth equals dieter's share, if allowed. Add salt for the regulars.

One Serving
(3 oz. meat,
cooked weight)

Without gravy

105	milligrams sodium
7	grams total fat
7	grams saturated fat
169	calories

VARIATIONS

Have your butcher remove the tiny glands at the shank end and into this hole put your herbs, Italian-fashion. A sprig of fresh rosemary, a slice of onion, and a clove of garlic are excellent used in this fashion.

Or, if you prefer to baste, the following sauce is one of our favorites:

½ cup water	⅛ teaspoon thyme
½ cup sauterne wine	½ clove garlic
1 teaspoon dried rose-mary	1 teaspoon chopped onion

This is sufficient for a 5-pound roast. Baste at least 4 times during the roasting period. Remove garlic before thickening for gravy—and be sure to portion that gravy carefully, if it is allowed.

SHISH KABOB
(Lamb Cabob; adapted from the Armenian)
8 Servings

Allow 2 servings per pound of lean raw meat with bone or 4 servings if boned.

When using leg of lamb, remove fat, gristle, and bone. Cut meat into squares 1½ to 2 inches in size. Put into a large flat bowl or pan, and add:

1 cup sliced onions
2 tablespoons vegetable oil
¼ cup white table wine (or sherry is excellent)
½ teaspoon pepper
½ teaspoon rosemary

Marinate overnight. Put meat with or without onions on skewers and broil over charcoal fire until crisp and brown on all sides, or broil in oven or rotisserie. Serve with rice. Pass the salt for the regulars.

One Serving
(3 oz. meat,
cooked weight)

With onions;
without rice

108	milligrams sodium
11	grams total fat
7	grams saturated fat
212	calories

One serving: ¾ teaspoon vegetable oil.

LAMB-IN-FOIL DINNER
4 Servings

Another Sunkist Growers' kitchen-tested recipe—delicious, a complete meal in itself, so easy to prepare, and only one pan to wash.

1 pound *lean* boneless lamb
1 medium onion
2 medium potatoes
1 zucchini squash, or 2 summer squashes
½ clove garlic, minced
½ teaspoon oregano
½ teaspoon sweet basil
2 tablespoons chopped parsley
Aluminum foil, cut into four 9 x 15-inch rectangles
4 slices lemon, ¼-inch thick

Cut meat into 1-inch cubes; cut each of the vegetables diagonally into 4 slices. Sprinkle meat and vegetables with seasonings and divide equally into 4 portions; pile or layer in center of each foil rectangle. Top each with lemon slice. Bring up lengthwise sides of foil. Seal together by making 2 folds toward center of package. At each end make 2 folds toward the center. (Be sure packages are air tight to avoid loss of steam and juices.) Lay them in shallow baking pan; bake in 450° (hot) oven for 1 hour or until meat is tender when pierced with a fork. Salt for those without sodium restrictions.

One Serving (3 oz. meat, cooked weight)	
110	milligrams sodium
7	grams total fat
7	grams saturated fat
258	calories

PORK

Pork is lower in sodium content than beef, lamb, or veal, but it is relatively fat. If you are on a restricted fat diet, you may find pork on your Don't list, or may be limited to the use of loin only, trimmed of all visible fat. If you are one of the lucky ones and can have it on your fare, you have exciting eating indeed. The rich flavor of pork, whether it be choice roast of pork or one of the lesser dishes, offers you an opportunity to use many of your own recipes and perhaps experiment with herbal seasonings. Pork lends itself particularly well to such treatment.

BAKED PORK CHOPS WITH RICE
6 Servings

1 cup brown rice	6 thick slices tomatoes
6 *lean* pork chops (about 2 pounds)	6 slices green bell pepper
6 slices Bermuda onion	Freshly ground pepper
2 cups hot tomato juice (low sodium dietetic)	

Cover rice with cold water and soak for at least 3 hours. Then place over low heat and bring to a boil to tenderize. Meanwhile, trim chops of all visible fat and lightly brown in skillet or broiler. Arrange chops in a large casserole or skillet and top with slice of onion, tomato, and green pepper. Lightly pepper. Cover each chop with drained rice, making a little mound on each one. There will be extra rice to fill spaces between chops. Pour tomato juice around meat-rice combination. Cover and bake in 325° (slow) oven, 50 to 60 minutes. Do not undercook. Add salt for those without sodium restrictions at time of serving. *Those with saturated fat restrictions will want to brown chops in ribbed-bottom skillet or in broiler so as to allow fat to drip away from meat.*

One of the beauties of this dish is that it can be prepared some time before use and baked when the rest of the meal is under way. Peas or asparagus combine well with it. Add a piece of broiled fruit, a tossed salad, and a light dessert, and you have a company meal at minimum effort.

One Serving
(3 oz. meat,
cooked weight)

74	milligrams sodium
11	grams total fat
10	grams saturated fat
380	calories

VARIATIONS

White or wild rice may be substituted for brown rice. Ala, the new Fisher Flouring Mills Company's bulgur wheat, is a delicious substitute for rice in this recipe.

Basil, caraway, or thyme may be sprinkled over chops when an herbal flavor is desired.

AMERICAN CHOP SUEY
3 Servings

Chop suey has become legend in the various Chinatowns of the country, and yet it is not a native dish in the true sense of the word. In fact, it is unknown in the Chinese language, and is considered the corruption of culinary tradition.

Its characteristic ingredients are bean sprouts, onions, meat, and soy sauce. We have to leave out the soy sauce because of its salt flavor. Let's substitute lemon juice for zest.

2 tablespoons vegetable oil

½ cup chopped onions

2 cups fresh bean sprouts

1 tablespoon lemon juice

½ pound *lean* loin of pork, shredded cross-wise

1 teaspoon sugar

1½ tablespoons corn-starch

¼ cup water

¼ cup blanched almonds, slivered

Warm oil in heavy skillet. Add onion and cook 10 minutes, stirring occasionally to prevent scorching. Wash bean sprouts; add them, dripping, to skillet. Sprinkle with lemon juice. Stir to prevent scorching, and add a tablespoonful or so of water if necessary. Cook just until tender (about 5 minutes). Pour onto warm platter and set in warming oven. Fry pork slivers in remaining oil mixture. Cover and let simmer until thoroughly done. Return bean sprout mixture to skillet and reheat. Meanwhile, make a glaze by blending sugar, cornstarch, and water; cook for 5 minutes. Pour over meat-bean sprout combination. Stir in almonds. Serve on platter. Rice is a natural accompaniment for chop suey. Add salt and soy sauce for the regulars. *Those with saturated fat restrictions will need to brown pork in broiler or in ribbed-bottom skillet to allow fat to drip away from meat; then add to vegetables.*

One Serving
(2 oz. meat,
cooked weight)
Without rice

50	milligrams sodium
22	grams total fat
6	grams saturated fat
343	calories

One serving: 2 teaspoons vegetable oil.

VARIATIONS

Broccoli may be substituted for the bean sprouts.
Veal, chicken, or turkey may be substituted for pork.

VEAL

Veal is one of the meats highest in sodium content but is low in fat content. Many cuts offer you variety in the way you serve it. The rump is usually considered the most flavorsome and coveted piece for roasting. It can be cooked plain or with herbs to enrich its natural good flavor. Boneless rolled shoulder, rib or loin chops, Frenched cutlets, steaks, shank, and breast all lend themselves to braising. Chops, cutlets, and steaks may, of course, be pan-broiled or oven-baked.

VEAL STEAKS, BAKED
8 Servings

Have your butcher cut 2 or 3 lean steaks (round or cutlets) weighing 2 pounds. Prepare as follows:

Put into a brown-paper bag . . .	½ teaspoon fresh pepper
½ cup flour	Steaks cut in 8 pieces

Shake until well blended. Remove from bag. Meanwhile, lightly oil a shallow baking dish and place steaks in it.

Sprinkle over top . . . . . 5 large mushrooms, sliced	½ cup low sodium nonfat milk

Bake in 325° (slow) oven for 45 minutes, or until thoroughly cooked. Add salt for those without sodium restrictions.

One Serving
(3 oz. meat, cooked weight)

113	milligrams sodium
4	grams total fat
4	grams saturated fat
235	calories

VARIATIONS

For variety, serve with low sodium dietetic tomato juice heated and slightly thickened. Add ⅛ teaspoon thyme for extra flavor.

Or substitute 1 crumbled shredded wheat for the flour and ¼ cup chopped onion for the mushroom. Add ⅛ teaspoon sweet basil.

Or substitute low sodium dietetic tomato juice for the low sodium milk. Sprinkle with 3 tablespoons chopped parsley and 1 teaspoon chopped chives, 1 tablespoon lemon juice.

Or substitute ¼ cup dry white wine and ¼ cup low sodium dietetic tomato juice for the low sodium milk. Gently heat. Add ½ teaspoon thyme and a dash of cayenne. Pour over meat and baste at least 3 times during baking period. (Cover your pan for this method.)

Or put a slice of Bermuda onion on the top of each steak and drip lightly with white wine and proceed as above with the basting.

Or bread steaks in crumbled shredded wheat, dip in low sodium non-fat milk and bake to doneness.

VEAL CUTLETS IN WINE
6 Servings

6 small cutlets (about 1½ pounds *lean* boneless meat)
½ cup flour
½ teaspoon pepper
2 tablespoons vegetable oil
1 cup sliced fresh mushrooms

1 clove minced garlic (optional)
2 cups cut-up fresh tomatoes *or* 1½ cups canned tomatoes (low sodium dietetic)
1 tablespoon minced parsley
1 cup sauterne

Allow 1 cutlet for each serving; wipe with damp cloth. Dredge in flour seasoned with pepper and place in hot skillet with 1 tablespoon oil. Turn to brown on both sides. Sauté mushrooms in 1 tablespoon oil in small skillet for 5 minutes; add garlic and simmer for 5 minutes longer. Combine with cutlets and add remaining ingredients. Cover skillet and gently simmer for 45 minutes. (Check to avoid scorching.) Add salt for regulars.

One Serving
(3 oz. meat,
cooked weight)

123	milligrams sodium
9	grams total fat
4	grams saturated fat
297	calories

LOW SATURATED FAT VARIATION

Brown cutlets in ribbed-bottom skillet or in broiler. Drain off drippings, then proceed as in Basic Recipe. *One serving: 4 grams saturated fat (1 teaspoon vegetable oil).*

PINEAPPLE-VEAL PATTIES
6 Servings

2 cups ground leftover cooked veal
¼ cup crumbled low sodium bread crumbs
¼ cup tomato juice, canned without added sodium
⅛ teaspoon black pepper
¼ cup minced onion
⅛ teaspoon thyme
1 egg, lightly beaten
6 pineapple slices
3 tablespoons vegetable oil
⅓ cup light brown sugar
½ cup pineapple sirup

Combine meat, bread crumbs, tomato juice, seasonings, and egg; mix all together. Shape into 6 medium patties. Place on pineapple slices in lightly oiled casserole. Combine vegetable oil, brown sugar, and pineapple juice; spoon over patties saving some for basting. Cover; bake at 325° (slow) oven for 30 minutes. Uncover and bake for 10 minutes longer, or until lightly browned. Baste once or twice with liquid mixture. Add salt for regulars at time of serving.

One Serving
(2⅔ oz. meat,
cooked weight)

117	milligrams sodium
12	grams total fat
4	grams saturated fat
343	calories

LOW SATURATED FAT VARIATION

Follow Basic Recipe except substitute 1 egg white for 1 whole egg. If no sodium restrictions, use regular tomato juice and add salt to taste. *One serving: 3 grams saturated fat (1½ teaspoons vegetable oil).*

TAMALE PIE
6 Servings

This tamale pie has a very Mexican flavor and is a morale builder for the person on restricted eating because it makes him feel he can have one of the good old stand-bys. It can be popular with you, too, because it's a good dollar-stretcher, in that only three quarters of a pound of meat is used to serve 6.

3 cups low sodium non-fat milk

1 cup brown granular wheat cereal, un-cooked

3 tablespoons grated onion

⅛ teaspoon black pepper

1 teaspoon curry powder

1 tablespoon vegetable oil

½ pound *lean* ground beef

¼ pound *lean* ground veal

1 cup fresh tomatoes, cut small

Heat low sodium milk. Add cereal slowly, stirring constantly to prevent lumping. Cook until thickened; then place over boiling water. Cover and continue cooking for 15 minutes.

Meanwhile, sauté onion in oil until golden brown in color. Add meat and cook until lightly brown. Add tomatoes, pepper, and curry powder.

Line a lightly oiled casserole with three fourths of the cereal. Pour the meat filling in next, and top with remaining cereal. Bake in a 350° (moderate) oven, 30 to 40 minutes, until topping is golden brown. Add salt for the regulars.

One Serving
(1½ oz. meat
cooked weight)

51	milligrams sodium
8	grams total fat
5	grams saturated fat
248	calories

LOW SATURATED FAT VARIATION

Follow Basic Recipe, except brown meat (top round for beef) in ribbed-bottom skillet or in broiler; discard drippings. Then combine with onion and other ingredients as directed. *One serving: 3 grams saturated fat (½ teaspoon vegetable oil).*

SCALLOPINI
4 Servings

Strips of veal steak, combined with fine seasonings, offer you a tasty and rich morsel for your meat dish. In our thinking, scallopini rates top billing even with its restrictions (and they are not many). The secret to good scallopini rests, in considerable measure, with the cooking. It must cook at very low heat, so the herbs and sauce have ample time to permeate the whole.

Have butcher cut thin *lean* veal steaks, allowing ⅓ pound per person (allow ¼ pound if boneless).

8 2-inch strips lean veal steaks	¼ cup chopped onion
¼ cup flour	½ cup water
½ teaspoon pepper	½ cup sauterne
2 tablespoons vegetable oil	1 cup low sodium dietetic tomato juice
1 clove garlic on wooden stick	½ teaspoon rosemary
	¼ cup minced parsley

Wipe meat with damp cloth; pound out each piece until it is half its original thickness. Roll in peppered flour and let stand for an hour or more. Put oil into heated skillet. Add meat; brown. Remove meat to warm platter. Put garlic and onion into skillet and gently simmer for 10 minutes. Return meat to skillet. Add ½ cup water slightly warmed. Meanwhile simmer over low heat the remaining ingredients; then pour over meat. Cover and simmer for at least 1 hour, or until meat is fork-tender. Add water if necessary to keep from scorching. The sauce will be thick at time of serving when you may add salt for the regulars if you think they will require it. This is so flavorsome that it may never be missed by dieter or the regulars.

One Serving (3 oz. meat, cooked weight)	
122	milligrams sodium
11	grams total fat
4	grams saturated fat
302	calories

LOW SATURATED FAT VARIATION

Do not roll in flour or use oil for browning. Rather, pan-broil in ribbed-bottom skillet or oven-broil; pour off drippings. Oil may be added according to diet requirements. *One serving, without oil: 4 grams saturated fat.*

MEAT STRETCHERS

With the sodium and fat content of meat as high as it is, it just seems plain prudent to use meat-stretchers often. By so doing, the person on the restricted program does not feel that he is being deprived of too much, and you, on the planning end, are able to save some of the precious count.

Stretcher devices have been used for long years by good homemakers. Some of the popular ones are:

(1) *Hash* with potatoes, onions, and leftover vegetables
(2) *Stew* with vegetables, macaroni, dumplings, or rice
(3) *Meat pies* with vegetables and a biscuit or mashed potato topping
(4) *Meat loaf* with low sodium bread crumbs, or crumbled shredded wheat, low sodium dietetic tomato juice, and egg
(5) *Casserole dishes*, combining meat with vegetables
(6) *Patties* with low sodium bread crumbs, mashed, or ground potatoes
(7) *Hearty soups* with meat or fish stock base
(8) *Rice* with meat balls, such as Pin Wheels, and accompanying sauce

(9) *Curries* served over rice or with baked potatoes
(10) *Meats stretched with sauces,* as in Scallopini
(11) *Meats stretched with low sodium white sauce,* as in croquettes

WHAT TO SERVE WITH MEATS

Think of the sauces, conserves, and specialties which combine with meats for appetite appeal, color and texture contrasts, and flavor pleasure.

Listed below are some of the combinations we have enjoyed:

With beef: Try cranberry sauce, broiled fruit, plain or with jelly centers

With lamb: Try currant jelly, mint sauce or jelly, cucumber sauce, wine jelly

With pork: Try spiced apple sauce, broiled pineapple slices or chunks, candied apples

With veal: Try cranberry jelly, currant jelly, mushroom sauce, broiled fruits

FAT-RESTRICTED BROWN GRAVY
1 Cup

- 3 tablespoons flour
- 1 low sodium beef bouillon cube
- ¼ teaspoon onion powder (not salt)
- ¾ cup boiling water
- ¼ cup red table wine

Brown flour in skillet. Combine crumbled bouillon cube, onion powder, and water; add slowly to browned flour to make smooth paste. Cook, stirring constantly to avoid lumping. When gravy begins to thicken add wine and reheat, but do not boil. If no sodium restrictions, use regular bouillon cube and add salt and other seasonings to taste.

Total Recipe
With wine

37	milligrams sodium
negligible	grams total fat
77	calories

VARIATIONS

Wine may be omitted and ½ teaspoon low sodium Worcestershire sauce substituted for the wine (regular Worcestershire sauce may be used if no sodium restrictions); or you may substitute herbs of your choice (sweet basil, garlic, and oregano are some of our favorites); or a sprinkling of low sodium meat tenderizer (regular meat tenderizer may be used if no sodium restrictions) may be added for zest.

8. CHICKEN EVERY SUNDAY

No wonder best-sellers are written about it, and restaurants selected for gourmet listings because of it! Chicken is just that good. It has been, for the stretch of our memories and more, the *pièce de résistance* of the Sunday dinner, whether that be on Sunday or some other day. In other words, chicken is a special occasion delicacy—to be served the most honored guest or as a family treat. Henry IV of France said at his coronation, "I wish that every peasant may have a chicken in his pot every Sunday."

Chicken is good *au naturel*, yielding its succulent juices for good eating, and is out of this world when combined with a bit of garlic, herb, and wine. In other words, chicken is good—whether it be boiled, baked, or broiled, plain or with the enrichment of added seasonings—any time you want fine and pleasurable eating.

Suggestions:

1. Always plan your complete menu carefully for the day when chicken is to be included, so that you stay within your allowance.

Measure the amount of chicken and gravy to be served with respect to the total sodium or fat content allowed.

2. Allow no more than ½ pound, *dressed weight*, uncooked, for the severely restricted dieter.

3. Use moderate heat for tender and juicy chicken. This holds for poultry of all ages, from the youngest spring bird to the oldest hen.

High heat hardens and toughens the protein of the

chicken, shrinks it more, and lessens its juiciness.

4. Do not start cooking chicken too long before it is to be served, for best results.

5. Vary your cooking method according to age and fatness of the chicken. Broiling, frying and oven-roasting lend themselves to *young* and *well-fattened* chickens. Braising or casserole dishes should be the choice if poultry is *lean* and *young*. *Old hens* take to the stew pot, for fricasseeing or steaming. (Steam, rather than fricassee, on diet programs where gravy must be omitted as most of the flavor goes into the gravy.) To sum up the cooking methods: use dry heat for young and tender birds, moist for old or lean.

6. Try some of the herbs or herb-wine combinations for high flavor and juicy goodness, if your count will permit. Green pepper, bay leaf, onion, and unsalted tomato juice; thyme, rosemary, and parsley; curry powder, onion, and vegetable oil; marjoram and thyme; onion and garlic with vegetable oil; sherry-herb basting sauce; a pinch of cinnamon or ginger, with dry red or white wines—many combinations of herbs, seasonings, and wines will add rich goodness to your chicken dishes.

7. Lightly oil chicken with vegetable oil for crisp skin for "regular" family members.

8. Chicken lends itself unusually well to casserole dishes. Give it that European flair by using herbs and wines for flavor—and stretch it (and so cut down the sodium and fat content) by combining with macaroni, rice, corn, or a macédoine of mixed vegetables.

9. From this day on, never let it be said that you use sage in stuffing for chicken or turkey. Try the gentler summer savory just once to become a convert to its subtle goodness. Combine with sweet marjoram, thyme, onions, green pepper, and vegetable oil. Above all, avoid mixed "poultry seasoning" as if it were a plague. It is much too strong for your chicken dishes. Use low sodium bread, of course, as your base.

10. Wrap chicken in aluminum foil before cooking, to seal in the juices and eliminate all basting if you like a steamed bird. Unwrap, the last 20 minutes of cooking, if you want a brown, crunchy outside.

11. Have handy the good old metal tongs, while cooking, for easy handling of the chicken. Fork handling pricks the tender skin and lets out juices.

Your method of cookery will depend in part upon the season of the year (unless you are a Deepfreeze planner) and the dish you want to concoct. We say "concoct" advisedly, because chicken cookery allows all kinds of interesting specialties. And these specialties are a boon to you, if you want to make your dieter's portion appear big, and yet remain within the allowable amount.

When you elect to *fry or broil* those young tender birds from 6 to 12 weeks old, weighing 1½ to 3 pounds, brush them lightly with unsalted butter or vegetable oil (depending upon your diet restrictions) and cook, remembering to start with skin side away from heat to seal in juices.

For the still young (5 to 9 months old) and well-fleshed chickens, try *stuffing and roasting* in an open pan. Place chicken breast side down in pan, and cover with aluminum wrap if you are not going to baste. Follow your own cooking directions as to temperature and cooking time.

REMEMBER: Braising and fricasseeing are the time-honored methods of chicken cookery for birds past their prime. When you stew your bird, you do so to tenderize it. In so doing you cause the chicken to give up some of its characteristic flavor to the liquid. *This can be recaptured only through the gravy, which, if allowed to your diet, must be calculated and measured carefully.*

For sodium restriction, do not use:

Chicken gravies, without consent of physician except special gravy (page 114-15)
Eviscerated frozen chicken, unless you first make sure it has not been treated in a light salt bath before freezing
Salt
"Spanish" sauces of the commercial sort
Worcestershire sauce, except sodium-restricted

For saturated fat restriction, do not use:

Broilers, hens (stewing chickens), or roasters (except for special occasions), as they are fat-rich. Choose *fryers*, although you won't be frying them by the old conventional methods. This seals in fat; you want it to drip out

Commercially prepared chicken dishes or canned chicken unless packed without gravy or fat (without added salt, too, if on sodium restriction)

Dark meat, as it contains more fat than light meat.

Regular gravies, as these are fat-rich. If drippings are to be used, chill gravy in refrigerator until fat solidifies and then remove. Better still, use recipe on page 114-15

BROILERS
4 Servings
(2-pound broiler—dressed weight)

The plain cooked broiler is a toothsome morsel at any time, but for variety try seasoning it with herbs. Broilers are higher in fat than fryers and should not be used on severely restricted fat diets.

Wipe dry your chicken. Rub with cut garlic clove and sprinkle with 2 teaspoons lemon juice. Brush lightly with ½ teaspoon vegetable oil and ¼ teaspoon fresh black pepper. Oil the bottom of your baster lightly and put the chicken on it, skin side away from the flame. Sprinkle with ⅛ teaspoon savory and ⅛ teaspoon rosemary for each half to be cooked.

As you turn your broilers, baste with wine sauce made from ½ cup Riesling and 1 tablespoon vegetable oil. This should be done at 10- to 15-minute intervals. Keep your basting sauce warm but not boiling.

Allow between 30 and 40 minutes for cooking. Fork-test for tenderness.

Skim drippings of excess fat by swirling ice cube in liquid. Thicken for gravy. Allow 1½ tablespoons flour to 1 cup liquid for 1 cup gravy; cook at least 5 minutes over low heat. If dieter is allowed gravy, portion carefully. One fourth equals special diet share. Add salt for those without sodium restrictions.

One Serving
(3 oz. white and dark
meat, cooked weight)

Without gravy

87	milligrams sodium
13	grams total fat
9	grams saturated fat
261	calories

VARIATIONS

Scatter minced herbs directly on broilers when high flavor is wanted. An epicurean treat.

Many herb-wine combinations will add character to your broiled chickens. For starters, try savory and thyme; rosemary and garlic; onion, vegetable oil, and garlic with wine—slightly warmed. Never add cold blends. Vary your wine-base sauces, too. Sherry is a wonderful substitute for the dry, white wines, when you tire of them, and gives body and richness to broilers.

BAKED CHICKEN
4 Servings
(2-pound fryer—dressed weight)

2-pound fryer, cut into serving pieces or quartered
1 teaspoon vegetable oil
1/4 teaspoon black pepper

Flour (optional)
2 teaspoons vegetable oil
1 tablespoon water
1/4 cup Chablis
Parsley sprigs

Place chicken on rack in baking pan. Brush pieces lightly with 1 teaspoon oil; sprinkle with pepper and flour. Bake 40 minutes, or until tender, in 350° (moderate) oven. Baste at least 4 times with warm basting sauce made of remaining oil, water, and wine. If gravy is allowed, skim off all fat by swirling ice cube in liquid or chilling in refrigerator; or make special gravy (page 114-15). Garnish with parsley sprigs and salt for those without sodium restrictions.

One Serving
(3 oz. white and dark meat, cooked weight)

Without gravy

86	milligrams sodium
6	grams total fat
3	grams saturated fat
241	calories

VARIATIONS

Substitute 2 teaspoons lemon or lime juice for wine.

Combine 2 teaspoons lemon or lime juice with ½ tablespoon of chopped parsley and green pepper, 2 teaspoons chopped onion, 1 clove finely chopped garlic, and 1 teaspoon vegetable oil. Mix well; baste over chicken.

Foil-wrap and bake for 30 minutes; unwrap for last 10 minutes of baking for browned skin. (But remember that skin is not for dieter.)

One teaspoon paprika and ½ teaspoon dry mustard may be rubbed over chicken before baking.

For herb flavor, try ½ teaspoon marjoram, rosemary, or basil.

LOW SATURATED FAT VARIATION

Follow Basic Recipe and Variations except omit flour as it absorbs fat which you want to drip away. Oil may be increased, reduced, or omitted according to your diet needs. Salt to taste if not restricted in sodium. Serve only breast meat to dieter. *One serving, with oil, without gravy: 1 gram saturated fat (¾ teaspoon vegetable oil).*

ROAST CHICKEN
8 Servings
(4-pound roaster—dressed weight)

Oven-baked chicken can be a gourmet's delicacy, or a dry disillusionment. Selection of your bird is of first importance for good results.

Stuffing and cooking:

In planning your stuffing, first consider the amount. Allow about 1 cup of low sodium bread crumbs for every pound of chicken (dressed weight), minus one pound from your total. So if you have a 4-pound roaster, allow 3 cups of bread crumbs. A standard size loaf of bread makes a full 4 cups of crumbs.

The next decision involves the use of crust. Many recipes call for trimmed loaves. Very good indeed, if you like a soft dressing, moist or not. For full flavor, however, try at least once the loaf as is, and see if you don't like the flavor of the crunchy crust. It adds variety and texture to the dressing, as well as flavor.

Now for seasoning. Celery is not allowed on the sodium-restricted diet. This situation simply creates a challenge to us in our kitchens to think through new flavor combinations. We find a little green pepper and parsley, with herbs, gives us a dressing both tasteful and harmonious to the savor of the chicken itself.

Amount of fat must also be considered on some programs to further limit the flavor of your dressing. If you can manage, do use a little unsalted butter with the vegetable oil for flavor-plus values.

For a 4-pound roaster, these proportions will give you a general guide to follow:

1 tablespoon vegetable oil
1 teaspoon unsalted butter (if diet allows)
½ cup finely cut onion
1 garlic clove, minced fine
1 teaspoon finely minced green pepper
3 cups flaked low sodium bread crumbs
1 tablespoon minced parsley
1½ teaspoons summer savory
½ teaspoon thyme
¼ teaspoon sweet marjoram
¼ teaspoon fresh black pepper

Heat oil and butter in skillet. Add onion, garlic, and green pepper; lightly brown. Combine bread flakes, parsley, and seasonings in bowl. Add oil-onion mixture to bread flakes and thoroughly blend; cool.

Meanwhile, put 2 tablespoons dry white wine into cavity and let stand while you are preparing stuffing. Drain before filling with stuffing.

Stuff bird, being careful not to pack stuffing in too tightly. Lace skewers to hold it in place. Set chicken in refrigerator until ready to roast (not overnight because of bacterial danger). At that time, brush chicken surface lightly with 1 teaspoon vegetable oil; wrap in aluminum foil; put in baking pan with low sides. Place chicken either sideways or on its breast, depending on its shape and other oven demands. Follow your range directions for cooking, but remember that low-temperature cooking will preserve juices and minimize shrinkage.

Unwrap and turn chicken the last 20 minutes of roasting for golden brownness.

Make gravy for regulars and use special recipe (page 114-15) for your dieter.

> *One Serving*
> (3 oz. white and dark
> meat, cooked weight)
> *With dressing;*
> *without gravy*

86	milligrams sodium
23	grams total fat
18	grams saturated fat
455	calories

VARIATIONS

One cup mushrooms may be added to stuffing for variety; or 1 tablespoon sliced mushrooms may be added to gravy.

Chicken may be marinated in special marinade (page 120).

LOW SATURATED FAT VARIATION

Since roasters are considerably higher in fat than fryers, you may be able to use this recipe only for extra special occasions, and then serve only white meat to dieter. Dressing for dieter should be cooked in custard cup, and not in chicken, as bread crumbs absorb animal fat during roasting. Oil may be increased, decreased, or omitted from stuffing according to your requirements; butter should be omitted. If oil is omitted, parboil onion, garlic, and green pepper in ¼ cup water or white table wine. Add salt if not restricted in sodium. *One serving, with oil, and dressing cooked separately: 8 grams saturated fat (½ teaspoon vegetable oil).*

FAT-RESTRICTED CHICKEN GRAVY
1 Cup

3 tablespoons flour
1 low sodium chicken
 bouillon cube
½ cup boiling water

⅛ teaspoon onion
 powder
½ cup Rhine wine (optional)

Brown flour in frying pan. Combine crumbled bouillon cube, onion powder, and water. Add slowly to browned flour, to make smooth paste. Cook, stirring constantly, to avoid lumping. When gravy begins to thicken, add wine and reheat. If no sodium restrictions, use regular bouillon cubes and add salt to taste.

Total Recipe *With wine*	
18	milligrams sodium
negligible	grams total fat
178	calories

BARBECUED CHICKEN
4 Servings
(2-pound fryer—dressed weight)

Whether you cook this in the oven, on the revolving spit of your broiler or outdoor barbecue, or over a homemade grill, the flavor of barbecued chicken is something very special and deserves your consideration summer or winter, Sunday or any day of the week.

2-pound fryer, cut up
½ cup low sodium catchup
2 tablespoons wine vinegar

1 teaspoon low sodium Worcestershire sauce
¼ teaspoon cayenne
1 cup water

Wipe cut-up fryer with a damp cloth and place on rack in baking pan. Make barbecue sauce by blending remaining ingredients. Pour over the chicken. Bake in 350° (moderate) oven for about 40 minutes, until done. Baste every 15 minutes. Add salt for those without sodium restrictions.

One Serving (3 oz. white and dark meat, cooked weight)	
93	milligrams sodium
3	grams total fat
3	grams saturated fat
222	calories

VARIATIONS

California red wine, such as Burgundy, may be substituted for high flavor for the wine vinegar, but for most, when wine flavor is desired, substitute dry sauterne.

Lemon juice or herb wine may be substituted for the wine vinegar.

LOW SATURATED FAT VARIATION

Follow Basic Recipe and Variations, except pour only half of sauce over uncooked chicken; reserve remaining half for basting. If no sodium restrictions, use regular catchup and Worcestershire sauce, and add salt to taste. Serve breast meat to dieter. *One serving: 1 gram saturated fat.*

BRAISED CHICKEN WITH VEGETABLES
6 Servings
(3-pound fryer—dressed weight)

3 tablespoons flour
¼ teaspooon pepper
3-pound fryer, cut up
1 tablespoon vegetable oil
1 cup sliced fresh mushrooms

½ cup cubed green pepper
2 tablespoons minced parsley
1 cup boiling water
½ cup fresh peas

Combine flour and pepper in paper bag; add chicken pieces and shake well. Brown chicken in oil in heavy skillet. Remove browned pieces to a casserole. Now put into frying pan in which chicken was browned, the mushrooms, green pepper, and parsley. Stir so they can absorb browned fat; then put into casserole with chicken. Add 1 cup hot water; cover. Let simmer slowly about 1½ hours, or until fork-tender. Add peas about 15 minutes before done. If oven-cooked, cook in 275° (very slow) oven with cover on casserole. Add salt for those without sodium restrictions just before serving.

One Serving
(3 oz. white and dark meat, cooked weight)

87	milligrams sodium
5	grams total fat
3	grams saturated fat
242	calories

LOW SATURATED FAT VARIATION

Follow Basic Recipe except omit pan-browning, and lightly broil chicken pieces if crusty skin is desired. Parboil mushrooms, green pepper, and parsley, if desired, but they may be added with boiling water after chicken has been placed on rack in Dutch oven or heavy-duty saucepan. Cover and simmer as in directions. Chill liquid and remove hardened fat before thickening with flour for gravy. Serve only breast meat to dieter; if not restricted in sodium, add salt to taste. Oil may be added to chicken according to diet requirements. *One serving, without oil: 1 gram saturated fat.*

CHICKEN CURRY
6 Servings
(3-pound fryer—dressed weight)

Put into a skillet	1 tablespoon vegetable oil
Add	3 small onions, cut fine
Brown, and add	1 tablespoon curry powder
Add chicken pieces, cut up, and cook until dry. Watch carefully, as curry powder burns easily.	
Add	2 cups water

Cover and simmer for about 1½ hours or until tender, and until sauce thickens a little. Salt for regulars. Serve over steaming rice, cooked with a pinch of turmeric.

One Serving
(3 oz. white and dark meat, cooked weight)

Without rice

88	milligrams sodium
5	grams total fat
3	grams saturated fat
225	calories

LOW SATURATED FAT VARIATION

Follow Basic Recipe except omit browning of onion and chicken in oil; instead, lightly broil chicken pieces. Place on rack in heavy skillet with onion, curry powder, and water (salt, too, if not restricted in sodium). Simmer for 1½ hours or until tender. Chill liquid and remove hardened fat; thicken. Serve with rice. Breast meat only to dieter. Oil may be added to chicken in skillet according to diet requirements. *One serving, without oil: 1 gram saturated fat.*

CHICKEN NAPOLI
6 Servings
(3-pound fryer—dressed weight)

The Wine Institute, San Francisco, has given us permission to use this tested recipe with its fine Italian savor.

3-pound fryer, cut up
¼ cup flour
¼ teaspoon pepper, freshly ground
¼ teaspoon marjoram (scant)
1 tablespoon unsalted butter
1 tablespoon vegetable oil
¼ cup chopped parsley

1 clove garlic, minced (optional)
1 cup fresh tomatoes (or canned dietetic low sodium)
½ cup cabernet
¼ cup fresh mushroom stems and pieces
1½ cups fresh peas (or canned dietetic low sodium)

Dredge pieces of chicken with flour, seasoned with pepper and marjoram. Heat butter and oil in a large, heavy skillet; brown chicken on all sides. Add parsley, garlic, tomatoes, and wine. Cover tightly and simmer gently for about 45 minutes, or until chicken is tender. Add remaining ingredients; simmer 5 minutes longer. Serve with boiled or steamed rice. Add salt for those without sodium restrictions.

One Serving
(3 oz. white and dark meat, cooked weight)
Without rice

89	milligrams sodium
7	grams total fat
5	grams saturated fat
300	calories

LOW SATURATED FAT VARIATION

Follow Basic Recipe but do not dredge chicken pieces with flour or pan-brown with butter and oil; instead lightly broil. Place on rack in skillet, add other ingredients and continue as directed. Before serving sauce, chill and remove hardened fat. (As flour was not used to dredge chicken, you may want to thicken slightly with

flour before serving.) If no sodium restrictions, use regular canned vegetables and salt to taste. Oil may be
added to sauce according to your diet needs. Serve breast
meat only to dieter. *One serving, without oil: 1 gram
saturated fat.*

CHICKEN PAPRIKA
6 Servings
(3-pound fryer—dressed weight)

For fine flavor and something exotic, it is hard to beat
Chicken Paprika.

2 tablespoons vegetable oil
3-pound fryer, cut up
¼ teaspoon black pepper
1½ teaspoons paprika

1 chopped garlic clove
2 tablespoons flour
1½ cups low sodium non-fat milk
1 tablespoon Riesling

Put oil into heavy-duty skillet and heat. Add chicken
pieces (after wiping them with damp cloth) rubbed with
pepper, paprika, and garlic. Sauté until golden brown,
turning as necessary. Blend flour in ½ cup milk until
smooth. Add remaining milk and blend thoroughly. Heat
over low heat until mixture begins to thicken. Pour over
chicken; cover, and *simmer* for 45 to 60 minutes, until
chicken is done. Check for scorching, adding a little water
if necessary to prevent scorching. Arrange chicken on
platter. Add wine to gravy and reheat. Pour over chicken
and serve. Portion the dieter's serving with care. Add
salt for those without sodium restrictions.

One Serving
(3 oz. white and dark meat, cooked weight)

86	milligrams sodium
8	grams total fat
3	grams saturated fat
262	calories

VARIATIONS

Omit garlic and substitute sherry for the Riesling. 1 tablespoon chopped parsley may be blended into white sauce.

LOW SATURATED FAT VARIATION

Follow Basic Recipe except omit pan-browning of meat; instead, lightly broil. Place on rack in skillet, add remaining ingredients and continue as directed. Before adding wine to gravy, chill gravy and remove hardened fat. If no sodium restrictions, use regular non-fat milk and add salt to taste. Oil may be added to sauce according to your requirements; serve only breast meat to dieter. *One serving, without oil: 1 gram saturated fat.*

POULTRY IN MARINADE

Roasters or fryers gain wonderful savors if put into a marinade for 6 to 8 hours before cooking and if the marinade is used for basting during the cooking. If you are roasting a whole fowl, rub the marinade inside the chicken and over skin surface; if preparing pieces of chicken, "anoint" each piece. Wrap marinated fowl in waxed paper and put into refrigerator. Remove 1 hour before cooking. Here is a marinade particularly good for chicken or turkey which we have adapted from Irma Mazza's recipe in *Accent on Seasoning*:

½ teaspoon rosemary *or* ½ teaspoon tarragon	Rind of lemon used
	2 tablespoons lemon juice
¼ teaspoon black pepper	1 tablespoon finely chopped parsley
2 tablespoons vegetable oil	Dash paprika
	¼ cup dry sauterne

Mix and crush herbs and lemon rind in a mortar with pestle. Combine and blend with remaining ingredients. When a marinade is used, omit all other seasonings in making except the marinade.

Total Recipe	
11	milligrams sodium
28	grams total fat
negligible	grams saturated fat
307	calories

CHICKEN PILAU
4 Servings

A pilau is an Oriental dish made with rice, combined with meat, fowl or fish, and spices. It is boiled or oven baked. Some of the old pilaus were made with cracked wheat.

We make ours with Fisher's American bulgur wheat, Ala. If this is not available, contact your local milling agent and use his product. Or use rice.

2 tablespoons vegetable oil	2 cups boiling water
1 cup Ala	¼ teaspoon oregano
1 tablespoon finely chopped onion	Few grains pepper
	1 tablespoon minced parsley
1 low sodium chicken bouillon cube	1 cup chopped chicken
	Paprika

Warm oil in heavy-duty skillet; add Ala and onion. Stir and cook until golden brown. Make bouillon; add seasonings. Pour over Ala. Cover, bring to boil. Reduce heat, simmer 15 minutes. The last 5 minutes of cooking, add chicken and heat thoroughly. Add a little hot water if necessary. Sprinkle each serving with a few grains of paprika. Add salt for those without sodium restrictions.

One Serving
(2 oz. meat,
cooked weight)

60	milligrams sodium
12	grams total fat
5	grams saturated fat
326	calories

VARIATIONS

Substitute brown rice for Ala.

For oven-baked pilau, brown Ala or rice first on top of range. Add other ingredients. Put into lightly oiled casserole. Cover with ½ cup crumbled low sodium bread crumbs, lightly oiled or buttered, and bake in a 350° (moderate) oven, 45 minutes, or until golden brown. With the chicken omitted, this is an excellent accompaniment to any chicken.

For variety, substitute 1 cup fresh tomatoes or unsalted tomato juice for one cup of water.

LOW SATURATED FAT VARIATION

Follow Basic Recipe and Variations except use white meat only. If no sodium restrictions, use regular bouillon cube and add salt to taste. *One Serving: negligible saturated fat (1½ teaspoons vegetable oil).*

OTHER DELICACIES

TURKEY-BROCCOLI AU GRATIN
8 Servings

2 cups fresh broccoli
(or 1 package frozen)
¼ cup boiling water
2 cups cooked minced
turkey
⅓ cup unsalted butter
⅓ cup flour

Few grains black pepper
2 cups low sodium non-
fat milk
¼ cup grated low so-
dium cheddar-type
cheese
1 cup Rhine wine

Cook broccoli in ¼ cup boiling water until fork-tender;
drain. Lightly oil casserole with vegetable oil. Place ½
broccoli in casserole; cover with ½ turkey. Repeat with
layer of broccoli and turkey. Make a white sauce of melted
butter, blended flour, pepper, and milk. Stir constantly to
keep smooth. Cook 5 minutes. Add wine. Blend, and remove from heat. Cover turkey-broccoli with sauce. Top
with grated cheese. Bake in a 350° (moderate) oven about
30 minutes, until mixture is bubbly. Salt for those without sodium restrictions.

One Serving
(2 oz. white and dark
meat, cooked weight)

60	milligrams sodium
13	grams total fat
12	grams saturated fat
273	calories

VARIATION

Chicken or veal may be substituted for turkey.

LOW SATURATED FAT VARIATION

Follow Basic Recipe except omit butter, and make white
sauce by blending 1 bouillon cube (low sodium, if restricted in sodium) with ¼ cup boiling water; add ¼ cup
cold milk. Blend flour with bouillon mixture to make a
smooth paste. Slowly add remaining milk, stirring constantly to blend; cook 5 minutes. Continue as directed in
recipe, but use all white meat. Omit cheese and top with

crumbs. If no sodium restriction, use regular non-fat milk and add salt to taste. *One serving: 4 grams saturated fat.*

ROAST DUCK IN WINE
4 Servings

Allow ½ pound for the dieter; 1 pound for others to be served. Breast meat, as with chicken, for the dieter. Fill the cavity with ½ cup cabernet and let stand for 2 hours. Remove and fill with 2 apples and 1 onion (as a change from the usual low sodium dressing). Rub the skin lightly with ¼ teaspoon vegetable oil, prick skin, and scatter over it ¼ teaspoon thyme and ¼ teaspoon marjoram. Put on rack in open baking pan. Roast in 325° (slow) oven, increasing heat to 425° (hot) oven, near end, until tender, allowing 30 minutes to the pound, dressed weight, for duck this side of well done. Baste with wine saved from marinating. Pour off fat as it accumulates; prick several times; and turn duck when you wine-baste. Serve with Cumberland Sauce (page 275), fluffy rice, fresh peas, cranberry molded salad, and a fruit dessert. *Duck is too high in fat content for those with fat restrictions.*

One Serving
(3-oz. breast meat,
cooked weight)

102	milligrams sodium
22	grams total fat
21	grams saturated fat
353	calories

RABBIT
6 Servings
(3-pound rabbit—drawn weight)

Young rabbit may be broiled or oven-baked in the same way as young chickens are cooked. For something special, however, why not try the European method?

Disjoint one 3-pound rabbit. Dice ½ cup onion, ¼ cup green pepper, and add to rabbit. Marinate for at least 12 hours in refrigerator in the following mixture: 1 teaspoon lemon juice, ½ cup white wine, 2 tablespoons sugar, 1 teaspoon black pepper, 1 small bay leaf, 3 whole cloves, ¼ teaspoon marjoram.

Remove rabbit and dry. Roll lightly in 3 tablespoons

flour and brown in 2 tablespoons vegetable oil. Strain the marinade and add it to rabbit, simmering over low heat until tender, 1½ to 2 hours. Add vegetables last 15 minutes of cooking. Serve the rabbit with brown rice, using vegetables as a dressing or garnish. Strain the sauce again. Heat but do not boil, and pour over rabbit. Add salt for those without sodium restrictions.

One Serving	
(3 oz. meat,	
cooked weight)	
Without rice	
63	milligrams sodium
14	grams total fat
9	grams saturated fat
318	calories

LOW SATURATED FAT VARIATION

Follow Basic Recipe but do not flour and pan-brown rabbit; instead, broil until golden brown. Chill sauce and remove hardened fat; thicken with flour mixed with water to make smooth paste. Oil may be added to sauce according to your diet requirements. If no sodium restriction, add salt to taste. *One serving, without oil: 9 grams saturated fat.*

SPANISH RICE WITH WINE
6 Servings

A savory accompaniment for that special chicken dish, we think this especially good when served with simple chicken dishes, not the highly seasoned ones.

1 tablespoon vegetable oil	½ cup Rhine wine
½ chopped onion	3 tablespoons minced parsley
½ cup finely chopped green pepper	¼ teaspoon thyme
1 minced garlic clove	Few grains black pepper
1 tablespoon flour	⅓ teaspoon cayenne
1 cup tomatoes, cut in small pieces	½ bay leaf, crumbled
1 cup water	1½ cups uncooked brown rice

Warm skillet and add oil. Heat over low heat; add onion, green pepper, and garlic. Cook slowly 5 minutes. Add and blend flour. Add all other ingredients except rice.

Bring to a boil and gently simmer for 5 minutes. Slowly add rice, stirring with fork to blend. Cover and let simmer for 30 minutes or until rice is tender and liquid is absorbed. Salt for those without sodium restrictions.

One Serving

9	milligrams sodium
3	grams total fat
negligible	grams saturated fat
246	calories

LOW SATURATED FAT VARIATION

If total fat is restricted, follow Basic Recipe but do not brown onion, pepper, and garlic in oil. Rather, simmer gently for 5 minutes in ¼ cup water. Salt to taste if not on sodium restriction. *One serving, with oil: negligible saturated fat (½ teaspoon vegetable oil).*

9. TRICKS WITH FISH

Fish must swim thrice—once in the water, a second time in the sauce, and a third time in wine of stomach. —JOHN RAY: *English Proverbs* (1670)

Some epicureans would agree one hundred per cent with this old proverb and would argue that a fish without its sauce is no fish at all. Thank goodness, many of us have learned that the delicate and bland flavor of fish is a treat in itself, when seasonings are delicately used to bring out its characteristic taste.

More good fish is spoiled by the way it is cooked than is almost any other food. Its natural juiciness is all but cooked right out of it, leaving us a dry, flat something to chew on. It is far too valuable in our diet for any such treatment, particularly for those of you on the fat-restricted program. (Most fish is low in total fat content, and all fish is low in saturated fat.) The albuminous or protein part of fish may be likened to the white of egg. Fish should be cooked only until this albuminous substance is "set" and no longer. Generally speaking, fish is cooked when it separates from the bones and may be "flaked" with a knife.

Fish does not require the slow cooking that meat does, as the sinews holding its fibers together are tender and jellylike and soften when heat is applied. When full heat is applied, the outside is soon cooked and the moisture and flavor are sealed inside. In baking fish, have high temperature to begin with, then reduce to normal baking temperature to complete. Remember that fish is at its best when cooked lightly and served at once.

Fish to Use:

The Frank A. Busalacchi Fish Company, in Stockton,

California, classifies fish as *lean* or *fat* for cooking purposes as follows:

Lean	Fat
Carp	Bass
Catfish	Bluefish
Codfish	Halibut
Flounder	Herring
Haddock	Mackerel
Perch	Millet
Pike	Porgy or scup
Pollock	Salmon
Red snapper	Shad
Sheepshead	Swordfish
Sole	Trout, sea
Trout	Tunà
Whiting	Whitefish

Cooking Methods:

Four methods of cooking fish may be used: Broiled, baked, boiled (steamed or poached), fried or sautéed. Although the small lean fish such as trout, filet of sole, and flounder are usually fried, this method is least desirable for dieters, particularly those who must limit fat. Such fish may be broiled or baked in parchment or aluminum wraps. Larger lean fish, as carp and haddock, may be baked or broiled and may be served with a sauce (pages 137 to 141) if desired. Cod and haddock are particularly good choices for you on fat dieting.

Fat fish, as bluefish, halibut, and mackerel, may be baked or broiled in smaller pieces. They are delicious with a wedge of lemon or tangy sauce, such as Tomato (page 140-41).

Some fish are more suitable for certain methods of cookery than others, and this should always be considered. Generally speaking, the method of cooking is determined by whether it is a fat or lean fish. Fat fish have oil mingled throughout the flesh, while "lean" fish have a drier flesh—the oil is contained in the liver and so removed when the fish is cleaned. We have used some general yardsticks in classifying fish according to leanness and fatness, but it must be remembered that the fat content of fish varies to an extent according to time of year. All fish is a blessing to the saturated fat-controlled diet.

Almost any kind of fish is good broiled, but fat fish are considered better for baking and lean fish for boiling, steaming, or for chowders. Lean fish is a natural for you who must also count calories. Have your dealer clean fish according to the way you plan to cook it. Fillets are the fleshy sides of fish and should be cut up to ½ inch thick, cut lengthwise and away from the bone. Steaks are cut crosswise from whole fish that have been scaled or skinned. Pan-dressed fish are whole fish, scaled and cleaned, with head, tail, and fins removed, if desired.

Some years ago, Evelene Spencer, the Fish Cookery Expert for the United States Bureau of Fisheries, described a Hot-Oven or Spencer method of fish cookery which lends itself to diet cookery to particular advantage. It cuts down the cooking fat or oil by more than a half and produces a better-looking product. It is useful for fish weighing up to a pound; for larger amounts, cut fish into strips or slices, as sea bass, sole, et cetera.

This is Miss Spencer's way of doing it: Place cut pieces of fish to your extreme left; next place a bowl of low sodium non-fat (or regular non-fat, depending upon diet regulations) milk, and seasoning. Next to this place a low-sided pan with finely sifted low sodium bread crumbs. Lastly, place a lightly oiled baking sheet with a teaspoon or more vegetable oil in a small measuring cup for "dabbing" the top of fish. With the left hand, put a piece of fish into the bowl of milk; then put into pan of crumbs. Now, with the right hand cover the fish with crumbs and place it in baking pan. Be sure to keep the left hand for the wet work, the right one for the dry. In this way you can keep the crumbs dry. After all of the pieces have been treated in the above manner, sprinkle each piece with a little vegetable oil, or brush lightly. This is the only fat used in this method or preparation. The same results cannot be obtained if a flour, corn meal, oatmeal, or general unsalted cracker dip is used. She states that with cracker or other dips, fish will be browned in splotches where fat has touched them; with bread-crumb dip and the addition of a little oil—about 1 tablespoon to a pound of fish—the product will be uniformly golden brown after cooking.

Preheat oven at highest temperature for 10 minutes; then place fish in oven. Most fish will cook in 10 minutes. Do not be afraid that it will burn, and never add water to fish cooked this quick way. If the heat has been sufficient, each piece may be easily removed to serving plate and pan will be quite dry underneath fish.

If herbs and seasonings are to be used, add about 4 minutes before fish is done. Garnish with lemon wedges or sauce (pages 137 to 141).

How to serve fish:

As most fish are light and pallid in color and mild in taste, strive for contrast in choice of vegetables and salads. Have flavorsome and colorful vegetables, as red cabbage, tomatoes, cucumbers, radishes, broccoli. Acid flavors make a good contrast for "fat" fish. This is one of the reasons that lemon is such an indispensable for your fish dishes. Use the juices to give a tangy savor to sauces; use a wedge per serving as a garnish.

For sodium restriction, do not use:

Canned fish, except dietetic without added sodium

Salted fish

Shellfish, except approved canned dietetic without added sodium

Frozen commercial fish fillet (usually treated in a salt bath in processing)

For saturated fat restriction, do not use:

Butter, margarine, or vegetable shortenings in preparation

Canned or commercially prepared fish with butter, whole milk, whole egg

Egg yolk or whole egg

Whole milk or cream

Suggestions to speed you on your way:

1. Serve fish as soon as cooked. It becomes soggy and unpalatable when allowed to stand.

2. Try parchment or aluminum foil for boiled or baked fish when you want to keep all of the juices "in."

3. Try Bakon Yeast for smoked flavor.

4. Basil, bay, crushed fennel, onion, thyme, dill, ginger root, nutmeg, paprika, green pepper, garlic, and white pepper do nice things for some fish dishes. Of course, lemon juice and white wines are naturals, too. And parsley is a love for garnishing and flavoring, as is curry when lightly sprinkled over fish before cooking.

5. Dry, white wines, such as Sylvaner, blend well with the delicate flavor of fish. Sherry is a zestful addition to scalloped fish and fish sauces.

6. Fish cookery allows you many methods. Choose from

baking or broiling when you want oven methods; from boiling, steaming, or pan-frying for top-of-the-stove methods. Leave the deep-frys for those who have cast-iron digestions and no overweight problems.

7. Do not serve sweet salads with fish, but choose crisp, crunchy greens with sharp dressings for flavor, color, and texture contrast.

STEAMED BLUEFISH
4 Servings

2 pounds bluefish, cleaned and cut in pieces
1 tablespoon vegetable oil
1 garlic clove
¼ teaspoon basil
2 tablespoons finely minced leek tops *or* chives
Paprika

Wipe pieces of fish with damp cloth. Oil fish with vegetable oil in which garlic has soaked for an hour or two. Put fish on steamer rack. Set in place with boiling water in lower part. Sprinkle basil and minced leek tops over fish. Cover tightly and steam for about 30 minutes, or until fork-tender. Serve with Cucumber Sauce (page 139-40). Garnish with paprika. Add salt for regulars and fat-restricted dieters without sodium restrictions.

One Serving
(3 oz. fish, cooked weight)
Without sauce

77	milligrams sodium
8	grams total fat
negligible	grams saturated fat
177	calories

One serving: ¾ teaspoon vegetable oil.

FISH IN CREOLE SAUCE
8 Servings

Another tested recipe from the Home Service Department of the Corn Products Company.

1 recipe Creole Sauce
3 cups cooked fish, cut in small pieces
Prepare Creole Sauce; add fish. If desired, serve on hot platter lined with mashed potatoes.

CREOLE SAUCE

⅓ cup corn oil
1 green pepper, cut in strips
1 cup sliced onion
1 clove garlic
1 teaspoon sugar
1 whole clove
¼ teaspoon pepper
⅛ teaspoon celery seed
3½ cups canned tomatoes without added sodium
2 tablespoons cornstarch
2 tablespoons water

Heat oil in saucepan; add green pepper, onion, and garlic; cover and cook slowly until slightly tender but not brown. Add sugar, whole clove, pepper, celery seed, and tomatoes; cook over low heat, stirring occasionally, about ½ hour. Blend cornstarch with water and add to sauce. Continue cooking 10 minutes, stirring constantly, until sauce thickens. Remove garlic and clove before serving. Add salt for those without sodium restrictions.

One Serving
(3 oz. cod,
cooked weight)
Without potatoes

94	milligrams sodium
12	grams total fat
negligible	grams saturated fat
207	calories

One serving: 2 teaspoons vegetable oil.

FISH SOUFFLÉ
3 Servings

1 cup cooked fish, flaked
¼ teaspoon dill weed
¼ teaspoon paprika
1 tablespoon lemon juice
Dash cayenne
⅓ cup low sodium bread crumbs
⅓ cup low sodium nonfat milk
1 egg, separated
1 tablespoon sherry

Flake fish. Add dill, paprika, lemon juice, and cayenne; blend. Add bread crumbs which have been soaked in milk until soft. Stir lightly to mix. Blend in 1 egg yolk, lightly beaten. Beat egg white until stiff but not dry. Add sherry; blend. Fold into fish mixture.

Turn into a casserole dish, lightly oiled with vegetable oil.

Set casserole in pan of hot water, and bake in 350° (moderate) oven for 30 minutes, or until soufflé is firm. Serve at once. Salt for those without sodium restrictions.

One Serving
(2⅔ oz. bass,
cooked weight)

93	milligrams sodium
15	grams total fat
2	grams saturated fat
256	calories

VARIATION

Any fish on your diet list may be used in this recipe, as haddock, cod, and halibut.

LOW SATURATED FAT VARIATION

Follow Basic Recipe except substitute 2 egg whites for whole egg. If no sodium restriction, use regular bread and non-fat milk and add salt to taste. *One serving: neg-ligible saturated fat.*

STEAMED HADDOCK IN COURT BOUILLON

A particularly good choice for those of you with fat re-striction.

6 Servings

3 pounds whole had-dock, cleaned and cut in pieces	3 peppercorns
	1 clove
	¼ bay leaf
1 tablespoon chopped onion	1 tablespoon wine vin-egar
1 tablespoon chopped parsley	1 quart water (about)
1 teaspoon vegetable oil	Parsley

Wipe haddock and wrap in cheesecloth so that you can lift it from pan without having it fall apart. Set on rack in large kettle. Simmer onion and chopped parsley in small amount of water for 15 minutes. Add remaining in-gredients to onion mixture; bring to a boil. Simmer 15 minutes longer. Pour over fish. Add water to kettle, if necessary, so that there are at least 2 inches liquid in bottom of pan. Cover tightly; simmer, being sure to keep liquid below boiling point. Cook until fork-tender. Allow from 24 to 30 minutes for a 3-pound fish. Lift fish carefully from pan. Strain liquid and thicken for sauce (2 tablespoons flour per cup of liquid) if desired. Garnish with parsley. Add salt for regulars or fat-restricted dieter without sodium restrictions.

One Serving
(3 oz. fish,
cooked weight)
Without sauce or
parsley garnish

70	milligrams sodium
1	gram total fat
negligible	grams saturated fat
94	calories

VARIATIONS

Fish may be poached in water or tomato juice (canned without added sodium for sodium-restricted dieters).

Wine may be used for the poaching liquid by substituting 2 cups red or white dinner wine for 2 cups water.

Other fish may be prepared in this way, as sea bass, halibut, and salmon.

We like to cut fish into serving pieces before boiling for better table appearance, avoiding that chopped-up look.

HALIBUT CASSEROLE
6 Servings

Steam or poach 2-pound halibut steaks as in recipe on page 130. Cool and flake. Make a low sodium non-fat milk sauce, using 1½ cups milk, 4 tablespoons unsalted butter, and 3 tablespoons flour. Add to it ½ cup white wine for flavor. Season with ¼ teaspoon pepper and a pinch of thyme. Brush casserole lightly with vegetable oil. Now, put a layer of fish in casserole. Top with white sauce and repeat. Top all with ½ cup low sodium bread crumbs and sprinkle with paprika. Bake 10 minutes in a 400° (very hot) oven, then reduce to 375° (moderate) oven for about 15 minutes. Salt for those without sodium restrictions.

One Serving
(3 oz. fish,
cooked weight)
With Sylvaner

63	milligrams sodium
14	grams total fat
8	grams saturated fat
309	calories

LOW SATURATED FAT VARIATION

Follow Basic Recipe except for white sauce. Use Basic Non-fat White Sauce (page 138). Add salt to taste if no sodium restriction. *One serving: negligible saturated fat.*

HALIBUT CONTINENTAL

½ cup seedless grapes (*skins removed*)	½ cup sliced onions
⅓ cup sherry	Few grains cayenne
2-pound halibut steaks, cut into 6 slices	1 cup low sodium White Sauce (page 137)
Few grains black pepper	¼ cup seedless grapes (for garnishing)
1 tablespoon lemon juice	

Put grapes into a small bowl; pour the sherry over them. Let stand for 30 minutes. Meanwhile, wipe the halibut slices with a damp cloth. Sprinkle with pepper and lemon juice. Cook onion slices in small amount of boiling water for 5 minutes; drain. Lightly oil a casserole; arrange fish slices in it. Top with drained onions; add cayenne to white sauce and pour over fish. Cover and bake in a 350° (moderate) oven, 25 to 35 minutes, until fork-tender. (Do not overcook.) Remove casserole from oven and strain off sauce. Drain grapes; add to the low sodium white sauce. Take 2 tablespoons sherry in which the grapes were soaked and blend with sauce. Reheat; pour over fish. Garnish casserole top with ¼ cup grapes. Add salt for those without sodium restrictions.

One Serving (3 oz. fish, cooked weight)	
65	milligrams sodium
11	grams total fat
4	grams saturated fat
251	calories

LOW SATURATED FAT VARIATION

Follow Basic Recipe except substitute Non-fat White Sauce (page 138). If no sodium restriction, add salt to taste. *One serving: negligible saturated fat.*

BAKED SALMON IN TOMATO SAUCE
6 Servings

Allow 6 servings to 1¾ pounds of salmon steak.

Put fish slices into a shallow pan and let soak for ½ hour in 1 cup white wine. Meanwhile, brush bottom of baking pan lightly with vegetable oil and place fish in it. Sprinkle each slice with a pinch of curry powder and fresh black pepper. Top each with a slice of onion. Place on top of onion 2 small slices of fresh tomatoes and a swirl of green pepper. Bake about 30 minutes in a 375° (moderrate) oven until flaky to fork-test. *Baste every 10 minutes* during cooking period with the wine in which the fish was soaked. As the cooking progresses, bits of tomato and pepper will break away and become parts of the sauce, to add to its wonderful flavor. Salt for regulars and fat-restricted dieters without sodium restrictions.

One Serving (3 oz. fish, cooked weight) With Sylvaner	
91	milligrams sodium
20	grams total fat
negligible	grams saturated fat
319	calories

VARIATION

Haddock, halibut, cod, bass, or other white fish may be used. Bass and salmon are higher in fat content than other fish except tuna, canned in oil, so should be used sparingly if total fat is restricted.

BROILED SWORDFISH
4 Servings

Cut 1-pound cross-section steaks into 4 portions. Wipe with damp cloth. Sprinkle each with ½ teaspoon lemon juice, ½ teaspoon thyme, and ¼ teaspoon dill. Pepper lightly. Drip 1 teaspoon sauterne over each steak and put in broiler about 2 inches under heat. Cook 15 to 20 minutes until tests done. Sprinkle with 2 teaspoons minced parsley when served onto platter, and garnish with wedges of lemon. Serve at once. Salt for regulars and fat-restricted dieters without sodium restrictions.

One Serving	
(3 oz. fish,	
cooked weight)	
With sauterne	
90	milligrams sodium
5	grams total fat
negligible	grams saturated fat
142	calories

VARIATIONS

For variety, try sliced fresh mushrooms on top of your fish fillets or steaks, or serve with non-fat milk-wine sauce (low sodium for sodium-restricted dieters).

A dash of allspice will give your swordfish an unusual flavor. It is particularly good with salmon or halibut, which may be prepared in the same way.

Ditto for curry powder.

In using such seasonings, scatter them over fish before broiling.

Or make an oil-herb sauce by soaking 2 split and crushed cloves of garlic in 2 tablespoons vegetable oil for 2 hours, then discard the garlic and brush fish with oil. Be sure to brush all sides for full flavor. Here we like a hot broiler so that steaks will cook in about 5 minutes for each side. Serve plain or with your favorite sauce.

CREAMED TUNA SUPREME
4 Servings

We are indebted to the Home Advisory Service of the Wine Institute, San Francisco, for this excellent recipe.

¼ cup unsalted butter	2 (6½ oz.) cans
¼ cup flour	dietetic-pack tuna,
1¾ cups low sodium	drained
non-fat milk	1 tablespoon finely
¼ cup sherry	chopped green pepper

Melt butter and stir in flour; add milk and cook, stirring constantly, until mixture boils and thickens. Add sherry, tuna, and green pepper. Heat thoroughly. Just before serving, add salt for those without sodium restrictions.

One Serving
(3¼ oz. fish, cooked
    weight)

42	milligrams sodium
12	grams total fat
11	grams saturated fat
278	calories

VARIATIONS

Instead of dietetic low sodium tuna, dietetic low sodium shrimps may be used. Or 1½ cups diced cooked chicken or veal may be substituted for tuna.

LOW SATURATED FAT VARIATION

Substitute the non-fat White Sauce (page 138) for the butter-flour-milk sauce in Basic Recipe. Add a sprinkling of dill weed or crushed fennel to heighten flavor. If no sodium restriction, use regular canned tuna (brine pack) or shellfish, and add salt to taste to white sauce. *One serving: negligible saturated fat.*

SAUCES

And now for a few sauces, so fish may come "swimming" in them to your table.

BASIC MEDIUM WHITE SAUCE
4 Servings

2 tablespoons unsalted butter (1 for thin, 4 for thick)
2 tablespoons flour (1 for thin, 4 for thick)
1 cup low sodium non-fat milk
⅛ teaspoon pepper

Melt the butter and blend with flour; gradually add the milk. Cook over hot water, or direct flame if you can stir constantly until mixture thickens. Add pepper and such other seasonings as you may wish (being sure to add sodium count of your choice of seasonings to total). This basic sauce has little flavor unless you "pep" it up.

One Serving (Medium)	Total Recipe	
2	9	milligrams sodium
6	23	grams total fat
6	23	grams saturated fat
84	337	calories

Note: Vegetable oil may be substituted for unsalted butter.

BASIC NON-FAT WHITE SAUCE
4 Servings

1 low sodium chicken bouillon cube
¼ cup boiling water
2 tablespoons flour (1 for thin, 4 for thick)
Few grains black or

white pepper
1 cup low sodium non-fat milk
Seasonings various (optional)

Dissolve bouillon cube in boiling water. Let cool slightly; blend flour and pepper with bouillon to make smooth paste. Slowly add milk, stirring after each addition to ensure smooth sauce. Stir constantly until mixture thickens (at least 5 minutes after bubbles appear). If no sodium restrictions, use regular non-fat milk and bouillon, and add salt to taste.

One Serving (Medium)	Total Recipe	
4	17	milligrams sodium
negligible	negligible	grams total fat
35	139	calories

VARIATIONS FOR
BASIC WHITE SAUCES

HERB SAUCE: Add ½ teaspoon of any of the following dried herbs; dill weed, fennel, gumbo file, powdered mushrooms, garlic powder, oregano, onion powder, paprika, or tarragon. Blend thoroughly. Pour over fish. Garnish as desired.

MUSHROOM SAUCE: Sauté ½ cup sliced, fresh mushrooms in 1 tablespoon vegetable oil for 5 minutes. Add to sauce and cook all together for another 5 minutes. Add 2 tablespoons white wine just before serving. One tablespoon lemon juice and ½ teaspoon dry mustard may be added when a sharper flavor is wanted.

PARSLEY SAUCE: Add ½ teaspoon grated onion and 3 teaspoons parsley when sauce is thickened. Add 1 tablespoon white wine just before removing from heat. When serving, sprinkle lightly with paprika and garnish with sprigs of parsley.

MOCK CHEESE SAUCE: Add 1 teaspoon Bakon Yeast with flour.

CHEESE SAUCE: Add 4 tablespoons grated low sodium cheese and ½ teaspoon paprika. Do not use if on saturated fat-restricted diet.

HOT TARTAR SAUCE
6 Servings

½ cup White Sauce (page 137)
⅓ cup low sodium mayonnaise
½ teaspoon chives, minced fine
¼ tablespoon scraped onion

½ teaspoon tarragon vinegar or wine vinegar
½ tablespoon chopped parsley
½ tablespoon low sodium pickles
Paprika

To Basic White Sauce, add the above ingredients in order. Stir constantly until well blended, but do not let boil.

Total Recipe

24	milligrams sodium
40	grams total fat
12	grams saturated fat
471	calories

LOW SATURATED FAT VARIATION

Use Never-Fail Mayonnaise (page 186) or Eggless "Mayonnaise" (page 185-86) with Basic Non-Fat White Sauce (page 138). If no sodium restrictions, use dill pickles and add salt to taste. *One serving: negligible grams saturated fat.*

CUCUMBER SAUCE
6 Servings

2 cucumbers pared, grated, and thoroughly drained
1 teaspoon chopped parsley

1 teaspoon minced chives
Vinegar

Season cucumbers to taste for a fish accompaniment. If no sodium restriction, add salt to taste.

One Serving	Total Recipe	
5	28	milligrams sodium
negligible	negligible	grams total fat
9	52	calories

ALMOND SAUCE

For every serving of fish allow:

1 teaspoon vegetable oil	½ teaspoon parsley, minced fine
½ teaspoon lemon juice	3 almonds blanched and slivered
Few grains cayenne	

Warm oil in small pan. Add almonds and cook slowly until they just turn color but do not brown. Add to other ingredients or pour over fish, as sole or Rex sole, when extra richness is desired.

One Serving	
negligible	milligrams sodium
7	grams total fat
negligible	grams saturated fat
64	calories

VARIATION

Wine may be substituted for lemon juice.

TOMATO SAUCE
4 Servings

If you don't like the low sodium milk sauces, no matter what you add for extra flavor, try a tomato sauce. Excellent when you want a Spanish tang to your fish dish.

2 tablespoons unsalted butter	1 tablespoon lemon juice
2 tablespoons flour	1 cup unsalted tomato juice
1 small bay leaf	
¼ teaspoon pepper	

Melt butter and blend in flour and seasonings. Add tomato juice and stir until sauce thickens. Pour at once

over fish, and garnish with parsley for color contrast.
Curry powder may be used in place of bay leaf.

One Serving	Total Recipe	
3	10	milligrams sodium
6	23	grams total fat
6	23	grams saturated fat
76	304	calories

LOW SATURATED FAT VARIATION

Vegetable oil may be substituted for butter; or fat may be
omitted. Combine flour and seasonings. Blend slowly with
tomato juice. Cook, stirring constantly, until sauce thickens. If no sodium restrictions, use regular tomato juice
and add salt to taste. *One serving, with oil: negligible
saturated fat (1½ teaspoons vegetable oil).*

10. A PARADE OF VEGETABLES

Where can you get so much for so little in restricted cookery? There are vegetables in abundance to use, and many of them have the good grace to be so low in sodium and fat content as to offer you opportunities to use some of the higher count foods in combination.

So it would seem that you will be able to pay court to vegetables on this diet and use them with a feeling of abandon (well, not quite all of them). If you want to make them appealing and nutritionally good, you will have to dream up something better than the old boil-and-butter method of cookery. Good as that method may be for some of the young and tender vegetables of early spring, it is hardly the treatment for all in all seasons. As with fish, many cooking sins are committed in the guise of vegetable cookery.

First of all, select only fresh vegetables and treat them to proper refrigeration once you get them home, if you want good results. You can't leave them standing around on your sink from time of purchase to preparation time. And they don't like to be prepared in the morning for evening use. Such treatment results in loss of vitamins as well as of flavor.

As for the cooking itself: most vegetables yield up their subtle flavors to the water in which they are cooked. When they are cooked in a bath of water, in other words when too much water is used, little of their true flavor remains when they come to the table.

Group A	Group B	Group C
Based upon ½ cup servings each of these vegetables contains about 9 milligrams sodium, and negligible calories and fat.	Based upon ½ cup servings, each of these vegetables contains about 9 milligrams sodium, 35 calories, and negligible fat.	Based upon ½ cup servings unless otherwise specified, each of these vegetables contains about 5 milligrams sodium, 70 calories, and negligible fat.

Group A	Group B	Group C
Asparagus	Onions	½ cup cooked beans, Lima or navy (dried)
Broccoli	Peas (fresh or dietetic low sodium canned only)	
Brussels sprouts		
Cabbage		
Cauliflower		⅓ cup cooked beans, Lima (fresh)
Chicory	Pumpkin	
Cucumber	Rutabaga (yellow turnip)	¼ cup beans, baked (without pork)
Eggplant		
Endive	Squash, winter (acorn, Hubbard, et cetera)	
Escarole		
Green beans		
Lettuce		⅓ cup cooked small ear corn
Mushrooms		
Okra		½ cup cooked lentils (dried)
Peppers, green or red		
Radishes		⅔ cup parsnips
Squash, summer (yellow, zucchini, et cetera)		½ cup cooked peas, split green or yellow, cowpeas, et cetera (dried)
Tomato juice (low sodium dietetic only)		
Tomatoes		
Turnip greens		1 small potato, white
Wax beans		½ cup potatoes, mashed
		¼ cup or ½ small sweet potato

Neither do they like to be cooked for so long that they are mushy in consistency when served. They invite a careful bit of timing in this department. All in all, they require careful handling.

There are many little cooking tricks to help bring out the natural flavors of vegetables. But before we go into that, let's take a look at the Do and Don't list on the page opposite.

Use as desired (fresh, frozen or dietetic canned without added sodium, as permitted by your physician).

See Appendix I if you are using count method of menu planning.

Do not use:

Artichokes, beet greens, beets, carrots, celery, Swiss chard, dandelion greens, kale, mustard greens, sauerkraut, spinach, turnips (white), canned juices, except low sodium dietetic packed without added salt. Fat-restricted dieters, without sodium restrictions, may use all kinds of vegetables—fresh, frozen, and regular canned—except baked beans prepared with added pork, or other vegetable combinations with added fat.

VEGETABLE COOKERY

A know-how of vegetable cookery involves a knowledge of the combining quality of vegetables with meats they so often accompany. We think of high-flavored meats with high-flavored vegetables. Let's see just how the principle does work out when the sodium count is so all-important.

Beef: With its fine flavor, beef invites such vegetable combinations as corn, string beans or Lima beans, broccoli, eggplant, sprouts, cauliflower, parsnips, yellow turnips, tomatoes, mushrooms, and onions.

Pork: This, too, is a high-flavored meat and is tasty with many of the vegetables listed above for beef—plus cabbage, succotash, parsnips, and sweet potatoes.

Lamb: Now let us turn to the milder meats. Young, succulent lamb is such a treat in the spring of the year that you will surely want to include it somehow if you can, and you can by using very low count vegetables with it. Peas, bless their low sodium content, are the most natural accompaniment to roast lamb, and hard to beat. Squash, asparagus, yellow turnips, cucumbers, baby Lima beans, may all take their turn. In serving lamb, be sure to remember that leg of lamb is lower in fat content than lamb chops.

Veal: With its delicate flavor, veal is a good choice for those of you on fat-restricted diets (but highest of the meats and poultry in sodium content) when you want to serve such vegetables as asparagus, succotash, squash, mushrooms, baby Lima beans, string beans, peas, young green corn.

Chicken (turkey, too): You will have to be pencil-wise again if you are restricting solid fats and may use only the breast of chicken whatever your vegetable selection. The vegetables that seem to combine most appropriately with chicken all have very low sodium content. They are corn, baby Lima beans, peas, sweet potatoes, and pearl onions.

Rabbit: Takes the same natural combinations in vegetables as does chicken, but because of its low sodium content, you can select vegetables of higher count, for variety's sake.

Hints on cooking vegetables:

1. Select only fresh vegetables to use. Wash them quickly, and store in closely covered jar or refrigerator container.

2. Prepare vegetables just before cooking for best flavor and nutrition. Under no condition let them soak in water. Whenever it is necessary to string beans, shell peas, or otherwise prepare vegetables before time of use, store in tightly covered jar and fill to top of container.

3. Cook vegetables in as little water as possible; steam whenever possible.

4. Do not overcook.

5. Save any remaining vegetable liquid for later cooking use in gravies, soups, and sauces.

6. You can get along very well without adding unsalted butter or margarine to cooked vegetables, particularly if you use lemon juice or wine to heighten flavor. But if you must add a fat, use small amounts (vegetable oil only for restricted fat diets).

7. For variety in flavoring, try herbs, too. In general, they should be sprinkled over tops of vegetables at end of cooking period. Cover utensil and let stand not more than 5 minutes. Some particularly good *vegetable-herb* combinations are:

Cauliflower with *tarragon* and *low sodium dietetic prepared mustard* (use regular mustard if no sodium restriction)
Summer squash with *nutmeg, mace* or *sweet basil*
Green beans with *marjoram, savory,* or *dill*
Peas with *thyme,* or *marjoram*
Broccoli with *dill, oregano,* or *garlic*

8. The red and white table wines for which you have sodium content (Burgundy, the clarets, Rhine, and sauterne) combine with many vegetables for improved flavor. The white wines blend well with light-colored vegetables; the red with the darker ones. Experiment with small amounts and let your own taste guide your use.

9. A *pinch* of sugar is a good accent where salt is omitted.

10. Don't overseason. Vegetables have fine flavors in their own rights.

Let us take a look at the methods of cooking vegetables and see what they have to offer.

Pressure Cooking: Preserves the bright color, natural flavor, and best in nutrition to the highest degree. Vegetables cook so quickly by this method that they require only about 1/3 of the usual boiling time.

Steaming: One of our favorite methods of vegetable cookery because of the consistency of good results—colorful and tasteful vegetables, with all of their natural flavor preserved and none of that mushy, all-boiled-out flavor. Place vegetables on rack, with just enough boiling water in the bottom of pan to generate steam. Cover and steam for length of time required for individual vegetable. In general, this will be from 5 to 15 or more minutes longer than for boiling.

A variation of this method and one that brings vegetables to the table chock-full of their true flavors is the lettuce leaf "cover." All you have to do is to place vegetables on rack as with ordinary steaming and cover them with a large piece or two of dripping lettuce. Do not use more than 1/4 to 1/2 inch of water in bottom of utensil. A real flavor-saver.

Pan-frying, also called sautéing and frying: Depends upon fat for the liquid in which the vegetable is to be cooked and is quite a favorite in Chinese cookery. Put a little vegetable oil in the bottom of your skillet, and add your vegetable, shredded or sliced thin, with 1 or 2 tablespoons of water. Stir occasionally and cook until fork-tender—from 5 to 15 minutes. Cabbage, lettuce, broccoli, and sprouts all lend themselves to this treatment (may not be your choice if total fat is restricted).

Baking: Will preserve the food values of your vegetables to a high degree. Beans, potatoes, and tomatoes lend themselves particularly well to direct oven cookery. Eggplant, cauliflower, or mixed vegetables and mushrooms are naturals for the oven casserole.

Boiling: This is the least desirable method of vegetable cookery. When you do elect to boil your vegetables, cook them covered in the smallest possible amount of *boiling* water. Bring your vegetables to a boil quickly, then turn down the heat and simmer gently. Do not overcook, and serve as soon as they are cooked. Save every bit of water left over for sauces and soups. Store it in a covered jar until time of use. Better still, cook in a low sodium dietetic beef bouillon cube liquid in place of water, if your sodium allowance will permit. (Use regular bouillon cube liquid if sodium is not restricted.)

Broiling: The method used for very young and tender raw vegetables, particularly when you are serving a broiled meat and want to conserve heat and cook your vegetables right along with the meat. It can sometimes be used for reheating cooked vegetables, too.

ASPARAGUS

This vegetable is altogether too often spoiled by improper cooking. It can arrive on the table limp and listless when cooked too long, or in too much water. Under such conditions, it is a doubtful addition especially without salt. On the other hand, it can be simply delicious if panned or steamed.

HOT ASPARAGUS
3 Servings

Prepare by breaking off all tough ends and removing scales of 1 pound. Put the stalks standing upright on a rack in saucepan or directly into pan if you are going to pan-cook it. Cover tops with dripping lettuce leaf to hold in moisture, and cut down amount of water needed for boiling or steaming. Whatever you do, use a minimum amount of water. Boil 10 to 20 minutes, steam 12 to 30 minutes; for tips only, boil 5 to 15 minutes, steam 7 to 15 minutes in a tightly covered pan. Serve plain, with lemon juice, or with mock hollandaise sauce. Add salt for those without sodium restrictions.

6 Stalks
Without sauce

3	milligrams sodium
negligible	grams total fat
20	calories

ASPARAGUS CHINESE STYLE
6 *Servings*

2 pounds fresh asparagus

¾ cup low sodium bouillon, chicken-flavored

1 tablespoon cornstarch

1 tablespoon cold water

1 garlic clove, finely chopped

Few grains black pepper

2 tablespoons vegetable oil

1 teaspoon lemon juice

Wash asparagus and break off tough lower stalks. Using a sharp knife, cut diagonally in very thin slices. Make chicken bouillon, stir in a mixture of cornstarch and water. Cook until thickened, stirring constantly to prevent scorching. Add garlic and pepper. Sauté asparagus slices in hot oil for about 3 minutes, until fork-tender. Blend lemon juice and sauce; pour over asparagus. Stir and cook 1 minute. Serve at once. Salt for those without sodium restrictions.

One Serving	Total Recipe	
5	30	milligrams sodium
5	30	grams total fat
negligible	negligible	grams saturated fat
71	426	calories

One serving: 1 teaspoon vegetable oil.

FRESH OR FROZEN STRING BEANS
4 *Servings*

Pressure-cook, steam, pan-cook, or broil. Allow from 20 to 35 minutes for boiled whole string beans; 15 to 25 minutes for cut.

To 1 pound of beans try adding a pinch of sugar, 1 teaspoon vegetable oil to water or bouillon. When ready to serve, add ⅓ teaspoon dill weed and ½ teaspoon lemon juice. Salt for those without sodium restrictions.

One Serving	Total Recipe	
Without low sodium bouillon		
or oil		
2	8	milligrams sodium
negligible	1	gram total fat
negligible	negligible	grams saturated fat
36	143	calories

VARIATIONS

Marjoram or thyme will accent the flavor of beans pleasantly.

For variety, add a few slivers of toasted almonds as you serve your string beans and 1 tablespoon dry red wine in place of lemon juice.

Prepare green beans as outlined above. Warm 2 tablespoons oil in a small skillet (for those without total fat restrictions), and add 1 tablespoon minced onion and 1 small clove garlic, minced. Cook all together 5 minutes. Pour over beans as you are ready to cook them by whatever method you elect.

LIMA BEANS
2 Servings

Baby Limas are delicious whenever available. Use 1½ pounds unshelled or ½ pound shelled beans. Simply cut off their outer rims and shell like peas. Boil 20 to 30 minutes; steam 25 to 35 minutes. Season with ½ teaspoon unsalted butter and 1 teaspoon minced parsley. (Savory may be used in place of parsley.) Salt for those without sodium restrictions.

One Serving	Total Recipe	
2	3	milligrams sodium
2	4	grams total fat
1	2	grams saturated fat
154	308	calories

LOW SATURATED FAT VARIATION

Substitute vegetable oil for butter or serve without fat. Salt to taste if no sodium restriction. *One serving, without fat: negligible grams saturated fat.*

BROCCOLI

Now, here is a versatile vegetable, distinctly flavorsome and equally good hot or cold. Its green flowers lend a decorative quality to the salad bowl; and flowers, stems, and leaves may be cooked. It will yield a marvelous flavor if you will only cook it pan or steam method.

Miss Lois Marr introduced us to it, Chinese-fashion, some years ago, and here we adapt it for diet cookery.

PANNED BROCCOLI
3 Servings

1 pound broccoli	1 cup low sodium
2 tablespoons vege-	chicken bouillon
table oil	1 teaspoon cornstarch
1 tablespoon water	¼ teaspoon oregano

Wash the broccoli; cut stems from flowering tops. Peel stems and cut crosswise. Heat the oil until very hot in a heavy skillet or Chinese wock. Add broccoli stems and stir constantly for 5 minutes. Add water and cut-up flowers; cook fast for 2 minutes. Heap to one side of utensil and stir into oil mixture the blended low sodium bouillon and cornstarch. (The amount specified provides a lot of sauce; reduce amount if desired.) Let cook slowly over low heat until it thickens. Now blend in broccoli; mix thoroughly and stir to prevent scorching. Cook until just fork-tender, about 10 minutes or less. Sprinkle oregano over top, cover and let stand 2 minutes. Serve at once. Salt for those without sodium restrictions.

One Serving	Total Recipe	
15	44	milligrams sodium
10	29	grams total fat
negligible	negligible	grams saturated fat
114	342	calories

One serving: 2 teaspoons vegetable oil.

VARIATION

Prepare 1 pound broccoli as above outlined. Parboil about 10 minutes or, better still, pressure-cook 1½ to 3 minutes. Meanwhile, put 2 tablespoons vegetable oil into your skillet and heat. Add 1 tablespoon minced onion, and 1 garlic clove split lengthwise and fasten on a wooden pick. Brown slowly and add drained broccoli. Sauté all together for about 10 more minutes or until done. Sprinkle with ⅛ teaspoon pepper and stir in 1 tablespoon lemon juice. Remove garlic and serve at once, adding salt for those without sodium restrictions. Vinegar or red table wine may be used in place of lemon juice.

CABBAGE

For variety's sake, when you want to serve cabbage raw, don't always depend upon a cabbage slaw. Use wedges, white savory or red, for that raw addition of the day. Its crunchy goodness is good to the last taste, served in just its natural state.

HOT CABBAGE
4 Servings

Shred a 1-pound head cabbage thin and wash thoroughly. Put the dripping cabbage into your saucepan, adding enough water to keep from scorching. Add ½ teaspoon unsalted butter, ½ cup sugar, ½ teaspoon caraway seed, and 2 tablespoons vinegar to make the whole tart. Boil only until tender. This takes from 3 to 10 minutes. Salt for those without sodium restrictions.

One Serving	Total Recipe	
13	52	milligrams sodium
1	3	grams total fat
1	2	grams saturated fat
122	486	calories

VARIATION

Follow directions as given in recipe above. After cabbage has cooked until tender, add ½ cup low sodium non-fat milk. Heat but do not boil, and serve. Some cooks like to add 1 egg white, beaten lightly, stirred into the hot creamed cabbage just before serving. If the count is very close, you'd better forget the egg white.

LOW SATURATED FAT VARIATION

Substitute vegetable oil for unsalted butter in Basic Recipe. Add salt if no sodium restrictions. *One serving: negligible grams saturated fat (⅛ teaspoon vegetable oil).*

CAULIFLOWER

It is delicious raw, and its dainty flowerets should be served in this form often.

Whatever you do, don't overcook cauliflower. Its flowerets need only 8 to 15 minutes, if you choose to boil them, while 10 to 20 minutes will give desirable tenderness if steamed. For real conservation of flavor and texture, try steaming this vegetable. Once tried, it's safe to predict you'll be a convert.

STEAMED CAULIFLOWER
3 Servings

Wash and cut up a 1-pound cauliflower and steam 10 to 20 minutes, depending upon the size of your flowerets. Season with ¼ teaspoon tarragon and a dash of cayenne, and let stand 5 minutes. Spread flowerets lightly with low sodium prepared mustard, using a brush to spread quickly. Use regular mustard and add salt for those without sodium restrictions.

One Serving	Total Recipe	
14	42	milligrams sodium
negligible	1	grams total fat
negligible	negligible	grams saturated fat
18	54	calories

SPANISH CAULIFLOWER
6 Servings

1-pound head cooked cauliflower
½ teaspoon thyme, minced
Few grains pepper
Dash allspice
2½ cups fresh tomatoes, cut up

½ cup soft low sodium bread crumbs (100 per cent whole wheat bread is particularly good)
1 teaspoon unsalted butter

Put cauliflower in a shallow, lightly oiled casserole. Add seasonings to the tomatoes and bring to a rapid boil. Pour over cauliflower, top with crumbs, and dot all with 1 teaspoon unsalted butter or margarine. Bake in 350° (moderate) oven 15 to 30 minutes, and serve at once. Add salt for those without sodium restrictions.

One Serving	Total Recipe	
11	64	milligrams sodium
1	7	grams total fat
1	4	grams saturated fat
50	301	calories

LOW SATURATED FAT VARIATION

Follow Basic Recipe except substitute vegetable oil for

unsalted butter. Put bread crumbs and oil into jar and shake to blend; add to cauliflower mixture. If not restricted in sodium, add salt to taste. *One serving: negligible grams saturated fat (⅙ teaspoon vegetable oil).*

GREEN CORN

The vegetable marts not only strip corn of some of its husks and therefore reduce a considerable part of its nutritional value, but let the ears stand around on the counters so long that kernels are withered often before you can make your purchase. Enough said. Don't purchase. The ideal way, of course, is to be able to get corn on the cob fresh from the field with its golden tassels gleaming. Hurry it home and set in a shallow pan of water so that its stubby bases are kept moist and fresh until time of husking. The natural sugars in corn begin to change to starch within one-half hour after picking. If you can't buy this vegetable fresh in your market, you may want to resort to the frozen variety that is packed under favorable conditions.

FRESH OR FROZEN CORN

Good on the cob, boiled or barbecued; cut from the cob and mixed with a little unsalted butter and pepper or made into fritters; with green peppers, or combined with an assortment of vegetables—fresh or frozen corn is good in so many ways! (By the way, frozen corn is the one vegetable that needs to be partly thawed before cooking. Follow the directions on your package for best results.) Put shakers of salt on the table for individual use of those without sodium restrictions.

One pound of cut corn will yield 4 servings.

Substitute a little vegetable oil for low saturated fat dieters.

CUCUMBERS

Perhaps you reserve cucumbers for salads when you want their crunchiness to add texture contrast. For variety, try them hot sometime and see if you don't like their "different" taste.

CUCUMBERS IN MILK
6 Servings

1 teaspoon unsalted butter	onion (or sliced thin)
3 cucumbers	¼ cup low sodium non-fat milk
⅔ cup sliced radishes	
¼ teaspoon grated	¼ teaspoon pepper

Melt fat and add cucumbers, radishes, and onions. Cover and cook rapidly 10 minutes, adding 2 tablespoons of water if necessary to prevent scorching. Uncover and continue cooking to let some of the juice evaporate. Add low sodium milk and pepper; reheat, but do not boil. Add salt for the regulars.

One Serving	Total Recipe	
11	68	milligrams sodium
1	5	grams total fat
1	4	grams saturated fat
23	135	calories

LOW SATURATED FAT VARIATION

Substitute vegetable oil for butter. Use regular non-fat milk if not restricted in sodium, and add salt to taste. *One serving: negligible saturated fat (⅙ teaspoon vegetable oil).*

BAKED EGGPLANT
4 Servings

This easy-to-do vegetable recipe came to us from the San Joaquin County Heart Association and is so good we hope you will try it often.

Preheat oven to 350° (moderate). Remove skin from eggplant. Cut into slices ⅜-inch thick. Place slices close together on a lightly oiled cookie sheet. Brush tops of the slices with 1 tablespoon vegetable oil. Bake 12 minutes. Turn slices and bake about 10 minutes longer. Serve at once with a light sprinkling of salt and white pepper for the regulars; or sprinkle with lemon juice for all.

One Serving	Total Recipe	
Without lemon juice		
2	8	milligrams sodium
4	15	grams total fat
negligible	negligible	grams saturated fat
55	219	calories

One serving: ¾ teaspoon vegetable oil.

BROILED MUSHROOMS
2 Servings

Remove stems from ½ pound large mushrooms and clean caps. Brush lightly with 1 tablespoon vegetable oil. Place caps, top side up, 3 inches below broiler unit. Broil 5 to 8 minutes. Fork-test, and do not overcook, as mushrooms toughen with too much and too long heat. Add a light sprinkling of salt for those without sodium restrictions.

One Serving	Total Recipe	
5	10	milligrams sodium
8	15	grams total fat
negligible	negligible	grams saturated fat
95	190	calories

One serving: 1½ teaspoons vegetable oil.

ONIONS

You may want to skip right over this section, believing that too much emphasis has already been given to onions as a flavor. True, they do appear frequently in this connection because they heighten the flavor of many dishes when salt is not used. As a seasoning, they can be cleverly used and disguised so that the taster is aware only of the flavor and not at all of onions.

As a vegetable, they add their hearty bit to many a meal. The small white pearl onions, boiled and buttered, are a natural combination with turkey or duck. Good with veal, too. The larger and lustier varieties lend themselves to baking. They combine well, also, with other vegetables where an onion, in combination flavor, is desired. Boiled, baked, pan-fried, or sautéed—onions offer you interesting vegetable variety.

BAKED ONION RINGS
6 Servings

Peel and slice 1 pound large onions crosswise, ¼-inch thick, and separate into rings. Dip in 1½ cups Fritter Batter (page 210) and put into shallow pan, coated with vegetable oil. Bake about 30 minutes in 400° (hot) oven, or until lightly brown. Check at half time to see whether additional oil is needed. Sprinkle lightly with paprika and serve with salt added for the regulars (without sodium restriction).

One Serving	Total Recipe	
20	121	milligrams sodium
3	17	grams total fat
3	16	grams saturated fat
138	827	calories

LOW SATURATED FAT VARIATION

Follow Basic Recipe except use Low Saturated Fat Variation for Fritter Batter (page 210). *One serving: negligible grams saturated fat (⅓ teaspoon vegetable oil).*

GLAZED PEARL ONIONS
6 Servings

1½ pounds pearl onions	Few grains pepper
2 tablespoons vegetable oil	2 tablespoons sugar
	¼ teaspoon fresh grated nutmeg

Peel onions and steam over water in covered pan for 25 to 35 minutes. Remove from heat before they are quite ready to serve. Drain. Meanwhile, heat 2 tablespoons vegetable oil. Add other ingredients and stir to blend. Add onions and cook slowly until they are golden in color, turning as needed to ensure uniform golden color and glaze.

One Serving	Total Recipe	
11	64	milligrams sodium
5	29	grams total fat
negligible	negligible	grams saturated fat
106	634	calories

One serving: 1 teaspoon vegetable oil.

PARSNIPS

Parsnips may be served with unsalted butter or vegetable oil, sautéed or baked. If quartered, they boil in 20 to 30 minutes; bake in 30 to 45 minutes in 350° (moderate) oven. Remember to remove the parsnip cores when you prepare them, so you will not get woody shreds.

BOILED PARSNIPS IN SAVORY SAUCE
2 Servings

½ pound parsnips
1 tablespoon flour
1 tablespoon unsalted butter *or* margarine
⅓ cup parsnip liquid
¼ teaspoon low sodium dietetic Worcestershire sauce

¼ teaspoon onion powder
Scant ¼ teaspoon low sodium dietetic prepared mustard
1 teaspoon minced parsley

Wash and scrape parsnips and cut into lengthwise strips. Barely cover with water and boil 20 to 30 minutes until just tender. Drain liquid and save. Combine flour with heated butter in small skillet. Add parsnip liquid and stir until mixture boils and thickens. Add remaining ingredients except parsley. Pour sauce over parsnips and serve garnished with parsley. Salt for those without sodium restrictions.

One Serving	Total Recipe	
8	16	milligrams sodium
6	12	grams total fat
6	11	grams saturated fat
132	264	calories

VARIATION FOR
SODIUM RESTRICTION

One tablespoon low sodium dietetic cheddar-type cheese may be added to sauce.

LOW SATURATED FAT VARIATION

Follow Basic Recipe but omit butter from sauce. Slowly blend parsnip liquid with flour, stirring constantly; or substitute vegetable oil for the unsalted butter. If no sodium restrictions, use regular Worcestershire sauce, prepared mustard, and add salt to taste. *One serving: negligible grams saturated fat (1½ teaspoons vegetable oil).*

FRESH PEAS

Peas may be panned, steamed, or boiled, although the last method is certainly the least desirable. Small and tender, the first peas of spring need little seasoning, except perhaps a pinch of sugar and a small amount of vegetable oil or unsalted butter or margarine. Do not add butter or margarine if you are on saturated fat restriction.

PEAS
2 Servings

Shell 1 pound of peas just before cooking, to preserve every bit of their goodness. Minister to their cooking time, lest they be overcooked and spoiled both in appearance and taste. For best results, pressure cook or steam them with dripping leaves of lettuce lining saucepan and covering peas. Cook at the very last moment and serve piping hot. Add salt for those without sodium restrictions.

One Serving	Total Recipe	
2	4	milligrams sodium
negligible	1	gram total fat
negligible	negligible	grams saturated fat
101	201	calories

VARIATION

Prepare and cook as outlined above. When tender, add ½ teaspoon savory, thyme, or onion powder. Stir well, so herbs blend with all of peas. Cover and let stand for 5 minutes for further blending, and serve at once. If you wish, you may cut up lettuce and serve with peas, for it is quite tasty. Also, you may place a few pea pods on top of lettuce leaves when you cook peas to add to flavor.

PEPPERS (GREEN)

A colorful addition to our lengthening list of vegetables. The green bell pepper, a perennial favorite for its color, taste, and texture, a buoyant addition to a plate of raw vegetables, is equally at home when cooked. In this connection, it is usually served whole, with some stuffing, and baked; or cut in slivers or rings, and sautéed.

STUFFED GREEN PEPPERS
6 Servings

6 bell peppers
1 tablespoon vegetable oil
2 tablespoons chopped onion
¼ teaspoon thyme
Dash savory

Few grains black pepper
2 cups cooked brown rice (or Ala)
½ cup tomato juice, canned without added sodium

Remove stem, seeds, and membrane from peppers. Wash inside and out. Cover with boiling water and cook 5 minutes to parboil. Meanwhile heat oil and lightly brown onion. Remove from heat; add seasonings, rice, and tomato juice. Fill peppers with rice mixture. Place in baking dish and bake in 400° (hot) oven about 20 minutes, until thoroughly heated and fork-tender. A tomato sauce may be added, if desired. Salt for those without sodium restrictions.

One Serving	Total Recipe	
With rice; without sauce		
3	20	milligrams sodium
3	17	grams total fat
negligible	negligible	grams saturated fat
88	525	calories

One serving: ½ teaspoon vegetable oil.

VARIATIONS

Chopped or ground leftover meat (veal or chicken are particularly good) may be substituted in whole or part for rice. Ground lean beef is also an interesting filling.

POTATOES
(White)

A well-cooked potato adds enjoyment and balance to a well-planned meal, and with its low sodium and low fat content is a welcome addition. Mashed potatoes are perhaps the least savory of the many ways they may be prepared without salt, and where low sodium milk must be used as a liquid, they are apt to be pretty flat. If your meal just seems to call for them in this form, try adding a little finely minced parsley and a bit of grated onion to bolster them. Buttered, baked, fried, or scalloped, they make wonderful contributions to our meals. For nutrition's sake, leave skins on whenever possible during cooking, or pare very thin.

NEW POTATOES
3 Servings

Use 1 pound for 3 servings.

Scrape and wash 1 pound potatoes. Boil whole about 25 minutes until fork-tender (depends upon the size of the potato). Instead of pan-frying in vegetable oil and sprinkling with parsley, which is a delicious treatment, try sprinkling with ½ teaspoon crumbled dill, 1 teaspoon vegetable oil, and ¼ teaspoon freshly ground pepper. Blend and serve with a sprinkling of salt for those without sodium restrictions.

One Serving	Total Recipe	
4	11	milligrams sodium
2	5	grams total fat
negligible	negligible	grams saturated fat
120	359	calories

One serving: ⅓ teaspoon vegetable oil.

STUFFED POTATOES
4 Servings

- 2 medium-sized potatoes
- ¼ cup low sodium non-fat milk, warmed
- ½ teaspoon vegetable oil
- ¼ teaspoon tarragon
- Dash onion powder
- Dash garlic powder
- Few grains black pepper
- Paprika

Select 2 potatoes of similar size; scrub thoroughly. Wrap in aluminum foil in individual packages. Bake 45 to 60 minutes in a 350° (moderate) oven until tender. Remove from oven and cut lengthwise. Scoop out potatoes and blend in warmed milk. Beat until snowy white and as fluffy as your whipped cream in the days before restricted cookery. Stir in oil and seasonings; blend carefully. Give one more beating to keep fluffy. Lightly spoon into potato shells, heaping full. Sprinkle with paprika and lightly brown if crusty top is desired. Otherwise, serve at once. Add salt for those without sodium restrictions.

One Serving	Total Recipe	
2	8	milligrams sodium
1	3	grams total fat
negligible	negligible	grams saturated fat
59	237	calories

SODIUM RESTRICTED VARIATION

Top each filled potato shell with a slice of low sodium dietetic cheddar-type cheese (not to be used by those with saturated fat restrictions).

SWEET POTATOES AND YAMS

MASHED SWEET POTATOES
2 Servings

Wash and boil ½ pound sweet potatoes, unpeeled. Remove from stove and peel. Mash thoroughly and add ½ teaspoon orange peel (or fresh, grated), two dashes Angostura Bitters, and ½ cup orange juice (or less) for piquant flavor. Beat until fluffy. Serve at once. Add salt for those without sodium restrictions.

One Serving	Total Recipe	
11	21	milligrams sodium
1	2	grams total fat
negligible	negligible	grams saturated fat
147	294	calories

VARIATION

One-half cup crushed pineapple and pineapple juice may be substituted for the orange juice.

CANDIED YAMS
6 Servings

Wash and boil 1½ pounds yams, unpeeled, until tender. Meanwhile, make a sirup of 1½ cups water, 1 cup light brown sugar, 1 tablespoon vegetable oil, and ⅛ teaspoon nutmeg. Heat all together and simmer gently. Remove yams from fire, peel, and slice. Arrange in lightly oiled baking dish. Pour sirup over yams and bake in a 400° (hot) oven until a light golden brown. No salt or substitute needed.

One Serving	Total Recipe	
19	115	milligrams sodium
3	18	grams total fat
negligible	negligible	grams saturated fat
276	1657	calories

One serving: ½ teaspoon vegetable oil.

ORANGE CANDIED YAMS
6 Servings

Prepare and boil 1½ pounds yams, unpeeled, until tender.

Remove from stove and peel. Meanwhile, combine ingredients:

¼ cup boiling water
1 tablespoon orange juice
½ tablespoon grated orange peel

1 orange, peeled and sliced
1 cup light brown sugar
2 tablespoons unsalted butter or vegetable oil

Pour over potatoes and dot with butter (use oil if saturated fat restrictions). Spread in shallow baking dish, lightly oiled, and bake until glazed, or pan-glaze on top of stove over low heat, for about 15 minutes. Baste frequently and turn potatoes at least once. No salt or substitute needed.

One Serving With butter	Total Recipe	
20	119	milligrams sodium
5	27	grams total fat
4	23	grams saturated fat
302	1810	calories

One serving, with oil: negligible saturated fat
(1 teaspoon vegetable oil)

SPROUTS

Brussels sprouts, with their moderate sodium content, can be combined with beef, pork or veal to their advantage because of their high flavor. One pound sprouts will give 4 servings.

BRUSSELS SPROUTS
4 Servings

Try cooking 1 quart with a pinch of sugar and sprinkle lightly with 1 teaspoon lemon juice; then serve. Add salt for those without sodium restrictions.

One Serving	Total Recipe	
12	48	milligrams sodium
1	2	grams total fat
negligible	negligible	grams saturated fat
41	165	calories

VARIATION

Use vinegar in place of lemon juice; or dress with a low
sodium hollandaise sauce (but not for those with saturated fat restrictions).

SQUASH

Squash is "in" every season, fortunately so, with its very
low sodium and fat content. Whether you choose to serve
on your menu the crookneck or zucchini, the delicate
green or white scallop of summer, or the Hubbard of
winter, you have a mild and versatile vegetable. Sliced or
cut in wedges, the spring and summer varieties can be
steamed to advantage and are delicious combined with a
small dribbling of oil or unsalted butter, sugar, or cinnamon. Winter Hubbard is best baked or mashed.

ZUCCHINI—ITALIAN STYLE
4 Servings

1 tablespoon vegetable oil	4 medium-sized zuc-chini squash (about 1 pound)
1 tablespoon chopped onion	1 tablespoon slivered blanched almonds
1 chopped garlic clove	1 teaspoon lemon juice
½ teaspoon rosemary	

Put oil into skillet; warm. Add onion, garlic and rosemary.
Stir and cook until oil is absorbed and onion-garlic is
tenderized. Add washed and sliced zucchini (unpeeled).
Add 2 to 4 tablespoons water. Cook about 10 minutes just
until tender. Blend in almonds and lemon juice. Toss
lightly. Serve at once. Add salt for those without sodium
restrictions.

One Serving	Total Recipe	
1	5	milligrams sodium
5	19	grams total fat
negligible	negligible	grams saturated fat
64	255	calories

One serving: ¾ teaspoon vegetable oil.

TOMATOES

Universally liked, tomatoes, fortunately, can be used often

on restricted dietaries. Conveniently low in sodium and fat content, they can be used as wedges, in salads galore, and as a vegetable. Boiled, baked, or broiled, alone or in combination, they will do much to add zest to your meals. They combine with such other vegetables as string beans (with a little rosemary and thyme), with corn and green peppers, with Lima beans—yes, and with okra too. We have already seen in meat cookery how tomatoes are used as a seasoning as well as a vegetable accompaniment. There is scarcely a vegetable which will work harder for you.

Thyme, curry, dill, marjoram, and parsley are herbs that combine favorably with this vegetable.

BAKED TOMATO SLICES
3 Servings

Use 3 tomatoes weighing about 1 pound.

Wash and cut in slices, ¼ inch thick. Bread in crumbled shredded wheat (about 1 biscuit). Sprinkle lightly with ½ teaspoon thyme, ⅛ teaspoon fresh black pepper, and a pinch of sugar. Place on baking sheet lightly oiled. Bake in 350° (moderate) oven for 15 to 30 minutes. Sprinkle with salt for the regulars.

One Serving	Total Recipe	
5	14	milligrams sodium
1	2	grams total fat
negligible	negligible	grams saturated fat
62	185	calories

VARIATION

Broiled tomatoes may be prepared in exactly the same way as Baked Tomatoes. Cut slices thicker, of course, for broiling.

BAKED STUFFED TOMATOES
6 Servings

6 tomatoes of even size (2 pounds)	¼ cup onion, minced
2 tablespoons vegetable oil	1 cup soft low sodium bread crumbs
⅛ teaspoon black pepper	⅛ teaspoon allspice
	½ teaspoon sugar

Wash and scoop out unpeeled tomatoes. Sauté onions in

vegetable oil. Stir in tomato pulp, bread, and seasoning. Stuff and place in lightly oiled baking dish. Add a little hot water to cover the bottom of the dish. Bake in 350° (moderate) oven for 20 minutes. Add salt for the regulars.

One Serving	Total Recipe	
5	30	milligrams sodium
6	33	grams total fat
negligible	negligible	grams saturated fat
105	628	calories

One serving: 1 teaspoon vegetable oil

BUTTERING

Unsalted butter or margarine may be used in moderation in many of these vegetable recipes for the fine seasoning that it is, if allowed on your diet. Be sure to count it in your fat allowance if you include it. Vegetable oils may be substituted for unsalted butter or margarine in the lemon, garlic, wine sauces (without egg), allowing ½ teaspoon oil per serving, for those with saturated fat restrictions.

LEMON BUTTER: Fastest way to perk up the flavor of sodium-restricted foods is with lemon butter or oil. Like the wave of a magic wand, a pat of this seasoned butter will transform a flat-tasting food into something pretty special. Versatile, too, with four variations on the basic mix:

BASIC LEMON BUTTER
4 Servings

A Sunkist tested recipe, used by permission from Sunkist Growers.

> 1½ teaspoons boiling water
> 2 tablespoons unsalted butter, softened
> 1 tablespoon fresh lemon juice

Add boiling water to softened butter. Mix well. Add lemon juice and whip mixture until smooth and creamy. Makes enough for two cups of vegetables.

VARIATIONS

Add 1 tablespoon chopped fresh parsley for sandwich

spread. Also fine for meats and vegetables.

Add 1 tablespoon chopped fresh herbs or 1½ teaspoons dried herbs (approximate, due to individual taste). Use on meats and vegetables. Begin with small additions, such as basil, garlic, or onion *powder*, mustard, rosemary, thyme.

Add 1 tablespoon grated onion or chopped chives. Excellent on baked potato. Try also on green beans and squash.

Add ½ teaspoon dry mustard and ¼ teaspoon marjoram. Very good on steamed cabbage.

BROWNED BUTTER: This is delicious with corn on the cob, steamed squash (particularly summer), string beans, and plain sweet potatoes. Melt the amount of unsalted butter to be used until it darkens. Add 2 tablespoons lemon juice or vinegar. Herbs of choice may be added for another variety.

GARLIC BUTTER: Melt unsalted butter and add 1 garlic clove, split lengthwise and fastened on a wooden pick. Let this stand until you are ready to add to vegetables. Remove garlic, blend, and serve. Minced parsley may be added to garlic butter for vegetables or toast topping.

BROWNED BUTTER CBUMBS (*au beurre*): These are called for in many scalloped vegetable dishes and as a topping in others. Melt 2 tablespoons unsalted butter and stir in 1 cup fine, dry low sodium bread crumbs. Cook over low heat until crumbs are lightly browned.

WINE-BUTTER SAUCE: Beat 1 egg yolk and add 2 tablespoons water, 1 teaspoon lemon juice, ⅛ teaspoon freshly ground black pepper, and 1 tablespoon dry white wine. Cook slowly in double boiler until about the consistency of custard. Add 2 tablespoons unsalted butter and dash nutmeg. Stir and heat but do not boil. Pour at once over hot vegetables and serve. In general, this can be used only for those of you on mild sodium restriction with a whole egg allowance. Remember when you use the yolk of an egg in cooking you must subtract it from your daily or weekly allowance.

Where fat is not restricted closely along with your sodium, you may elect to use butter seasonings as sauces and serve them in a pitcher at the table.

LOW SATURATED FAT VARIATION

Substitute the following spread from the Home Service Department of Corn Products Refining Company as your basic mix for herb mixtures or use plain as a "butter" substitute. Spreads well but does not melt as do the "butters." Be sure to include amount used in your daily oil or total fat allowance.

OIL SPREAD

1 tablespoon cornstarch	⅔ cup water
⅔ cup low sodium non-fat dry milk powder	2 cups corn oil
1 tablespoon lemon juice	Few drops yellow food coloring

Sift cornstarch and instant non-fat dry milk together into top of double boiler. Combine lemon juice and water; gradually add to starch mixture stirring until smooth. Cook over boiling water, stirring constantly, until mixture thickens, about 4 minutes. Remove from heat. Add corn oil, ¼ cup at a time, beating with rotary beater after each addition. Add coloring to give desired shade. Do not use electric blender. Makes about 1 pound 5½ ounces.

Use regular non-fat milk and add salt if no sodium restrictions.

One level tablespoon: negligible grams saturated fat (2½ teaspoons vegetable oil).

11. WITH A CRUET IN EACH HAND

> *Oh, herbaceous treat!*
> *'Twould tempt the dying anchorite to eat;*
> *Back to the world he'd turn his fleeting soul,*
> *And plunge his fingers in the salad bowl;*
> *Serenely full the epicure would say,*
> *"Fate cannot harm me,—I have dined today."*
> —SYDNEY SMITH in *A Receipt for a Salad*
> (c. 1810)*

And treat indeed is a succulent salad for persons on the sodium-restricted or fat-restricted diet. It is refreshingly good and adds much to the pleasure of eating. The health benefits also abound in its store of minerals and vitamins.

You can be in style, too, for the approved way of serving many of the best salads is to bring all ingredients and mixings to the table and assemble them in full view of all, respectfully and with care. This little ceremony of mixing the salad is not without its psychological benefits. The dribbling of oil and vinegar, the addition of seasonings, and the final tossing of the salad can stimulate appetites for the good food to come. With so many limitations in the choice and preparation of food, the very appearance of salad in its many gay garbs can set the stage for complete acceptance of the entire meal.

Discount it, if you will, but salad, from its inception to the last mouthful eaten, can be a plus-value to you, if you will give it Number One billing at your festive board. Select it with care in relation to the rest of the meal, and prepare it with all the skill you have. Its rewards will be worth your "trouble."

There are some limitations in salads, of course, but no one but yourself need be aware of them. You have many

---

* From *A New Dictionary of Quotations*, selected and edited by H. L. Mencken; New York, Alfred A. Knopf, Incorporated, 1942. Quoted by permission of Alfred A. Knopf, Incorporated.

tools (ingredients) with which to concoct good salads. Gone are the dandelion greens, nasturtium, celery, chard, and spinach for those with sodium restriction. So what? You still have a wide selection of lettuces and greens— butterhead, roseleaf, Boston and Los Angeles head lettuce, as well as the delectable romaine; and endive, cabbage, zucchini squash, and broccoli. Cucumbers, radishes, and parsley are available, too. Besides which, a wealth of fruit is at your disposal when a sweet salad is the choice.

When you are planning your menus, don't make the mistake of thinking any salad will do for any meal. In the first place, there is the ever-present matter of the sodium and fat content of its ingredients; you may be surprised to see how those lettuce leaves and other makings add to the meal's total. Salad must, therefore, be thought of in relation to the count of a particular meal as well as for its eating qualities. It should be planned in the context of the meal in its entirety and *should complement the whole*.

Taking it by and large, vegetable salads are better appetite-stimulants than sweet fruits. This is also true when salads are to be served with the main course. Vegetable-tossed salads, the raw combinations, seem to combine naturally with most meats. Perhaps the outstanding exception is veal and fowl. You can use almost any light fruit combination with them and have a good effect, taste-wise, if you must have your fruit in salad form.

The fruit and molded salads should be considered primarily dessert salads, to follow the main course or be used as the main interest in a lunch meal.

Just sit down and *think* through the different flavors you have used in your recent salads and evaluate their contribution to your meals before you do too much new planning. Then make up your mind that you will turn out good salads without making too much extra work for yourself. The women's magazines are full of good time-saving suggestions and recipes for you to adapt.

For sodium restriction, do not use:

Prepared dressings, such as mayonnaise or French, except dietetic without added salt
Prepared fruit gelatin except dietetic low sodium
Salt
Shellfish except canned, dietetic low sodium
Vegetable salts (such as garlic, celery, and so on); pure powders may be used

For saturated-fat restriction, do not use:

Prepared hydrogenated salad dressings, such as may-
onnaise
Olive oil, unless specifically allowed
Cheese-flavored dressings
Regular prepared dressings, all varieties, for severely
restricted total fat

Hints on salad making:

1. Have a work center for salad-making and keep your
stand-bys always ready to use.

This should include such indispensables as a mixing
tray, measuring spoons and cups, a *wooden* salad fork
and spoon for dressing the salad, a large salad bowl, a
pepper mill and peppercorns, sugar, paprika, salt for those
without sodium restrictions. You will also want to have,
on a tray or near by, curry powder, cayenne, dry mustard,
fresh or dried herbs (fresh are much better), garlic buds,
young onions, and parsley sprigs, various salad oils, and
vinegars.

2. Regardless of how you plan to serve your salad, do
have your plates or bowls thoroughly chilled. You can't
serve a crisp, chilled salad on tepid plates. That's right:
set salad bowl and serving plates in the refrigerator to
cool before using. Ditto for salad servers.

3. Pay special attention to your dressings. They add
quality to your salad flavor.

4. Include the sodium content of lettuces and dressings
if you must "do the count."

5. Be generous in your use of herbs and use fresh ones
if possible for salads. Avoid blended seasonings and herbs.
Concoct your own combinations and so make your salads
distinctively your own creations.

6. Our recipes are developed with corn oil, but you may
substitute any oil on your diet list. (Walnut oil will give
you a French-tasting oil while olive oil emphasizes the
Italian, but use them only if they are on your list.)

7. Let your own palate dictate use of lemon juice or
vinegar. For steady use it is hard to beat a straight wine
vinegar blended with an herb one when you want a tangy,
robust flavor. But when you want the subtle savors of
fruit juices, try lemon, lime, or orange. We like to rub
our fruit salad bowls with the rind of citrus fruit to be
used.

8. Always consider the color, texture, and shape of your
salad "makings" in relation to the rest of the meal. Eye

and taste appeal go hand in hand here again.

Making a tossed salad:

Whether you like the modern emphasis in home decorating or not, you can be grateful to it for the increase in large salad bowls and platters. All salad fanciers emphasize the point that a tossed salad can be well made only in a huge bowl. For best results, you will want one that has some depth as well as width, so you can gently lift your greens up and down and roundabout in the tossing period.

When you harvest your greens from your garden patch, or bring them home from the store, trim off all inedible leaves and cut away brown spots. Store your greens in tightly covered containers in refrigerator until time of use. Before salad-making time, cut out core of head lettuce and hold the cavity under cold running water until its leaves separate and all are thoroughly washed. For the leaf lettuces and endive, put in a deep mixing bowl, separate each leaf, and wash thoroughly. This may require more than one water if much sand is imbedded. Dry greens by putting them in a clean towel, then transfer to lettuce bag and place in refrigerator until you are ready to use them. *Be sure they are completely dry before use.*

To assemble: Put greens and other salad ingredients into large bowl, and add garlic—not directly, as we pointed out in the chapter on herbs, but split in two, and rubbed over the heel of a piece of low sodium bread and tossed into the salad bowl with the greens. Dress greens with *chapon* and remove it at time of serving.

Now you are ready for the oil. For good tossed salad, it is imperative that oil and vinegar be used separately and that you forget all about your homemade mixtures so carefully stored on your shelf. The reason for adding oil first is to seal the tiny pores in the leaves and protect them from quick wilting. The amount of vegetable oil to use will depend upon your particular medical restrictions, your own taste, and the size of the salad.

As a beginning, allow 1 teaspoon to 1 tablespoon per person, according to your allowance. Let the oil *dribble* slowly over the greens, then take wooden fork and spoon and lift gently. Toss until each leaf is coated with the oil, and "so sealed from the invaders."

Add bits of "bruised" herbs, discarding bitter stems as you use them.

Now grind a sprinkling of fresh black pepper over your greens. Invest in a pepper mill if you do not already own one, and use peppercorns freshly ground at each making for improved salad flavor. Now you are ready for vinegar or lemon juice. Allow ½ teaspoon or more per serving. Use any good vinegar to bring out the taste you want. There is nothing like wine vinegar for epicurean results. The amount, again, is a matter of taste and the brand you use. Allow about ½ tablespoon per serving in the beginning and increase if you want greater sharpness.

Toss salad again, after this addition, until seasonings and vinegar are well blended with the greens. Taste before you ask others to sit in judgment. When your salad is dressed to your liking, remove the garlic bread and serve at once.

Add salt for those without sodium restrictions.

SOME SIMPLE TOSSED SALADS

BASIC TOSSED SALAD
6 Servings

½ head romaine lettuce
½ head red crinkle lettuce
1 chopped garlic clove *or* 1 *chapon*
3 tomatoes, peeled and cut in wedges
½ cup thinly sliced onion rings
½ cup wafer-thin cucumber slices
4 tablespoons vegetable oil
2 tablespoons wine vinegar
¼ teaspoon freshly ground peppercorns

Wash each leaf of lettuce and thoroughly dry. Break leaves into bite size and toss into large salad bowl. Add garlic and vegetables. Drip oil over entire surface and toss with salad fork and spoon, lifting and turning mixture to be sure that oil has a chance to coat all surfaces. But use a gentle hand to avoid any bruising of greens. Now grind pepper and blend. Add vinegar and toss again. Taste for desired tartness. (With tomatoes you may use less vinegar than with other vegetable combinations because of their tartness.) Serve the sodium-restricted dieter's portion; add salt for those without sodium restriction.

One Serving	Total Recipe	
19	111	milligrams sodium
10	59	grams total fat
negligible	negligible	grams saturated fat
116	695	calories

One serving: 2 teaspoons vegetable oil.

VARIATIONS

We favor the fresh, uncooked vegetables for their crisp-ness. You may combine any of the vegetables on your list that appeal to you, raw flowerets of broccoli or cauliflower, slices of green pepper or squash (summer or zucchini), leeks—tops and all—are good choices.

Cooked vegetables—leftovers or freshly cooked—may be substituted for all or part of the fresh vegetables in the Basic Recipe.

Orange, grapefruit, or tangerine sections combine with greens when a more delicate and piquant tossed salad is the choice. An excellent accompaniment to a veal dinner.

Lemon or lime juice may be substituted for wine vinegar in Basic Recipe.

For special ingredients, try *garbanzos*, slivers of cold veal, chicken, or beef, dietetic low sodium tuna or shrimps (regular for fat-restricted dieters who do not have to limit sodium), onion or garlic croutons (made of low sodium bread for sodium-restricted dieters), red beans, or a topping of dietetic low sodium cheese (but not for fat-restriction).

ZUCCHINI-RADISH SALAD
4 Servings

Combine two lettuces, such as ½ head romaine and ½ head Los Angeles head lettuce. Add ¼ cup sliced radish and ½ cup zucchini, slivered thin and quartered, a garlic heel of low sodium bread, and a bulb of a new onion. Dress with 3 tablespoons vegetable oil, freshly ground pepper, 2 tablespoons white wine vinegar. Add salt for those without sodium restriction. See directions for tossing.

One Serving	Total Recipe	
22	89	milligrams sodium
11	43	grams total fat
negligible	negligible	grams saturated fat
118	471	calories

One serving: 2¼ teaspoons vegetable oil.

VARIATION

Dress with French or Italian Dressing (pages 183-84) spiked with 1 teaspoon or less fresh or dried dill leaves.

OTHER SALADS

CABBAGE SLAW
4 Servings

Wash in ice water 2 cups finely shredded cabbage. Drain, wrap in towel. Dry and chill. Now put cabbage into a mixing bowl. Add 3 tablespoons Cooked Salad Dressing (page 184) and an extra pinch of mustard. Toss all lightly with a fork to blend and serve immediately on beds of lettuce. Add salt for those without sodium restrictions.

One Serving	Total Recipe	
11	45	milligrams sodium
2	7	grams total fat
negligible	negligible	grams saturated fat
42	169	calories

VARIATION

Add 1 cup crushed pineapple to the above (6 servings) or ½ cup crushed pineapple and ¼ cup yoghurt (non-fat for fat-restriction).

POTATO SALAD PIQUANT
8 Servings

We are indebted to the Home Advisory Service of the Wine Institute, San Francisco, for this excellent recipe.

4 cups diced, cooked potatoes	1 tablespoon white wine vinegar
2 hard-cooked eggs, chopped	2 teaspoons dry mustard
1 cup diced cucumber	1 teaspoon dill seeds
¼ cup chopped onion	½ cup low sodium mayonnaise
¼ cup chopped parsley	½ teaspoon pepper, freshly ground
1½ cups California white table wine	

Combine potatoes, eggs, cucumber, onion, and parsley in a mixing bowl. Add wine. Cover and chill in the refrigerator for 1 to 2 hours. Drain thoroughly. Add remaining ingredients, using just enough mayonnaise to moisten the mixture. Mix gently to avoid mashing the potatoes. Chill again until time to serve. Serve in crisp lettuce cups. This salad makes a delicious filling for a low sodium tomato aspic ring. Add salt for those without sodium restrictions.

One Serving	Total Recipe	
With Rhine wine		
40	317	milligrams sodium
12	98	grams total fat
2	17	grams saturated fat
219	1750	calories

LOW SATURATED FAT VARIATION

Omit eggs and substitute ½ cup Cooked Salad Dressing (page 184) for mayonnaise. Add salt for those without sodium restrictions. *One serving: negligible grams saturated fat (⅜ teaspoon vegetable oil).*

MAIN-DISH SALADS

When we think of more elaborate salads, we immediately think of shellfish and avocados. Avocado, fish, chicken, and meat are all important ingredients for the low sodium dietary when a rich main-dish salad is the choice. And don't neglect the dietetic low sodium shrimps, salmon, tuna, chicken, and ham.

Where total fat-restriction is the order, avocado, in spite of its high unsaturated fat content, will probably be tabooed because of its high total fat and calorie content. But you have many choices from the above and, if you are not restricted in sodium, you will not have to select dietetic fish or poultry when such canned additions are used.

MEAT SALAD
6 Servings

In Mrs. Irma Goodrich Mazza's delightful book *Herbs for the Kitchen*, she gives adaptations of very old French salads using cold meats for "the most inspired way of serving cold roast one can imagine."

Meat leftovers can be adapted to the sodium-restricted and fat-restricted diet in the following way:

Chop ¼ cup parsley into small bits; put in a bowl with 1 tablespoon vinegar, 2 tablespoons vegetable oil, ½ teaspoon dry mustard, and mix. Add, by degrees, 6 slices cold beef roast (about 1 ounce per serving), cut *very thin* and narrow. Put in a few strips at a time. Then add ¼ teaspoon rosemary, ½ teaspoon sage; shake, and stir well.

Cover the bowl, and let meat marinate a good 3 hours before serving. For each serving, garnish with parsley sprig and serve with crunchy accompaniment such as 1 radish, 1 small wedge of lettuce, and 1 thin slice green pepper. Let those without sodium restrictions salt to taste.

One Serving (1 oz. meat, cooked weight)	Total Recipe	
32	194	milligrams sodium
7	41	grams total fat
2	12	grams saturated fat
109	655	calories

One serving: 1 teaspoon vegetable oil.

VARIATIONS

Sliced roast lamb, veal, or chicken may be used in place of beef. Use chives or rosemary in your marinade.

STUFFED TOMATOES
4 Servings

Peel and scoop out 4 medium tomatoes. Cut the amount scooped out into small bits and combine with 1 cup flaked halibut. Try using ¼ cup small cubes of zucchini squash instead of the usual celery. Marinate by dribbling ¼ cup homemade French Dressing (page 183). Fill tomatoes. Chill thoroughly and serve on romaine lettuce. Add salt for those without sodium restrictions.

One Serving (2 oz. fish, cooked weight)	Total Recipe	
47	189	milligrams sodium
8	33	grams total fat
negligible	negligible	grams saturated fat
177	709	calories

One serving: ¾ teaspoon vegetable oil.

VARIATIONS

Use ¼ cup thinly sliced radishes in place of zucchini. Tuna, salmon, or other cooked fish may be used in place of halibut. Or use 1 cup cut-up chicken instead of fish as a tasty variation.

MOLDED AND FRUIT SALADS

Although we lean toward vegetable salads for many meals, there are times when fruit salads play their part as introductory or accompanying salads.

The appetizer salads should be light in flavor and texture. A tangy sharpness is pleasant in such a salad. Such selections as citrus fruits alone or in combination with thick onion slices, or melon combinations, are delicious first courses, and avoid the sweetness of many fruits that cloy rather than sharpen appetites.

Molded salads—apple with lemon juice, cabbage, and citrus fruits—are good combinations with cold meats provided their dressings are kept on the tart side, when you want to get fruit into your meal in this way.

Dessert salads can use avocados, if allowed, bananas, prunes, pineapple, peaches, and other sweet fruits. In both flavor and consistency, they seem to go *after* rather than *before* the main part of the meal.

BASIC RECIPE FOR MOLDED SALAD
6 Servings

The ready-made flavors are out, as you know, for sodium restriction, except low sodium dietetic ones. You must be content to build flavor into your molded salads. Wonderful for buffets, for luncheons, for hot weather coolness—molded salads have the proverbial 1001 uses. Most of the molded salads are computed without the addition of dressing, because the choice is so often a matter of individual preference. Be sure to add the dressing count to your daily total.

Prepare unflavored gelatin according to directions on the package, using one package or 1 tablespoon to stiffen one pint of liquid, as a general rule. However, when fruits or nuts are added, a jelly may require more gelatin. This also applies if the recipe is enlarged and is to be molded in a large container. Be sure to measure gelatin with care, remembering that an overly stiff, rubbery jelly is most unappetizing. Should your jelly be too quivering to hold its shape, serve in dessert glasses.

Gelatin dissolves more evenly if first softened in cold liquid. Measure the amount of cold liquid specified into a bowl and sprinkle gelatin over it; let stand 5 minutes. Then add hot liquid and stir until gelatin is completely dissolved. *Do not let mixture boil* after gelatin has been added as this affects the gelatin so that it will not stiffen.

Prepare unflavored gelatin according to directions on package, using one package of gelatin, dissolved in ½ cup cold water, or ¼ cup liquid if fruit juice and fruit additions are to be used. Add 4 tablespoons lemon juice or vinegar, when you want a sharper flavor, and 1½ cups boiling water, vegetable, or fruit juices. Chill, and when partially set, add about 1½ cups strained and cut-up fresh or canned fruit, leftover vegetables, chicken, or fish.

When partially set again, pour into a ring mold (8 inches), and chill until firm (about 4 hours). Unmold onto a large platter or chop plate, and garnish with any of the lettuces.

APPLE CIDER RING
6 Servings

We are indebted to Mrs. Frederick Bauer of Berkeley, California, for this delicious recipe, and for the Cranberry Pie which appears in the dessert chapter (page 256-57). Mrs. Bauer, a sodium-restricted dieter herself, believes in sharing from one homemaker's kitchen to another's—to widen selection for all.

Put into a mixing bowl .	1 package unflavored gelatin
Soften in . . . . ,	½ cup apple cider
Heat to boiling point the following ingredients, and add to the above. . .	½ cup pineapple juice
	1 scant cup apple cider
	1 tablespoon sugar
Stir thoroughly until gelatin is dissolved.	
Add	1 tablespoon lemon juice
	1 teaspoon orange rind, grated

Let stand until jelly begins to thicken.

Add	¼ cup broken walnuts
	½ cup crisp-cut canned pineapple bits
	¾ cup diced apple

Rinse mold with cold water, or lightly oil, and fill with mixture.

Chill until gelatin is set. Unmold onto a bed of lettuce greens and serve with dressing of choice.

One Serving With walnuts Without dressing	Total Recipe Without walnuts	
5	27	milligrams sodium
3	1	grams total fat
negligible	negligible	grams saturated fat
113	515	calories

SHERRIED AVOCADO AND GRAPEFRUIT RING
6 Servings

We are indebted to the Home Advisory Service of the Wine Institute, San Francisco, for this excellent recipe.

1½ envelopes (1½ tablespoons) unflavored gelatin
¼ cup cold water
1½ cups grapefruit juice
½ cup California sherry
⅓ cup sugar
1½ cups well-drained grapefruit segments
1 cup diced avocado
1 tablespoon grated green pepper

Soften gelatin in cold water 5 minutes; dissolve over hot water. Add grapefruit juice, wine, and sugar, stirring until sugar is dissolved. Chill until mixture begins to thicken, then fold in grapefruit, avocado, and green pepper. Turn into slightly oiled ring mold; chill until firm. Unmold on crisp salad greens and serve with dressing of choice.

One Serving Without dressing	Total Recipe	
9	55	milligrams sodium
7	41	grams total fat
negligible	negligible	grams saturated fat
190	1138	calories

CHICKEN MOLD WITH WALNUTS
6 Servings

Follow the preceding Basic Recipe (page 177) substituting ½ cup lemon juice for the water and add 1 cup diced cooked chicken, ⅓ cup Special Never-Fail Mayonnaise (page 186), ¼ cup toasted slivered nuts. Serve on lettuce cups. Sprinkle lightly with salt for those without sodium restrictions.

One Serving (1⅓ oz. chicken)	Total Recipe	
44	264	milligrams sodium
18	109	grams total fat
3	20	grams saturated fat
227	1363	calories

One serving: 2⅔ teaspoons vegetable oil.

VARIATION

Substitute salmon for chicken in the preceding recipe.

MOLDED CRANBERRY SALAD
6 Servings

2 cups fresh cranberries
½ cup sugar
1 package unflavored gelatin
½ cup cold water
½ cup boiling water
¾ cup orange juice

1 tablespoon lemon juice
1 teaspoon grated orange rind
½ cup walnut pieces (optional)

Put raw cranberries through food chopper. Add sugar. Make gelatin according to Basic Recipe (page 177). Chill gelatin until slightly thickened. Add cranberries; nuts, too, if extra richness is desired. Pour into molds and chill in refrigerator until firm.

One Serving With walnuts	Total Recipe Without walnuts	
5	25	milligrams sodium
6	2	grams total fat
negligible	negligible	grams saturated fat
160	630	calories

WHITE FISH MOLD
6 Servings

Follow the Basic Recipe for molded salad (page 177), substituting ½ cup lemon juice for the water. Use 1 cup flaked halibut, ½ thinly sliced or cubed cucumber, ½ teaspoon dry mustard, and follow as outlined. Serve on

crisp lettuce cups and sprinkle with salt for those without sodium restrictions.

One Serving (1⅓ oz. fish, cooked weight)	Total Recipe	
32	189	milligrams sodium
3	19	grams total fat
negligible	negligible	grams saturated fat
89	532	calories

LIME-CUCUMBER MOLDED SALAD
6 Servings

1 envelope granulated gelatin	1 cup cucumber, minced fine
½ cup cold water	½ cup Special Never-Fail Mayonnaise (page 186)
1 tablespoon sugar	
1 cup hot water	
¼ cup lime juice	Paprika

Soften the gelatin in cold water. Add sugar and boiling
water, and stir until dissolved. Add the lime juice, mix
well, and pour into mixing bowl that has been rinsed
with cold water. Let stand until mixture begins to jell
slightly. Add mayonnaise and cucumber, stirring thoroughly. Pour into individual molds, or a ring, or melon
mold (rinse mold in cold water before using), and put
in refrigerator to set and chill. To serve, turn out onto
shredded lettuce; sprinkle with paprika. Dress to taste,
being sure to include your choice of dressing in daily
count. (Excellent, as is, for family use, too.)

One Serving	Total Recipe	
9	56	milligrams sodium
18	111	grams total fat
negligible	negligible	grams saturated fat
185	1112	calories

One serving: 4 teaspoons vegetable oil.

VARIATION

One-fourth cup lemon juice may be used in place of lime.

LUNCHEON SALAD OF FRUITS
4 Servings

Use 1 large red-skinned apple and 1 peeled avocado, cut
in wedges, and grapefruit, sectioned. Arrange in mixed

order on lettuce bed for flavor and eye appeal. Serve with ½ cup Cooked Salad Dressing (page 184).

One Serving	Total Recipe	
5	20	milligrams sodium
2	10	grams total fat
negligible	negligible	grams saturated fat
125	498	calories

VARIATIONS

Unsalted nuts, as walnuts, pecans, and almonds, add flavor and texture to fruit salads. For total fat restriction, use only if allowed on your diet.

Orange chunks and pineapple chunks may be added to the Basic Recipe for variation. Top with equal amounts of sugar and lemon juice for a light, piquant dressing.

TOMATO ASPIC
4 Servings

Follow the Basic Recipe for Molded Salads (page 177), substituting unsalted tomato juice for boiling water.

Add . . . .
1 teaspoon sugar
1 tablespoon scraped onion *or* ½ teaspoon onion powder
Dash paprika
¼ teaspoon thyme *or* sweet basil
1 tablespoon vinegar *or* lemon juice

Proceed as outlined in the preceding recipe and pour into individual or small mold. Unmold on salad greens, and serve with dressing of choice. Sprinkle with salt for those without sodium restrictions. Fat-restricted dieters without sodium restrictions may use regular tomato juice and add salt to taste.

One Serving	Total Recipe	
Without dressing		
7	29	milligrams sodium
negligible	1	gram total fat
negligible	negligible	grams saturated fat
38	143	calories

DRESSINGS

You will want to experiment with basic dressings and modify their flavors in terms of basic salad ingredients. Experiment with wine, cider, and herb-flavored vinegars, the ever-popular citrus additions—lemon, grapefruit, and orange juice—and a galaxy of herbs for your choice flavors. Remember to dilute vinegars with a little water if their tartness is too sharp.

FRENCH DRESSING
1 Cup

If the idea of French Dressing without salt sounds impossible to you, you haven't tried this one! The paprika, dry mustard, and onion combined with lemon juice or vinegar make as tangy a dressing as anyone could wish:

½ cup fresh lemon juice
½ teaspoon paprika
⅛ teaspoon black pepper
¼ teaspoon dry mustard
1 teaspoon finely chopped onion
1 tablespoon sugar
½ cup vegetable oil

Combine the lemon juice, paprika, pepper, dry mustard, onion, and sugar. Mix well. Slowly add vegetable oil, beating constantly with rotary or electric beater. Makes 2 cups. Add salt for those without sodium restrictions.

One Tablespoon	Total Recipe	
negligible	2	milligrams sodium
3	110	grams total fat
negligible	negligible	grams saturated fat
33	1052	calories

One tablespoon: ¾ teaspoon vegetable oil.

VARIATIONS

Substitute ¼ cup vinegar and increase oil to about ¾ cup in the Basic Recipe.

Catchup, chile sauce, or relish (dietetic low sodium

for those with sodium restrictions) may be used to spark dressing.

For an Italian slant with plenty of tartness, use ⅓ cup fresh lemon juice or vinegar with ⅔ cup vegetable oil. Here we like to put oil in bowl first, then add lemon juice or vinegar *slowly*, beating vigorously to emulsify. Add freshly ground pepper and other seasonings as desired.

COOKED SALAD DRESSING
2 Cups

Good with most any kind of salad and a change from the perennial "pour" type dressing, here's a cooked one that is clear and thick yet delicate. Lemon juice is skillfully combined with mustard and paprika to result in a delicious tart flavor in this tested Sunkist Growers' recipe.

1 cup sugar	1 cup fresh lemon juice
2 tablespoons flour	1 tablespoon grated
2 teaspoons dry mustard	onion
1 tablespoon paprika	¼ cup vegetable oil

Mix sugar, flour, mustard, and paprika. Add lemon juice and mix well. Cook 8 minutes; cool. Add grated onion. Beat oil slowly into the mixture. Chopped parsley may be added when served. Makes 2 cups. Add salt to taste for those without sodium restrictions.

One Tablespoon	Total Recipe	
negligible	6	milligrams sodium
2	56	grams total fat
negligible	negligible	grams saturated fat
43	1370	calories

One tablespoon: ⅜ teaspoon vegetable oil.

VARIATION

Diluted wine vinegar may be substituted for the lemon juice.

CRANBERRY DRESSING
4 Servings

This is particularly good with orange salads because of the blending qualities of cranberry and orange.

Beat with a fork ½ cup cranberry jelly. Add 4 tablespoons vegetable oil, 2 tablespoons lemon juice, ¼ teaspoon finely grated onion. Blend all together until smooth.

One Serving	Total Recipe	
1	2	milligrams sodium
14	56	grams total fat
negligible	negligible	grams saturated fat
195	779	calories

One serving: 1 tablespoon vegetable oil.

"EASY-MIX" SALAD DRESSING
1½ Pints

Another Corn Products Company tested recipe.

¼ low sodium non-fat dry milk
3 tablespoons sugar
1½ teaspoons dry mustard
⅓ cup water
2 cups vegetable oil
½ cup wine vinegar *or* lemon juice

Combine first four ingredients in deep bowl. Beat with rotary beater until thoroughly mixed. Add vegetable oil, ¼ cup at a time. Beat after each addition until oil is blended and mixture is smooth. Add vinegar, all at once, and beat until smooth and thick. (After vinegar is added, dressing thins slightly but thickens immediately when beaten.) Store in refrigerator in covered jar. For those without sodium restrictions, use regular non-fat milk powder and add salt to taste.

One Tablespoon	Total Recipe	
With wine vinegar		
1	36	milligrams sodium
9	440	grams total fat
negligible	negligible	grams saturated fat
85	4071	calories

One serving: 2 teaspoons vegetable oil.

EGGLESS "MAYONNAISE"
1 Cup

⅓ teaspoon paprika
¼ teaspoon dry mustard
Dash cayenne
½ cup double-strength low sodium non-fat milk
1 teaspoon plain gelatin
½ cup hot low sodium non-fat milk
¼ cup lemon juice

Mix dry seasonings in cold milk and dissolve gelatin. Add hot milk and blend. Add lemon juice. Chill in refrigerator until half congealed. Beat until fluffy. Return to refrigerator and chill until firm. Remove, and beat once again. Store in covered jar in refrigerator. Stir vigorously before serving. Thin with lemon juice as desired. (If no sodium restriction, use regular dry milk powder and add salt to taste.)

Total Recipe	
13	milligrams sodium
negligible	grams total fat
157	calories

SPECIAL NEVER-FAIL MAYONNAISE
1 Cup

We are indebted to the Home Service Department of Corn Products Refining Company for this tested egg-white mayonnaise made with their product, Mazola.

½ teaspoon sugar	1 egg white
½ teaspoon dry mustard	1 cup corn oil
Few grains red pepper	4½ teaspoons vinegar

Combine first three ingredients in a bowl. Mix well. Add egg white; beat well with rotary beater. Continue beating and add corn oil a little at a time, beating continually until ½ cup is used. Then add 1½ teaspoons vinegar, and continue adding remaining corn oil a little at a time. Beat in last tablespoon vinegar. Add salt if not restricted on sodium.

One Tablespoon	Total Recipe	
3	47	milligrams sodium
14	220	grams total fat
negligible	negligible	grams saturated fat
123	1971	calories
	One tablespoon: 1 tablespoon vegetable oil	

TRANSPARENT SALAD DRESSING
6 Servings

This dressing is particularly good with cabbage or cabbage-fruit slaws and with cooked vegetable salads. The mustard and vinegar are the sources of its authority.

2 tablespoons flour
1½ teaspoons sugar
1 teaspoon mustard
Few grains cayenne
⅔ cup water

1 egg yolk
2 tablespoons vegetable oil
¼ cup mild cider vinegar

Mix flour, sugar, mustard, and cayenne in the top of a double boiler. Stir in water and egg yolk. Stir until thick, about 10 minutes. Add vegetable oil and cider vinegar. Mix well and chill. Add salt for those without sodium restrictions.

One Serving	Total Recipe	
3	15	milligrams sodium
6	34	grams total fat
1	5	grams saturated fat
65	390	calories

LOW SATURATED FAT VARIATION

Substitute 1 egg white for egg yolk.
One serving: Negligible grams saturated fat (1 teaspoon vegetable oil).

12. THE STAFF OF LIFE

Here is bread, which strengthens man's heart, and therefore called the staff of life.

—MATHEW HENRY in *Commentaries*.
Psalm CIV

This is one area in which you need make no apologies for the product. Low sodium breads can be so good you will have a hard time keeping them on hand.

They may never take blue ribbons at county fairs; they may be a little coarser in texture than the commercial breads we use today; they may "tear" occasionally due to absence of salt; but they are still so good you will even have family members clamoring for them. And they are low in saturated fats, too, when made with non-fat milk and vegetable oil. Most commercial breads are taboo because of their lard or hydrogenated shortening content for those of you with saturated-fat control.

It's a wonderful family experience to introduce bread-making to the modern home. The fragrance of freshly baked loaves offers a cheap but treasured excursion for many oldsters into the memories of childhood, when Mother's breadmaking was taken for granted and held to be one of her most popular tasks. If you missed out on sifting her carefully measured flours and stirring the mixes in your yesteryears, you have a most exciting cooking experience ahead of you. It is one the family may want to share in, too.

There is also an inner secret to breadmaking for the maker. Dough can be to her what Plasticine and clay are to the young child. Do you remember how he punches and pulls, stretches and pats his material? Well, these very same manipulations are part and parcel of good bread-making. The very plastic qualities of dough make it a live thing to handle and the rhythm of kneading can relax and heal tired or anxious feelings or muscles. There can be such inner satisfaction in this kneading process that baking days can become adventures in contentment for you.

We say baking day advisedly, for there is little economy

of effort in making just one loaf of bread, particularly if you have a home freezer. You may as well make a batch of dough while you are about it. The same dough can be used for bread, pan rolls, raised biscuits, or certain sweet breads. You can make up the dough all at once, or shape dough for different purposes, lightly bake, store in freezer, and complete baking at time of need.

Now for a quick look at the prohibitions and ingredients you may use.

For sodium restriction, do not use:

> Baking powders (except low sodium)
> Bicarbonate of soda
> Corn sirup
> Milk, except kind specified on diet list
> Molasses
> Ready mixes, except approved dietetic
> Salt
> Self-rising flours

For saturated fat restriction, do not use:

Butter or margarine (except special margarine, if allowed)
Cheese
Cream
Hydrogenated fats such as Crisco or Spry
Whole egg, or egg yolk, unless on your "allowable" list
Whole milk

YEAST

There are two types of yeast for your use—just as in ordinary breadmaking. The older and more familiar variety is the little cake of compressed yeast, which must be stored in the refrigerator and used within a few days of purchase. To use compressed yeast successfully, you must crumble it into water that is just *lukewarm*. We consider this to be about 95°. With compressed yeast, it is better to be on the cold side, rather than the hot, for good fermentation to take place.

More than half the yeast now being used by American homemakers is the new active dry yeast—the granular type. It has only been available to us in our kitchens since the end of World War II, but is certainly popular today. And no wonder, for it is packaged in a moisture-proof

container, and may be kept as long as four months if
stored in a cool, dry place. It must be used, however,
fairly soon after being opened.

Unlike compressed yeast, granular yeast must be dissolved in water that is a little warmer than lukewarm
water (115°). If the water is too cool, the active dry yeast
will be "shocked" and will not give you its best fermentation.

Either yeast may be used interchangeably in recipes
and in the same amounts (1 package equals 1 cake)—
just remember the slight difference in temperature of
water to use: *lukewarm for the compressed; warm, not
hot, for the active dry yeast.* Crumble yeast in ¼ cup
water (temperature regulated to type used) or sprinkle
granular yeast over the water and proceed with mixing
directions. It is no longer necessary to let yeast stand in
water before mixing.

And now to introduce you to some of the substitutes
and supplements available for low sodium breadmaking.
Some of the most important ones are:

MILK

Lucky indeed are many of you city-dwellers who can
get fresh low sodium whole or non-fat milk according to
your needs. But since this will not be available to many of
you, we are using a specially processed milk, *Cellu Low
Sodium Non-Fat Dry Milk,* in our various bread and baked
goods recipes. If you are on fat restrictions but do not
have to limit sodium, you may substitute fresh or powdered regular non-fat milk according to your diet list. For
sodium counters, use of the low sodium non-fat dry milk
will give you low-count, high nutrition products and you
will save some of those precious milligrams of sodium
for broader menu selection.

FLOURS

Wilma Lord Perkins points out, in *The New Fanny Farmer
Boston Cooking School Cook Book,* that gluten flours make
the best bread, because they make the dough strong and
elastic as the yeast causes it to expand. Special bread
flours are high in gluten—but all-purpose flours make

good breads and are satisfactory for our purposes. Unbleached flours are high in flavor and nutrition, so deserve to be used often in low sodium breads. But don't overlook the dark flours—rye, graham, and wheat—for their fine flavor and source-rich nutrients. If a flour is marked 100 per cent whole-grain, it must be just that according to Federal Food and Drug Administration regulations. In the case of wheat, the 100 per cent means that the germ of the wheat is included. When white flours are used, you may want to add some wheat germ to your recipe, allowing about 1 tablespoon to 1 cup of flour. (Toast wheat germ lightly in oven, if its addition seems to retard the rising of your breads.) Wheat germ may be purchased in retail grocery stores in handypack sizes.

FATS

Because many of our readers are restricted in the use of the saturated fats—butter, hydrogenated shortenings, margarine—most of our recipes are tested using vegetable oils. Those of you who are allowed the use of saturated fats may want to substitute unsalted butter or margarine, or shortenings such as Crisco or Spry, for the vegetable oils. In general, to change recipes from solid fat to oil, allow ¾ cup oil for each cup of solid fat; on the other hand, to change recipes from oil to solid fat, allow about one-third more fat.

A small amount of unsalted butter mixed with the sugar-cinnamon topping of coffee cake, or spread as the filling of sweet rolls, does add plus-flavor to these breads.

GENERAL RULES FOR YEAST BREADS

If it is results you are concerned with in making yeast breads:

1. Do read the recipe carefully. If you are using your own recipe, rather than a special one, sit down with pencil and paper and make necessary modifications before you begin preparations.

2. Check your shelves to see that you have adequate equipment. You will need:

Baking pans
At least 1 liquid measuring cup with lip and line

above the cup line

Graduated measuring cups in ¼, ⅓, ½, and 1 cup amounts for dry ingredients and shortening

Graduated measuring spoons for amounts less than ¼ cup

Mixing bowl 3 times the bulk of dough

These kitchen aids will save you time, effort, and failures.

3. Get mixings together at work center before you begin preparations. This goes for utensils, too.

4. Measure carefully for best results in texture and taste. All measurements in our recipes are level.

5. Sift flours before measuring them and resift with other dry ingredients as outlined in the various recipes. An easy way to do first sifting is to use a double square of wax paper as a receiving base. Store in flour drawer for frequent use.

6. Watch the temperature of water in all yeast recipes.

7. Take short cuts only after you have mastered basic recipes. Every effort has been made to think through shorter steps in breadmaking, but no one kitchen or one homemaker has all the answers.

8. Spend effort now for later timesaving. Double your recipe whenever practicable. Bake what you need; freeze the remaining dough, or bake all and freeze the finished product.

9. Compressed yeast or dry granular yeast may be used interchangeably in all recipes and in equivalent amounts. Compressed yeast cakes must be stored in refrigerator and be used within a few days. Granular yeast will keep as long as four months, properly stored. Note expiration date on package.

10. Do not let yeast doughs rise more than double in size for "good" bread.

11. After you have mixed yeast dough, round up, and let stand for 10 minutes to tighten for easy kneading.

12. Don't handle dough any more than necessary—and keep light and easy to handle.

13. Oil your hands lightly before kneading dough to avoid stickiness.

Method of breadmaking:

We use the straight dough method in the recipes in this chapter—that is, adding the flour all at once. Let the dough rise once in the bowl, shape into loaves, put into pans, let rise again, and bake.

Kneading:

Turn dough onto a lightly floured board, cover with a bowl, and let stand 10 minutes to tighten up. Oil hands lightly with vegetable oil to make handling easier. Knead dough by folding it toward you, then pushing away from you with "heel" of hand. Turn the dough as you work it. These two actions in manipulating the dough are all there is to kneading. Repeat until dough is smooth and elastic and you can see little bubbles forming beneath (about 40 turns). Your dough will be free of the board and light enough so you will be able to hold it in your hand a few seconds without any sticking.

Raising low sodium dough:

Use a large mixing bowl for bread that is to rise—one about 3 times the size of dough. Place the dough after kneading it in the bowl, lightly oiled with vegetable oil. Turn dough once, so top is greased. Cover with a *damp* cloth and let rise in a warm place (about 85°) until double in bulk (45 to 60 minutes). If your kitchen is very warm in midsummer, place a pan of water at 75° under the bowl. If the temperature of the room is less than 80°, put bowl of dough over a pan of hot water (do not let it touch bowl) and cover with a damp cloth. Remember that the water you used in dissolving it started the yeast's work— and the temperature you keep around the dough will complete it. When your room is too cold, the growth of the yeast is retarded; when too hot, the yeast is killed.

For perfect bread, let the dough rise just the exact time needed. Salt, you may remember, is used in regular breadmaking to give flavor and to slightly retard yeast action. Without it, dough will rise in about half the time required for ordinary breadmaking. If you let dough rise too long, your product will be coarse and full of holes; if not long enough, it will be heavy.

Perhaps you are thinking you will have to set the minute hand on your stove to achieve this exactness in rising. But this is not the case; the best method to determine when to shape dough is the finger indention method. With the variables in different flours, temperature of water, and room temperature, this method will give you most uniformly good results. To test for handling, press two fingers deeply into dough. If indention remains when fingers are withdrawn, the dough is double in bulk and ready to handle.

Punch dough down with fist to let gas escape and let fresh oxygen into the yeast.

To mold bread:

Turn onto a lightly floured board again and cut dough in two with a sharp knife. This breaks any remaining bubbles. Make into 2 balls—cover with a cloth and let stand for 10 minutes.

Now you are ready to shape the dough into loaves and rolls. To shape for bread, flatten out dough and press all air out of it with closed fists. Fold dough lengthwise, and stretch and pull to lengthen. (Slap against table to stretch out if necessary.) Bring the two ends to center and overlap together tightly. Have seam on the underside to give a smooth top. Place the shaped loaf, side down, in lightly oiled bread pan (use 9 x 5 x 3"). Fill pan about two thirds full.

Cover and let rise again until dough comes to top of pan with center rounding. Finger test in 25 minutes. If indentation remains, loaves are ready to bake.

Baking and care of bread:

Bake bread in a preheated 400° (hot) oven about 30 to 40 minutes or until golden brown, or at 350° if a glass baking dish is used; plain yeast rolls, 400° to 425° for 15 to 25 minutes; sweet yeast rolls, 375° for 20 to 30 minutes.

Bread will shrink from sides of pan and be light brown in color when done. A good test is to remove bread from oven at minimum time, loosen from sides of pan, and tap bottom of loaf. A good hollow sound indicates that bread is done. Turn onto a rack to cool.

For a *soft crust,* cover top of loaf with a damp cloth for 5 minutes.

For a *shiny top,* brush lightly with ½ teaspoon vegetable oil or melted unsalted butter (if you are not restricted on saturated fat). Cover with a towel for a few minutes to soften crust.

For a *crisp crust,* do not grease or oil bread. Allow it to cool uncovered.

To keep breads fresh, wrap in wax paper or save bread wrappings from bakery bread. Store in refrigerator or cool bread box. Low sodium bread without salt must be carefully cared for; otherwise, it will mildew.

BASIC BREAD AND ROLL RECIPE

Good ingredients go into this bread, and with proper mixing and handling of dough, the product can merit raves. Note the addition of wheat germ (optional) for improved flavor and nutrition. (If no sodium restrictions, use regular non-fat milk powder and add ¾ teaspoon salt per loaf of bread.)

For One Loaf *16 slices*	*For Two Loaves* *32 slices*
¾ cup hot water	1¾ cups
1½ tablespoons sugar	3 tablespoons
1 tablespoon vegetable oil	2 tablespoons
¼ cup warm, not hot, water (cool to lukewarm for compressed yeast)	¼ cup
½ package or ½ cake yeast, active dry or compressed	1 package or 1 cake
¼ cup low sodium non-fat dry milk powder	½ cup
2½ to 3 cups *sifted* all-purpose flour	5½ cups, more or less
2 tablespoons wheat germ	¼ cup

Combine the hot water, sugar and oil in a large mixing bowl. Beat to blend and emulsify. Let cool to desired temperature. Meanwhile, put warm water (cool to lukewarm for compressed yeast) into a measuring cup and sprinkle or crumble in yeast. Stir; then add to large mixing bowl. Add milk powder sifted with one-half of the flour. Stir in wheat germ. Work in remaining flour (reserving some for dusting of mixing board) until there is just enough to prevent sticking to bowl. When dough comes away from sides of bowl, turn onto floured board, round into a ball, and cover with a cloth; let stand for 10 minutes to tighten up to handle. Knead, let rise, mold, let rise in pan(s), and bake in preheated 400° (hot) oven, 30 to 40 minutes. If a glass loaf pan is used, set oven at 350°, because oven-glass holds heat longer than metal.

One Slice Crisp	One Loaf Crust	One Slice Shiny	One Loaf Top	
1	15	1	15	milligrams sodium
1	19	1	21	grams total fat
neg.	neg.	neg.	neg.	grams saturated fat
97	1551	98	1572	calories

VARIATIONS
2 *Loaves*

WATER: Add 2 tablespoons vegetable oil and omit low sodium milk powder.

POTATO: Substitute potato water for low sodium milk powder and water, keeping liquid measurements the same. Add a mashed and sieved potato. As the sieved potato provides some bulk, you may be able to decrease flour by ¼ cup.

CRACKED WHEAT: Substitute ½ cup cracked wheat and 2½ cups 100 per cent whole wheat flour for 3 cups white flour. Omit wheat germ. Reduce sugar to 1 tablespoon and add 2 tablespoons honey.

WHOLE WHEAT: Substitute 2 cups 100 per cent whole wheat flour for 2 cups white flour. Omit wheat germ.

100 PER CENT WHOLE WHEAT: Substitute 6 cups 100 per cent whole wheat flour for white flour. Omit wheat germ. Decrease sugar to 2 tablespoons, and add 4 tablespoons honey.

SOY: Substitute 6 tablespoons soy flour for 6 tablespoons white flour.

1 *Loaf*

DATE: Knead in 1 cup finely chopped dates (be sure to select *sun-dried* variety only, as the addition of sulphur and other preservatives can be injurious to the low sodium diet).

RAISIN: Knead in 1 cup *sun-dried* raisins.

HERB: Wonderful for stuffing or with special meat dishes and salads. For a stuffing bread, add 1 teaspoon summer savory, ½ teaspoon thyme, and ½ teaspoon rosemary to dry ingredients. For general use, try nutmeg with caraway or savory, or mace with savory.

CHEESE: Delicious toasted and served with salads or thick soups, and is good for sandwiches, too. Add ¾ cup grated low sodium cheese, mixing it with the last flour added. *Not for you on fat-restriction.*

STANDARD ROLLS
12 *Rolls*

Make up your Basic Recipe as for 2 loaves and divide into 2 balls. Reserve 1 for bread, the other for rolls. After the "resting" period, make 1 long roll about 18 inches long, cut into twelve 1½-inch pieces, and shape into round balls. Put into a lightly oiled, round baking pan (you can use a 9-inch deep pie plate, if nothing else is available). Let rise in a warm room until light (about 45 minutes). Bake until a golden brown in a 425° (hot) oven, 15 to 25 minutes.

If you don't want to serve these rolls on the day of making, shape them, let rise, lightly bake, cool, and prepare for freezing. All ready for later light baking to serve.

One Roll
(White, whole wheat, or cracked wheat)

1	milligram sodium
2	grams total fat
negligible	grams saturated fat
129	calories

VARIATIONS

BREAD STICKS: Cut dough into 12 pieces, and pull and stretch into long thin sticks. Put in a shallow baking pan, lightly oiled. Cover with damp cloth to rise. Bake as directed above. Good with thick soups, casserole dishes, and as salad accompaniments.

PARKER HOUSE ROLLS: Roll dough ⅓ inch thick and cut with biscuit cutter (12 rolls). Place on a lightly oiled pan and brush tops with ½ teaspoon vegetable oil. Make a crease across each roll with the rounding handle of a knife. Fold over, so top half slightly overlaps. Press edges together at crease. Place close together or separately on pan, depending on crustiness wanted in finished roll. Let rise and bake as directed above.

CLOVER-LEAF ROLLS: Cut dough into 12 pieces, and then divide each piece into thirds. Make little balls of each piece of dough. Place 3 balls in each cup of a lightly greased muffin tin. Let rise and bake as directed above.

SWEET YEAST BREADS

For breakfast, tea, and between-meal "snacks," sweet yeast breads get triple-star rating. Quick to make and chock-full of good ingredients, they win both homemaker's and eater's approval.

BASIC SWEET YEAST BREAD
12 Servings

1 cup low sodium non-fat milk

2 tablespoons vegetable oil

¼ cup sugar

1 package or cake yeast, active dry or compressed

¼ cup warm, not hot, water (cool to lukewarm for compressed yeast)

3 cups (more or less) *sifted* all-purpose flour

2 tablespoons wheat germ (optional)

Scald milk. Add oil and sugar and beat to emulsify. Cool to required temperature (warm for dry yeast; lukewarm for compressed). Dissolve yeast in water; add to milk mixture and blend. Add 1½ cups flour and wheat germ, if used. Beat thoroughly for 5 minutes with electric beater. Add enough more flour to make dough just barely firm to handle. Knead. Shape immediately into any of the shapes suggested in Variations. Let rise until light (about 30 minutes); then bake in 375° (moderate) oven for 20 to 30 minutes. Frost with confectioner's icing (½ cup sugar moistened with water and flavored with vanilla or grated lemon rind). If no sodium restrictions, use regular non-fat milk and add ¾ teaspoon salt.

One Serving	Total Recipe	
With wheat germ		
1	13	milligrams sodium
3	33	grams total fat
negligible	negligible	grams saturated fat
169	2033	calories

One serving: ½ teaspoon vegetable oil.

VARIATIONS

CINNAMON BUNS: Flavor with ½ teaspoon cinnamon or sprinkle cut shapes with ½ teaspoon cinnamon blended with 2 tablespoons sugar. Cut with 3-inch cutter or fancy shape. Follow Basic Recipe for rising and baking.

CINNAMON ROLLS: Proceed with Basic Recipe and flatten dough to ¼-inch thickness. Brush dough with ¼ teaspoon vegetable oil and spread with sugar-cinnamon mixture. Dot with ⅓ cup cut-up *sun-dried* dates. (If dates are very sticky, dip in flour before dotting dough.) Or spread dough with applesauce or crushed pineapple, thoroughly drained. Roll as for jelly roll, beginning at wide side. Be sure to pinch edges of roll firmly to seal. Cut to 1-inch slices. Place on lightly oiled baking sheet or in muffin cups. Allow space between rolls for doubling in size. Follow Basic Recipe for rising and baking.

CINNAMON TWISTS: Add ½ teaspoon caraway to dry ingredients. Follow Basic Recipe and flatten dough to oblong piece, about ⅓-inch thick. Sprinkle half of dough with ¼ cup light brown sugar blended with ½ teaspoon cinnamon and 2 tablespoons *sun-dried* raisins. Fold other half over spread half. Cut into 12 strips 1 inch wide. Hold strips at both ends and twist in opposite directions. Place on lightly oiled baking sheet, 2 to 3 inches apart, pressing both ends of twist to baking sheet to seal. Brush with ½ teaspoon vegetable oil. Follow Basic Recipe for rising and baking.

ORANGE ROLLS: Use orange juice in place of milk and add 1 tablespoon grated orange peel. Shape like Parker House Rolls, putting a cube of sugar, dipped in orange juice, in each. Follow Basic Recipe for rising and baking.

RICH COFFEE ROLLS OR CAKE: If you are allowed whole egg, you may add 1 medium egg to milk mixture when it is cool; blend thoroughly. But this must be calculated as part of your egg allowance for the day.

QUICK BREADS

You can adapt many of your own favorite recipes for quick breads after you have learned a few basic principles. The milk, eggs, baking powder, salt, and soda of your recipes will have to be altered or eliminated in terms of your dietary requirements.

The total fat content of quick breads is higher than in plain yeast breads. For this reason, some of you may have to omit these products from your diet. However, by using vegetable oil in place of shortening or butter, and substituting 2 egg whites for 1 whole egg, the saturated fat content of quick breads is made negligible.

The recipes in this section are worked out with low sodium non-fat milk (but other types of milk may be substituted). The quick breads will meet the needs of the severe sodium restrictions, in most instances. As explained before, if you have a more generous allowance of milk and eggs, it is easy enough to make substitutions upward, insofar as the sodium content is concerned.

A low sodium baking powder is used in all quick bread recipes. It may be ordered at drugstores (page 24) or may be purchased commercially at health stores under the name of Cellu, *green label*. Or ordered direct from this big dietetic firm.* (Regular double-action baking powder may be substituted if you have fat and *no* sodium restriction.)

Lida Jamison, dietitian of the Chicago Dietetic Supply House, tells us she gets best results with Cellu Baking Powder by sifting it with flour, as usual, using same amount as Calumet. It is always well to shake the jar before measuring baking powder, as special powders tend to separate somewhat. Miss Jamison advises increasing the baking powder approximately 1 teaspoon per cup of flour if whole milk or eggs are omitted from the recipe, or if 2 egg whites are substituted for a whole egg.

To make good quick breads you must do good planning. You will have to depend upon the low sodium baking powder and air beaten into your mixtures to *raise* quick breads (soda and acids such as sour milk and molasses are taboo). Where you elect to use your egg allowance in your quick bread, the egg will help keep mixture light. In some of the fruit breads, where neither egg nor whole milk is used, you may get a sticky product. The bread is good to taste but somewhat inferior in quality to that produced when egg is included as an ingredient.

For good results:

1. Read over the recipe carefully before you begin.
2. Assemble all "tools" and ingredients at your work center.
3. Preheat oven to required temperature for baking.
4. Sift flour and measure.
5. Add other dry ingredients and sift.
6. Add shortening (vegetable oil in most of our re-

---

* The Chicago Dietetic Supply House, Inc., 1750 West Van Buren Street, Chicago 12, Illinois.

cipes), egg, if any, and low sodium milk, pouring all at once over entire surface of flour mixture.

7. Mix together with a pastry blender and stir until flour is moist and all of the ingredients are blended. (Don't try to stir out all the lumps in quick breads.)

8. Mix wet and dry ingredients as quickly as possible.

9. Turn into lightly oiled pan and bake at once in middle of oven or as directed in recipe.

MUFFINS
12 Muffins

This excellent Basic Recipe comes from the Home Service Department of Corn Products Refining Company and it offers you many variations. (We have adapted it for diet requirements.)

2 cups sifted all-purpose flour	1 egg, well-beaten
3 teaspoons low sodium baking powder	1¼ cups low sodium non-fat milk
2 tablespoons sugar	⅓ cup corn oil

Mix and sift dry ingredients. Make a well and add remaining ingredients all at once; stir only enough to dampen flour. Batter will be lumpy. Fill lightly oiled muffin pans ⅔ full. Bake in 425° (hot) oven, 20 to 25 minutes, until golden brown.

One Muffin	Total Recipe	
7	86	milligrams sodium
7	81	grams total fat
1	6	grams saturated fat
144	1732	calories

VARIATIONS

BLUEBERRY MUFFINS: Increase sugar to ⅓ cup. Add 1 cup fresh, frozen, or drained canned blueberries to mixed, sifted, dry ingredients. (Other fruits may be used, as cherries, peaches, or crushed pineapple.)

CHEESE MUFFINS: Add ½ cup grated low sodium dietetic cheese to mixed and sifted dry ingredients. Sprinkle tops of muffins with paprika before baking. And for special flavors, use ½ teaspoon basil, caraway, dill, or sage with dry ingredients. *Cheese muffin variation not to be used by those with total fat or saturated fat restrictions.*

GRAHAM MUFFINS: Use ⅔ cup graham flour with 1 cup

all-purpose flour in the Basic Recipe.

NUT MUFFINS: Add ½ cup coarsely chopped walnuts to mixed and sifted dry ingredients.

SUGARED APPLE MUFFINS: Add 1 cup chopped apples to mixed and sifted dry ingredients. Combine ½ teaspoon cinnamon with 2 tablespoons sugar. Sprinkle over tops of muffins before baking.

LOW SATURATED FAT VARIATION

Follow Basic Recipe except to substitute 2 egg whites for the whole egg. All Basic Recipe Variations may be used except Cheese. Nut Variation should be omitted if total fat is restricted. If no sodium restrictions, use regular baking powder and non-fat milk, and add 1 teaspoon salt. *One muffin, Basic Recipe: negligible saturated fat (1⅓ teaspoons vegetable oil).*

CORNMEAL MUFFINS
12 Muffins

1 cup *sifted* all-purpose flour

1 cup enriched yellow cornmeal

¼ cup sugar *or* 3 tablespoons honey

1 tablespoon low sodium baking powder

1 cup low sodium non-fat milk

2 tablespoons vegetable oil

1 egg, well-beaten

Mix and sift the dry ingredients together three times. Make a well and add remaining ingredients all at once. Mix quickly, just enough to moisten dry ingredients. Batter will be lumpy. Pour into lightly oiled muffin tins, filling them ⅔ full. Bake in 400° (hot) oven, 20 to 25 minutes. Or pour into lightly oiled 8 x 8 x 2-inch baking pan for 9 servings of corn bread. Increase baking time to 30 to 40 minutes; use a 425° (hot) oven.

One Muffin With sugar	Total Recipe	
7	85	milligrams sodium
3	37	grams total fat
1	6	grams saturated fat
132	1581	calories

LOW SATURATED FAT VARIATION

Follow the Basic Recipe except to substitute 2 egg whites for the whole egg. If no sodium restrictions, use regular

non-fat milk and baking powder, and add 1 teaspoon salt.
*One muffin: negligible saturated fat (½ teaspoon vege-
table oil).*

BAKING POWDER BISCUITS
10 Biscuits

1 cup *sifted* all-purpose flour	2 tablespoons vegetable oil
1½ teaspoons low sodium baking powder	⅓ cup low sodium non-fat milk
1 teaspoon sugar	

Mix and sift dry ingredients. Combine oil and milk and
pour over entire surface of flour mixture. Mix with fork
to make a dough light and soft to handle. Shape lightly
with hands to make a ball. Place on waxed paper and
knead about 10 times or until smooth. Pat out to ½-inch
thickness for average biscuits (thinner for Southern Type,
thin and crusty biscuits; slightly thicker for the tall,
fluffy ones). Or roll between 2 squares waxed paper
(about 12 inches square). Remove top sheet of paper;
cut biscuits with unfloured 2-inch biscuit cutter. Place
biscuits on unoiled baking sheet—2 inches apart for
crusty biscuits or close together for soft ones. Bake in
450° (very hot) oven, 10 to 15 minutes. (If no sodium
restrictions, use regular non-fat milk and baking powder,
and add ½ teaspoon salt.)

One Biscuit	Total Recipe	
1	6	milligrams sodium
3	29	grams total fat
negligible	negligible	grams saturated fat
69	694	calories

One biscuit: ½ teaspoon vegetable oil.

VARIATIONS

DROP: In a hurry? Try Drop Biscuits by increasing liquid
by about 2 tablespoons. Drop by spoonfuls on an oiled
baking sheet or put in muffin pan, filling two-thirds
full. Bake as outlined.

CHEESE: Add ¼ cup graded low sodium cheese to dry
ingredients. A real delicacy with salads: *But not for
those with fat restrictions.*

CURRY: Add ½ teaspoon curry powder to dry ingredients.
Something very special when split and topped with
"creamed" leftover meats or croquettes.

HERB: Add ¼ teaspoon nutmeg, ¼ teaspoon sage, and ½

teaspoon caraway seeds to dry ingredients. Elegant split for "creamed" chicken or mushrooms. Good with tossed salads, too.

ORANGE: Add 1 tablespoon grated orange rind to dry ingredients. When biscuits are shaped and on pan, place ½ cocktail cube sugar dipped in orange juice on top of each biscuit.

PARSLEY: Cut in 2 tablespoons chopped parsley with dry ingredients.

COFFEE CAKE
9 Squares

2 cups *sifted* all-purpose flour

1 teaspoon powdered orange peel

½ cup sugar

2 teaspoons low sodium baking powder

1 medium egg, slightly beaten

½ cup low sodium non-fat milk

½ cup fresh or diluted frozen orange juice

⅓ cup vegetable oil

Mix and sift dry ingredients. Make a well and add the remaining ingredients. Stir only enough to dampen flour —the batter will appear lumpy. Turn into lightly oiled 10-inch pie pan or a 9-inch square baking pan. Spoon topping over surface and bake in 375° (moderate) oven, 25 to 35 minutes. Delicious plain or with topping.

MARMALADE TOPPING

¼ cup sugar (more or less)

¼ cup flour

1 teaspoon unsalted butter

1 tablespoon water

½ cup pure marmalade

Mix in order given and blend to a coarse mix. Spoon onto batter and spread lightly over surface. The topping will melt down through coffee cake during baking to give it a rich flavor.

One Square With marmalade topping	Total Recipe Without topping	
11	82	milligrams sodium
10	81	grams total fat
1	6	grams saturated fat
308	2011	calories

VARIATIONS

One-fourth cup white or light brown sugar combined with 1 teaspoon cinnamon may be sprinkled over coffee cake in place of topping.

Thin slices of apple may be substituted for the marmalade. Combine with ½ cup water and ½ cup sugar. Simmer gently for 5 minutes. Then arrange on the batter. (A few broken walnuts may be scattered over the top if fat content will allow.) This gives a glazed topping.

One teaspoon caraway may be added to the apple mixture.

LOW SATURATED FAT VARIATION

Follow Basic Recipe or Variations except substitute 2 egg whites for 1 whole egg and omit unsalted butter. If no sodium restrictions, use regular non-fat milk and baking powder, and add ¾ teaspoon salt. *One serving: negligible saturated fat (1¾ teaspoons vegetable oil).*

FRUIT AND NUT BREADS

No wonder fruit and nut breads are so popular. They are chock-full of good nutrients and are flavorful and appealing in texture—whether plain, thinly spread for tea, or as general sandwich bread when variety is wanted.

Like other quick breads, they are higher in fat content than plain yeast breads. However, when made with egg white and vegetable oil, the saturated fat content is negligible. When a large loaf of bread is made with as much as a cup of walnuts, little or no oil is needed; but when the nuts are omitted, oil or shortening is necessary to give a good product.

Fruit breads should be cooked with an inverted loaf pan cover for the first 20 minutes of baking; then remove to complete. Allow to stand overnight for best slicing, and whatever you do, use a sharp, straight-edged knife, not a saw-toothed one.

Don't worry if your fruit breads crack in the center. This is quite typical of these heavy, rich breads. They are really half bread, half cake, and may be used in a variety of ways to give interest to your meals.

APRICOT NUT LOAF
1 Loaf (12 slices)

This recipe comes to us from the Home Advisory Service, Wine Institute, San Francisco, California.

1 cup *sun-dried* apricots
¾ cup water
½ cup California muscatel
1 egg, lightly beaten
Liquid from cooking apricots
Low sodium non-fat milk (about ½ cup)
1 tablespoon vegetable oil

2 cups *sifted* all-purpose flour
½ cup sugar
4 teaspoons low sodium baking powder
1 teaspoon grated lemon rind
½ cup chopped walnuts

Rinse apricots, add water and wine; boil, uncovered, about 10 minutes. Cool; drain, reserving liquid, and slice apricots. Beat egg lightly. Turn liquid from apricots into measuring cup and add low sodium milk to make ¾ cup. (Mixture may curdle slightly, but this will not affect baked loaf.) Combine with egg and oil. Sift flour, sugar, and baking powder. Add lemon rind, walnuts, and liquid mixture, and mix until all of flour is moistened. Carefully blend in apricots. Turn into lightly oiled loaf pan (8½ x 4½ x 2½ inches). Bake in 350° (moderate) oven about 1 hour. Turn out onto wire rack to cool.

One Slice	Total Recipe	
11	129	milligrams sodium
5	55	grams total fat
1	6	grams saturated fat
195	2342	calories

LOW SATURATED FAT VARIATION

Follow Basic Recipe except substitute 2 egg whites for 1 whole egg. If no sodium restrictions, use regular non-fat milk and baking powder, and add ½ teaspoon salt. *One serving: negligible saturated fat (¼ teaspoon vegetable oil).*

ECONOMY FRUIT BREAD
18 Slices

This recipe has been developed without eggs or fat for the highly restricted diet.

Put into a mixing bowl ..	1¼ cups light brown sugar
Sift together and stir in	3 cups all-purpose *sifted* flour
	5 teaspoons low sodium baking powder
	¼ teaspoon nutmeg
Stir in	1½ cups low sodium non-fat milk
Blend in and stir well	1 cup *sun-dried* cooked prunes, cut in small pieces

Pour into a lightly greased loaf pan and let stand 15 minutes. Bake in a 350° (moderate) oven, 1 hour or until center of loaf is dry to wooden pick test. Turn onto rack to cool and let stand overnight, if possible, for best slicing. This bread is an excellent accompaniment to a salad meal.

One Slice	Total Recipe	
5	93	milligrams sodium
negligible	5	grams total fat
negligible	negligible	grams saturated fat
155	2783	calories

ORANGE BREAD
2 Loaves (20 slices)

3 cups *sifted* all-purpose flour

1 tablespoon low sodium baking powder

1 tablespoon grated orange rind *or* powdered peel

½ cup sugar

1 medium egg, lightly beaten

¼ cup orange juice

1¼ cups low sodium non-fat milk

2 tablespoons vegetable oil

Mix and sift dry ingredients 2 times. Combine egg, orange juice, milk, and vegetable oil. Add to dry ingredients and mix just enough to blend. Pour into 2 slightly

oiled and waxed paper lined loaf pans (8 x 3½ inches).
Bake in 350° (moderate) oven, 60 to 75 minutes.

One Slice	One Loaf	
5	45	milligrams sodium
2	19	grams total fat
negligible	3	grams saturated fat
103	1025	calories

VARIATIONS

Add 1 cup *sun-dried* raisins or prunes to dry ingredients.
Add 1 cup broken walnut meats to batter.
For a cakelike loaf, increase sugar to ¾ cup.

LOW SATURATED FAT VARIATION

Follow Basic Recipe and Variations except substitute 2
egg whites for 1 whole egg. If no sodium restriction, use
regular non-fat milk and baking powder, and add ½ teaspoon salt. *One slice: negligible saturated fat (¼ teaspoon
vegetable oil).*

PRUNE BREAD
1 Loaf (12 slices)

1 cup *sun-dried* prunes
½ teaspoon grated
    orange rind
½ cup orange juice
Hot water
¾ cup sugar
2 cups *sifted* all-purpose
    flour

4 teaspoons low sodium
    baking powder
½ teaspoon cinnamon
1 tablespoon vegetable
    oil
1 medium egg, lightly
    beaten

Cut prune meat from pits with knife or sharp scissors;
add rind. Add enough hot water to orange juice to make 1
cup; pour over prunes and rind. Let stand 10 minutes.
Sift dry ingredients 4 times. Add oil and egg to prune mixture; then add dry ingredients and beat to blend well. Pour
into lightly oiled loaf pan (8 x 4 x 2 inches); bake in
350° (moderate) oven, 1 hour, or until fruit bread tests
done. Turn out onto wire rack to cool.

One Slice	One Loaf	
7	82	milligrams sodium
2	23	grams total fat
1	6	grams saturated fat
168	2010	calories

VARIATIONS

One-half to 1 cup broken walnut meats may be added to batter.

Sun-dried dates may be substituted for the prunes.

LOW SATURATED FAT VARIATION

Follow Basic Recipe and Variations except substitute 2 egg whites for 1 whole egg. If no sodium restrictions, use regular baking powder and add ½ teaspoon salt. *One slice: negligible saturated fat (¼ teaspoon vegetable oil).*

PANCAKES AND WAFFLES

Pancakes, with their few ingredients, are relatively easy to make and are very good with substitutions—so do include them plain or dressed up as a special treat for any meal.

The secret of making good pancakes is to combine the liquid and dry ingredients quickly, and stir only until flour mixture is dampened. Of course, the cooking is important, too. A griddle must be "seasoned" right if it is going to cook right. Try two coatings of one of the new long-lasting "surfacings" to condition it. Preheat as directed, and then brush with unsalted fat if necessary. So treated, the griddle can be wiped after each use without washing. Since you can't use a good old salt-in-the-bag rub to clean griddle of batter pieces, you may have to brush lightly with vegetable oil from time to time to keep in shape.

GRIDDLECAKES OR PANCAKES
6 Griddlecakes

1 cup *sifted* all-purpose flour	⅔ cup low sodium non-fat milk
2 teaspoons low sodium baking powder	2 tablespoons vegetable oil
1 medium egg, lightly beaten	1½ tablespoons sugar

Mix and sift dry ingredients. Combine egg, milk, and oil; add to dry ingredients, beating just enough to dampen flour. The batter should be lumpy. Add more milk, if necessary, to make batter just thin enough to pour. Heat griddle or frying pan over moderate heat, lightly oiled if necessary. To ensure pancakes of uniform size, use a ¼-cup measure to dip the batter onto the griddle. Turn pancakes as soon as they are puffy and full of bubbles and nicely browned on under side. Using a spatula, turn to other side to brown. Serve immediately with 100 per cent maple sirup or honey. Or top with fruit or confectioner's sugar.

One Pancake	Total Recipe	
Without sirup or fruit		
13	79	milligrams sodium
6	35	grams total fat
1	6	grams saturated fat
143	856	calories

VARIATIONS

WHOLE WHEAT: Use ⅔ cup white flour and ⅓ cup whole wheat flour. If desired, omit sugar and substitute 2 tablespoons honey.

BUCKWHEAT, WITHOUT EGG: Use ¼ cup white flour and ¾ cup buckwheat flour. Increase baking powder to 2½ teaspoons. Two tablespoons of honey may be substituted for sugar.

WHEAT GERM, WITH EGG WHITE: Use ½ cup white flour, ⅓ cup graham flour, 2 tablespoons wheat germ, and 2 tablespoons cornmeal. Increase baking powder to 2½ teaspoons. Increase milk to about 1 cup. Omit egg yolk; beat egg white and fold in with light strokes at very end.

FRITTERS: Useful for left-over vegetables or fruits, but good with almost any combination. Follow Basic Recipe, but reduce baking powder to 1 teaspoon. Separate egg and add beaten egg white after other ingredients are blended. Fold in 1 cup drained fruit or vegetable. This addition may be made to dry ingredients if you prefer a particularly light fritter. Makes 8 medium fritters.

LOW SATURATED FAT VARIATION

Follow Basic Recipe and Variations for Whole Wheat and Fritters except substitute 2 egg whites for 1 whole egg. Buckwheat and Wheat Germ Variations may be used without any changes. If no sodium restrictions, use regular

non-fat milk and baking powder, and add ½ teaspoon salt.
One pancake, Basic Recipe: negligible saturated fat (1 teaspoon vegetable oil).

FRENCH PANCAKES
20 Four-inch Cakes

A real dessert or luncheon delicacy, and so good when cooked to perfection in a small frying pan, or on your griddle. They glamorize many simple leftovers which may be used as fillers. They may be made ½ hour before meal is to be served and kept hot between the folds of a warm towel in warming oven, if you don't want to prepare them at the last moment.

1 cup *sifted* pastry flour	fat milk
½ teaspoon sugar	2 medium eggs
1 cup low sodium non-	

Mix flour and sugar. Add milk and stir until batter is smooth. Add eggs and beat thoroughly. Let batter stand a half hour or more. Heat a 4-inch or other small frying pan. Brush lightly with vegetable oil and cover pan with very thin layer of batter. Tilt pan to spread mixture evenly over surface. When cooked on one side, quickly loosen edges with spatula and toss or turn to cook other side. (French pancakes may be turned again if necessary to brown evenly.) Spread with jelly or jam, roll and dip in confectioners' sugar, and serve.

One Pancake	Total Recipe	
Without jelly or sugar		
8	149	milligrams sodium
1	12	grams total fat
1	11	grams saturated fat
33	650	calories

SPECIAL WAYS OF SERVING PANCAKES

WITH CHICKEN: Spread each pancake with 1 tablespoon chopped, cooked chicken. Roll and place in casserole. When ready to serve, pour mustard-cayenne flavored hot low sodium cheese spread over pancakes. Set in broiler to lightly brown. Or spread each cake with 2 tablespoons low sodium "creamed" chicken. Roll and garnish with parsley sprig. (Leftover meats may be used in the same way.)

WITH VEGETABLES: Spread with 1 rounded tablespoon cooked vegetables. Sprinkle with paprika or serve with sauce of choice. Set rolls of pancakes in a casserole and place in broiler to heat sauce. Watch carefully so as not to overcook and toughen pancakes.

LOW SATURATED FAT VARIATION

Follow Basic Recipe except substitute 3 egg whites for 2 whole eggs; add ½ teaspoon low sodium baking powder. When using Variations, omit cheese because of its saturated fat content. If no sodium restrictions, use regular non-fat milk and baking powder and add ½ teaspoon salt. *One pancake, Basic Recipe: negligible saturated fat.*

WAFFLES
6 Large Waffles or 12 3 x 6 inch Waffles

This recipe is straight from the Home Service Department of the Corn Products Company, and thanks to Jane Ashley, we have made the necessary adaptations for this diet.

2 cups *sifted* all-purpose flour	2 medium eggs, lightly beaten
1 tablespoon low sodium baking powder	1½ cups low sodium non-fat milk
2 tablespoons sugar	½ cup vegetable oil

Mix and sift dry ingredients. Combine eggs, milk, and vegetable oil (corn oil in the tested recipe). Add to dry ingredients; blend well. Bake in a hot waffle iron about 3 minutes, or until batter stops steaming. Lift from iron with fork and serve at once.

One Waffle 3 x 6 inches	Total Recipe	
13	158	milligrams sodium
11	126	grams total fat
1	11	grams saturated fat
181	2175	calories

VARIATIONS

SOYBEAN FLOUR WAFFLE: Substitute ½ cup *sifted* soybean flour for ½ cup white flour in Basic Recipe.

WHOLE WHEAT WAFFLES: Substitute *sifted* whole wheat flour for white flour in Basic Recipe.

LOW SATURATED FAT VARIATION

Substitute 3 egg whites for whole eggs and increase baking powder to 4 teaspoons in Basic Recipe and Variations.

If no sodium restrictions, use regular non-fat milk and baking powder, and add 1 teaspoon salt. *One serving, Basic Recipe: negligible saturated fat (2 teaspoons vegetable oil).*

MISCELLANEOUS

WHEAT GERM SQUARES
48 Squares

When you want a crisp and nutty-flavored cracker, try this quickie recipe graciously given to us by Mrs. Frances Prout, former Home Economics teacher and a member of the Special Diets committee of the Alameda County Heart Association.

½ cup *sifted* cake flour	1½ cups wheat germ
½ cup *sifted* all-purpose flour	3 tablespoons vegetable oil
4 teaspoons low sodium baking powder	⅓ cup water
	Pinch sugar, if desired

Mix sifted flours, baking powder, and 1 cup wheat germ. Cut in oil with 2 knives until well blended. Turn onto lightly floured board on which has been sprinkled part of the remaining wheat germ. Form mixture into a ball and pat out to ½-inch thickness. Sprinkle with some of the wheat germ; roll until paper-thin. Add more wheat germ as needed. Cut in 1½-inch squares with pastry edger or kitchen knife. Use a spatula to place wafers on unoiled baking sheet. Bake in 350° (moderate) oven, 12 to 15 minutes, until *lightly* browned. (If no sodium restrictions, use regular baking powder, and add ½ teaspoon salt.)

One Square	Total Recipe	
negligible	15	milligrams sodium
1	39	grams total fat
negligible	negligible	grams saturated fat
21	1004	calories

Three squares: ½ teaspoon vegetable oil.

MELBA TOAST

For authentic Melba toast, slice low sodium white bread (pages 194-95) from ⅛ to ¼-inch thick. Lay on a shallow baking pan and bake in a 250° (very slow) oven until perfectly dry and crisp. Toast should be golden brown and not curled. Good plain or with a spread.

Some of the dietetic supply houses * also make commercial Melba toasts, bread sticks, and zwieback—low in sodium and fat, too.

* The Chicago Dietetic Supply House, 1750 West Van Buren Street, Chicago 12, Illinois.

Stella D'Oro Biscuit Co., Inc., 184 West 237th Street, New York 63, New York.

Venus Wheat Wafers, Inc., 678 Columbus Avenue, Boston, Massachusetts.

13. DESSERTS FOR EVERY OCCASION

"I am glad that my Adonis hath a sweet tooth in his head."

—JOHN LILY in *Euphues and His England*

We Americans do like to finish off our lunches and dinners with a sweet. Not a bad idea, nutritionally speaking, if that dessert is planned to complete and round out the meal. Too often, we think of desserts only as rich pies, pastries, and puddings that, inappropriately used, cloy rather than satisfy at the end of a hearty meal.

Fortunately for sodium- and fat-restricted dieters, fruit is abundantly available. It has long been the favored dessert of many epicureans, who use tortes, soufflés, and pastries only when dessert is to be the featured attraction. The emphasis on fruit and fruit-made desserts in this book does not mean that all of the richer desserts have to be forsaken entirely. Not at all—but they will have to be planned and used with care and according to your allowables. They often call for large amounts of eggs and fats to give them their luscious richness. These ingredients must always be watched and used only as allowed. But with so many choices, surely there will be enough desserts to tickle your palate and give you variety.

What is left, you ask? There are the presently popular fruits-in-wine and flaming desserts, many of which feature fruit. They are pleasing in color, subtle in flavor, and a real addition to the diet. Then there are the gelatin whips, the delicate, frothy bits of flavor that add delightful piquancy to a hearty meal; simple tortes; low sodium cakes and cookies; puddings old and new; and pies. Do you think you will suffer for want of a toothsome dessert?

For sodium restriction, do not use:

Bakery products of the commercial variety, such as cakes, cookies, doughnuts, pastry

Cake, cookie, pudding, and pie mixes and toppings

Commercial ice cream and sherbet (except low sodium dietetic), candy (except low sodium dietetic), molasses

Condensed milk

Crystallized or glazed fruit

Desserts containing baking powder (except low sodium) or baking soda

Desserts of prepared gelatin (except low sodium dietetic), such as flavored Jell-O

Maraschino cherries

Salt

Sweet fountain sirups and ice cream mixtures, beverage mixes, instant cocoa mixes

For saturated fat restriction, do not use:

Bakery products, except homemade with vegetable oil, egg white, and non-fat milk

Butter

Chocolate

Cocoa

Coconut

Commercial desserts, mixes, and hydrogenated toppings, such as cake, cookie, ice cream, milk sherbet, pie, pudding

Cream

Egg yolk or whole egg desserts unless kept within your allowance; egg white desserts unless sodium allowance will permit

Hydrogenated fats, such as Crisco and Spry

Lard

Margarine (except special margarine, if allowed)

Whole milk

SPECIAL FLAVOR AIDS

A squeeze of lemon or lime juice on bananas, cantaloupe, or peaches for delicious flavor. Add sugar or honey as desired

Angostura Aromatic Bitters for a spicy tangy flavor; try 2 to 3 drops in center of apples to be baked; 5 to 6 dashes to a pound of prunes or apricots during stewing; 3 to 4 drops per serving to half grapefruit; 5 to 6 drops added to each cup sirup of canned fruits or puddings

Freshly ground nutmeg over bland puddings

Calcium Sucaryl to sweeten fruits and other desserts when you must be calorie conscious; one tablet, or ⅛ teaspoon solution, is equal to about 1 level teaspoon of sugar. Regular Sucaryl may be used for those without sodium restrictions if sugar must be curtailed. In baked goods and frozen desserts, Sucaryl does not give the same texture as sugar, so use tested recipes in this book or in material from manufacturer.

FRESH SEASONAL FRUITS

There are times when a bowl of fresh, colorful fruit is just the answer for dessert. Be sure to think of texture and taste differences in making up your selections. Whatever you do, use *fresh* (or frozen) fruit if you expect the plaudits of family or friends.

Fruit combinations, too, are becoming increasingly important in dessert planning. Here, you control color combination, taste, and texture differences, and can produce many different varieties.

A few suggestions to get you on your way:

Avocados, if allowed, with mixed fruit
Orange sections with stewed cranberries
Melon combinations
Pineapple chunks and raspberries
Mixed fruit compotes
Pineapple or watermelon, hollowed out, and filled with a blend of fruits

CANTALOUPE FRUIT CUP
2 Servings

Cut cantaloupe in half. Remove seeds. Fill centers with ¼ cup orange sections and ¼ cup raspberries. Sprinkle lightly with 1 teaspoon lemon juice and 1 tablespoon sugar. Chill thoroughly.

One Serving	Total Recipe	
25	49	milligrams sodium
1	1	grams total fat
negligible	negligible	grams saturated fat
126	252	calories

CALIFORNIA AMBROSIA
6 Servings

Peel and slice 6 Sunkist oranges. Arrange slices in serving dish; sprinkle with ½ cup powdered sugar, and ½ cup chopped walnuts.

One Serving	Total Recipe	
2	13	milligrams sodium
6	34	grams total fat
negligible	negligible	grams saturated fat
166	994	calories

FLAMING DESSERTS

We have already stated the importance of presenting sodium- or fat-restricted foods to their best advantage to make the simple diet you have to offer as attractive as possible. Steaming soups ladled from a tureen, the tossing of a green salad for the ceremony as well as flavor improvement, and now exploration with desserts "on fire" served for all to admire. Indulge yourself in a chafing dish, if your budget will allow, or prepare these simple desserts in the kitchen at the last moment—and bring them to the table, *flaming,* in all of their glory.

PEACHES JUBILEE
6 Servings

Use large Elberta peaches (·canned) for this delectable dessert. Drain sirup from one 2½ size canned peach halves. Lightly thicken sirup with 1 tablespoon cornstarch (thickness of sirup will alter the amount of thickening you will need). Blend and boil until clear, stirring to prevent lumping. Add peach halves and poach until thoroughly heated. Arrange peach halves in chafing dish or on platter, cut side up. Cover with sirup; add 1 jigger heated brandy; light, and serve flaming.

One Peach	Total Recipe	
3	18	milligrams sodium
negligible	1	grams total fat
negligible	negligible	grams saturated fat
99	595	calories

FRUITS IN WINE

There has been an increasing interest in combining fresh fruit (or frozen) in wine the last few years. No wonder, for the delicately blended savors of the fruit in the wine and the wine in the fruit make this a truly gourmet dessert. Easy to prepare, greatly improved with hours of "standing," here is a boon to you who must plan ahead to get everything done.

STRAWBERRIES IN PORT WINE
3 Servings

Wash, sort, and stem 1 pint basket of strawberries. Sugar with ¼ cup powdered sugar. Sprinkle with ½ cup port. Cover. Set in refrigerator to cool, allowing at least 6 hours for fruit and wine to blend. Many seasonal fruits, or their frozen varieties, may be fixed in this way. Prepared ahead of time, they demand no last-minute effort.

One Serving	Total Recipe	
5	14	milligrams sodium
negligible	1	grams total fat
negligible	negligible	grams saturated fat
140	421	calories

VARIATIONS

Substitute honey for sugar; or substitute 1½ teaspoons Calcium Sucaryl for sugar if you must count calories.
Raspberries-pineapple chunks with claret.
A blend of fruit with muscatel.
Sliced peaches in port.

FROZEN FRUIT DESSERTS

FROZEN DESSERTS, *by Hilda Faust (Extension Nutritionist, University of California, Agricultural Extension Service), has some excellent suggestions for making homemade frozen desserts. We are indebted to Miss Faust for permission to adapt this material for our purposes, and to share with you her recipe for Cranberry Ice.*

Practically any dessert that can be ice-frozen without stirring can be frozen in your refrigerator tray under the same conditions. Of course, you will want a smooth-grained product. Some of the usual ingredients used to accomplish this are denied you, but egg white, flour, or gelatin will help. Allow about 1 tablespoon of any one of the three for 1 quart of mixture.

Here are some other aids for frozen desserts:

1. It is important to thicken frozen mixtures enough to prevent large crystals from forming. Flour, cornstarch, cooked strained tapioca, mashed fruit, and honey will improve your product in this regard.

2. Try making up your frozen fruit desserts with a minimum amount of water.

3. Freeze under highest temperature possible. Have all of your ingredients *equally* cold when you mix them.

4. Try adding sugar to the fruit, instead of making all the sugar into a sirup. Let the sugared fruit stand for a few hours or overnight, then, if your recipe calls for a sirup, make it by boiling fruit juice and adding a little water, if necessary. When menu count permits use of egg white, try adding some of the sugar into the white for texture goodness.

5. Remember that excess sugar prevents freezing. Try substituting honey for some of the sugar in the fruit mixtures. In making this substitution, consider that honey is slightly sweeter than your granulated sugar, so use only two thirds honey for the sugar called for in the recipe.

6. In making sherbet calling for beaten egg white, freeze the chilled mixture to a mushy consistency (30-60 minutes). Remove to a chilled bowl, beat until product is light; then add the egg white, and return to freezing tray, and freeze.

Now, for some recipes.

CRANBERRY ICE
8 Servings

1 quart cranberries	2 cups sugar
2 cups water	½ cup lemon juice

Poach the cranberries in the water for about 10 minutes, then rub through a sieve. Add sugar and lemon juice. Stir all until sugar is dissolved. Pour into refrigerator tray and freeze until mushy consistency. Remove to chilled bowl and beat until light. Return to freezer tray and freeze. (A second beating during freezing process will improve texture.)

One Serving	Total Recipe	
1	6	milligrams sodium
negligible	4	grams total fat
negligible	negligible	grams saturated fat
223	1786	calories

VARIATIONS

CRANBERRY GINGER ALE ICE: Simply combine 1 can jellied cranberry sauce with ¾ cup ginger ale. Beat until well blended.

LEMON WATER ICE: Make a sirup by boiling 1 quart water with 1¾ cups sugar. Add ½ teaspoon lemon rind or 1 tablespoon lemon peel. Cool; add ¾ cup lemon juice and blend.

GRAPE ICE: Soften 2 teaspoons plain gelatin in ¼ cup cold water; then place gelatin over hot water to melt. Add 2 tablespoons lemon juice, 1 cup grapefruit juice, 1 quart pure unsweetened grape juice, and 1 cup sugar. Stir thoroughly to dissolve.

SHERBETS

When your count permits, add 1 egg white to any of your water ice recipes in the following way:

1. While sirup is still hot, pour gradually over freshly beaten egg white. Cool mixture and combine with fruit juices.

2. When you want to increase the volume and airiness, add to mixture when half frozen, as explained before.

BLACKBERRY VELVA
6 Servings

This recipe, adapted from a U.S. Department of Agriculture bulletin, may be frozen in a crank or electric freezer, or packed at once into a moisture-vapor-resistant container, sealed, and placed in the home freezer.

1 quart blackberries	2 teaspoons plain
½ cup (or more) sugar	gelatin
1 tablespoon lemon	¼ cup cold water
juice	

Sort, wash, and drain blackberries. Press through sieve to make 1½ cups purée. Add sugar and lemon juice to purée and stir thoroughly. Soften gelatin in cold water 5 minutes, then soften over hot water. Add to fruit, being sure that purée is around room temperature when added. If purée is too cold, the gelatin will congeal before it has a chance to bind the fruit. Stir to completely blend. Pour into ice cream freezer or freezer tray; or prepare for quick-freezing. Serve soft-frozen over fruit salads or fruit cups; or reduce freezer temperature to normal when mixture is soft-frozen and let "ripen" for at least an hour.

One Serving	Total Recipe	
2	10	milligrams sodium
1	6	grams total fat
negligible	negligible	grams saturated fat
123	740	calories

VARIATIONS

Any fresh or water-pack fruit may be used. Allow about 1½ cups fruit, such as fresh peaches or apricots, for the purée.

BANANA LOW SODIUM LOW FAT ICE CREAM
4 Servings

This recipe has been developed by Lida Jamison, dietitian for The Chicago Dietetic Supply House, and is built around their low sodium non-fat dry milk. We are indebted to them for permission to use it here. (If no sodium restriction, use regular non-fat dry milk.)

½ cup cold water
2 tablespoons lemon
  juice
½ teaspoon vanilla
¼ cup sugar

½ cup low sodium non-
  fat dry milk powder
1 cup mashed or puréed
  bananas

Put water into bowl; add the lemon juice, vanilla, and sugar. Stir and add low sodium non-fat dry milk powder. Beat vigorously until of a thick foamy consistency. Add bananas and blend. Pour into a refrigerator tray; freeze for ½ hour. Remove mixture to chilled bowl and beat well. Return to freezing unit until ready for use. Allow 3 to 4 hours for freezing. Turn refrigerator to normal for 1 hour of "ripening."

One Serving	Total Recipe	
5	20	milligrams sodium
negligible	1	grams total fat
negligible	1	grams saturated fat
139	554	calories

VARIATIONS

Crushed or sieved berries, drained crushed pineapple, puréed apricots or peaches may be substituted for the banana. Or you may use baby-food purée if there are no additives. Or pineapple, apricot, or loganberry nectar or juice, a blend of cranberry and orange juice. For a lower calorie dessert, substitute water-pack fruit and sweeten with Calcium Sucaryl. Add 1 tablespoon vegetable oil after ice cream is blended and beat a few seconds longer to mix oil and give smooth-textured product.

BANANA-ORANGE PARFAIT: Pour 2 tablespoons of honey over 1 cup orange pieces 2 hours before serving. Alternate orange and honey and low-fat ice cream in tall sherbet glasses. A topping of chopped walnuts may be added if desired. This fruit combination makes 4 servings.

FRUIT DESSERTS, COOKED

APPLE CRISP
6 *Servings*

Place 6 peeled, thin-sliced apples into a lightly oiled oblong baking dish. Sprinkle with 2 tablespoons lemon juice and ¼ cup water. Mix ½ teaspoon cinnamon and ½ cup sugar, and sprinkle over apples. Combine ½ cup sugar, ¾ cup flour, and 2 tablespoons vegetable oil, using pastry blender until crumbly. Spread over apples and pat well through with back of spoon. Bake in 350° (moderate) oven about 40 minutes, until apples are tender and crust is crisp and golden brown. May be served with hard sauce or "Whipped Cream" Topping (page 244).

One Serving	Total Recipe	
Without hard sauce or topping		
1	8	milligrams sodium
5	32	grams total fat
negligible	negligible	grams saturated fat
297	1783	calories

One serving: 1 teaspoon vegetable oil.

APPLE PANDOWDY
6 *Large Servings*

This is a deep-dish apple pie, handed down from early Colonial days, and a great favorite.

Line a casserole with shortcake pastry (page 233). Pare 6 medium cooking apples and slice thin into casserole. Sprinkle apples with a mixture of ½ cup sugar, 1 teaspoon caraway seed, ¼ teaspoon cinnamon. Add ½ cup light brown sugar, ¼ cup water blended with 1 tablespoon vinegar. Cover with pastry, or drop pastry by spoonfuls onto fruit. If you cover, you will have to cut slits for steam to escape. Line up edges of casserole even. Bake in a 400° (hot) oven about 30 minutes, or until fork-tender.

To make it really authentic, if you use a complete pastry cover over the fruit, you will want to break the top crust with a spoon when it is baked. Fold into apples. Bake about 8 minutes longer and serve warm.

One Serving	Total Recipe	
7	43	milligrams sodium
10	61	grams total fat
negligible	negligible	grams saturated fat
410	2459	calories

One serving: 2 teaspoons vegetable oil.

APPLE TORTE
4 Servings

This delicious apple dessert was first served us by Mrs. William Right Patton, of Oakland, California. We busied ourselves immediately to make the necessary adaptation and share it with you.

Beat 1 egg and add ¾ cup sugar. Continue beating until well blended. Add ½ cup broken walnuts, ¾ cup (scant) peeled, sliced thin apples, ½ teaspoon caraway seed, 1 teaspoon vanilla or lemon, 2 tablespoons flour.

Mix all together and add 1¼ teaspoons low sodium baking powder.

Sprinkle this lightly over the surface of your mixture and stir until it is blended well. Pour into an 8-inch baking pan (1 inch deep), lightly greased with vegetable oil. Bake in a 350° (moderate) oven about 40 minutes until a light, golden brown. This is so rich it is apt to crack, and is best served from the kitchen. Serve with "Whipped Cream" Topping (page 244).

One Serving	Total Recipe	
Without topping		
19	74	milligrams sodium
10	38	grams total fat
1	6	grams saturated fat
274	1094	calories

LOW SATURATED FAT VARIATION

Substitute 2 egg whites for 1 whole egg. If no sodium restrictions, use regular baking powder and add ½ teaspoon salt. *One serving: negligible saturated fat.*

BAKED APRICOT TAPIOCA
8 Servings

Put 2½ cups cooked, *sun-dried* apricots in an oblong lightly oiled baking dish. Sprinkle lightly with ½ teaspoon caraway seed.

Combine in a saucepan ½ cup minute tapioca, ½ cup honey, 3 cups cold water, and 2 tablespoons lemon juice. Bring all to a boil over medium heat, stirring constantly. Pour over fruit in baking dish. Cover and bake in 375° (moderate) oven about 15 minutes. Serve plain to dieter and with cream for regulars.

One Serving	Total Recipe	
6	47	milligrams sodium
negligible	1	grams total fat
negligible	negligible	grams saturated fat
173	1382	calories

VARIATIONS

Canned apricots may be used in place of dried apricots.

Try different fruit combinations with this recipe for interesting and simple tapioca desserts. Apples, peaches, and cherries have been favorites with us. Vary seasonings, too.

BAKED BANANAS
4 Servings

Peel 4 bananas and place in baking pan. Sprinkle lightly with 1 tablespoon lemon juice and ¼ cup light brown sugar. Bake in a 400° (hot) oven for about 15 minutes, or until slightly brown. Baked bananas may be served with veal or as a dessert.

One Serving	Total Recipe	
5	18	milligrams sodium
negligible	1	gram total fat
negligible	negligible	grams saturated fat
140	559	calories

BROILED GRAPEFRUIT
2 Servings

There are times when your meal calls for a hot fruit dessert. This is one of the best.

Cut medium grapefruit in half and separate the sections. For each grapefruit half, sprinkle the top with 1 tablespoon light brown sugar, ¼ teaspoon cinnamon, dash of mace, or a dash of Angostura Aromatic Bitters in center of cavity. Place under broiler and cook until lightly browned. Serve at once.

One Serving	Total Recipe	
6	12	milligrams sodium
negligible	1	gram total fat
negligible	negligible	grams saturated fat
126	252	calories

VARIATION

Honey may be substituted for light brown sugar for slightly different flavor in broiled grapefruit.

One tablespoon sherry may be sprinkled over top of each grapefruit in place of bitters.

FRUIT TAPIOCA
6 Servings

Blend in your saucepan 2 cups pineapple juice, ½ cup water, ½ cup sugar, ¼ cup tapioca. Place over double boiler, stirring constantly, and cook until mixture slightly thickens. This takes 5 to 8 minutes. Remove from heat and cool. Stir in 1 cup crushed pineapple. Chill to serve.

Other fruits and juices may be used, alone or in combination.

One Serving	Total Recipe	
1	8	milligrams sodium
negligible	1	gram total fat
negligible	negligible	grams saturated fat
161	968	calories

GELATIN DESSERTS

Use only plain, unflavored or approved dietetic low sodium gelatins in your recipes for those of you with sodium restrictions. One envelope gelatin (1 tablespoon) will set 2 cups liquid, with the exception of acid fruit, which uses only 1¾ cups liquid. Your basic gelatin recipe on the envelope can be adapted in a variety of ways, for fruits, salads, or desserts.

FRUIT GELATIN
4 Servings

Put 1 tablespoon gelatin into mixing bowl and soften with ¼ cup orange juice. Dissolve with ¾ cup boiling water. Stir in ½ cup sugar (this may be decreased where canned fruit juices are used). When gelatin and sugar are dissolved, add ¾ cup orange juice, 1 tablespoon lemon juice, and ½ teaspoon grated lemon rind. Chill mixture; when it begins to set, add ½ cup fresh strawberries and 1 banana, sliced. Pour into a ring mold or individual molds and chill until set.

One Serving	Total Recipe	
2	7	milligrams sodium
negligible	1	gram total fat
negligible	negligible	grams saturated fat
162	646	calories

VARIATIONS

LEMON GELATIN: Substitute ¼ cup sherry for ¼ cup liquid the next time you make Lemon Gelatin. It gives you something pleasingly different. (4 servings.) Other fruits and juices, alone or in combination, may be used.

ORANGE-PRUNE-WALNUT WHIP
6 Servings

We are indebted to the Consumer Service Division of Sunkist Growers for this delicious recipe.

1 tablespoon unflavored gelatin
⅓ cup sugar
½ cup cold water
1 cup fresh orange juice
3 tablespoons fresh lemon juice

1 cup chopped, cooked *sun-dried* prunes
½ cup chopped walnuts
1 cup orange chunks, drained (2 medium oranges)

Mix gelatin, sugar and water in top of double boiler. Heat over hot water until gelatin and sugar dissolve, stirring constantly. Remove from heat; cool, then stir in orange and lemon juice. Chill until mixture is slightly thicker than the consistency of unbeaten egg white. Beat with rotary or electric beater until light and fluffy and double in volume. Fold in chopped prunes, walnuts, and orange chunks. Pour into 1-quart mold and chill until firm.

One Serving	Total Recipe	
3	19	milligrams sodium
6	34	grams total fat
negligible	negligible	grams saturated fat
222	1333	calories

PUDDINGS

BLANCMANGE
3 Servings

Mix 1½ tablespoons cornstarch with 2 tablespoons sugar, ½ cup low sodium non-fat milk, until smooth. Heat 1 cup low sodium non-fat milk, then pour a little of it on the cornstarch mixture. Blend smoothly. Add remaining milk and put in double boiler. Stir constantly, until pudding begins to thicken. Cover and let cook 25 minutes, stirring as needed. When pudding is cool, add ½ teaspoon vanilla extract. (If no sodium restrictions, use regular non-fat milk, and add ⅛ teaspoon salt.)

One Serving	Total Recipe	
4	11	milligrams sodium
negligible	negligible	grams fat
90	271	calories

VARIATIONS

This pudding separates if not used rather quickly, so instead of making just one flavor, divide into three servings and make three different ones for individual servings. Many combinations are possible. These are some that are good:

Jelly or Jam: Into one, put 1 teaspoon pure jelly or jam.

Banana: Into a second, substitute ½ teaspoon banana flavor, cut up ½ banana at the time of service.

Cinnamon: For the third, try chilling with a small cinnamon stick. Remove when serving, and sprinkle lightly with cinnamon on top.

Peppermint flavoring may be used also. Or *Angostura Aromatic Bitters.*

BREAD PUDDING
6 Servings

2 cups low sodium non-fat milk

1 cup low sodium bread cubes

1 egg

¼ cup sugar

½ cup chopped, *sun-dried* prunes

½ teaspoon vanilla extract

½ teaspoon nutmeg

Warm milk; remove from heat. Add bread cubes. Beat egg lightly and add sugar. Add milk mixture, prunes, and vanilla extract. Blend; pour into lightly oiled baking dish and sprinkle with nutmeg. Set in pan of hot water. Bake in 350° (moderate) oven, 30 to 60 minutes, or until inserted knife comes out clean. (*This recipe is not for those with egg yolk restrictions.*)

One Serving	Total Recipe	
16	93	milligrams sodium
1	9	grams total fat
1	6	grams saturated fat
149	894	calories

LOW CALORIE BAKED LEMON PUDDING
4 Servings

½ cup *sifted* all-purpose flour

½ teaspoon low sodium baking powder

2 eggs, separated

2 teaspoons grated lemon rind

¼ cup lemon juice

1½ cups low sodium non-fat milk

2 tablespoons Calcium Sucaryl

Sift flour and baking powder. Beat egg yolks until lemon-color; add lemon rind, juice, milk, and Sucaryl. Beat until blended. Stir in flour mixture and beat until smooth. Beat egg whites until stiff enough to form peaks; fold into egg mixture. Pour into a lightly oiled 1-quart casserole. Set in pan containing ½-inch hot water. Bake in 350° (moderate) oven, 30 to 60 minutes. Chill at least 1 hour for cakelike topping and custard to set and cool.

One Serving	Total Recipe	
38	153	milligrams sodium
3	12	grams total fat
3	11	grams saturated fat
126	502	calories

LOW SATURATED FAT VARIATION

Substitute 3 egg whites for 2 whole eggs. If no sodium restrictions, use regular non-fat milk and add ¼ teaspoon salt. *One serving: negligible saturated fat.*

RICE PUDDING
4 Servings

½ cup brown rice
½ cup chopped, *sun-dried* apricots
1 cup low sodium non-fat milk
½ teaspoon nutmeg
¼ cup sugar
½ teaspoon vanilla extract

Follow directions on package for washing rice. (Some rice does not need washing.) Combine all ingredients. Pour into lightly oiled baking dish and bake in 300° (slow) oven, 2 hours or more, until rice and fruit are tender. Stir several times during the first hour. (If no sodium restrictions, use regular non-fat milk, and add ¼ teaspoon salt.)

One Serving	Total Recipe	
6	25	milligrams sodium
1	2	grams total fat
negligible	negligible	grams saturated fat
213	850	calories

UNCOOKED RICE PUDDING: Combine 1 cup cooked rice with 1 cup whole cranberry sauce. Add ½ cup confectioners' sugar. Fold in 1 cup "Whipped Cream" Topping (page 244) just before serving. Pile into individual serving dishes and top with a rounded tablespoonful of whole cranberry sauce.

MERINGUE SHELLS
12 Medium

Quick as a whip to make, and delicious with almost any fruit or sherbet, don't overlook these shells for party or family fare.

Beat ½ cup egg whites until foamy but not dry; add slowly 1 cup sugar, beating after each addition. Continue to beat until meringue forms sharp little peaks when you raise beater. Then add 1 tablespoon lemon juice, and beat again.

Shape meringue with spoon or pastry bag on unwaxed paper on oiled baking sheet. Allow space for meringues to spread. Bake in 250° (very slow) oven 1 hour and 15 minutes, until shells are thoroughly dried and tops are a delicate cream color. Remove from paper carefully, using a wet towel on the hot baking sheet so that meringues can be eased off. Let cool completely before storing.

Fill shells as desired. Makes 8 very large or 12 medium-sized shells.

One Serving (1/12 recipe)	Total Recipe	
16	188	milligrams sodium
negligible	negligible	grams total fat
70	834	calories

SCONES
6 Servings

1½ cups *sifted* all-purpose flour	¼ cup vegetable oil
2 teaspoons low sodium baking powder	1 egg, slightly beaten
2 teaspoons sugar	⅓ cup (more or less) low sodium non-fat milk

Sift dry ingredients together. Combine oil, beaten egg, and milk. Pour all at once over entire surface of dry ingredients. Mix with fork to make soft dough. Turn onto lightly floured board or wax paper and knead ten times or until smooth. Stretch into strips and form coils; or keep ¼-inch thick and shape into triangles; or into whatever shape you desire. Place scones on ungreased baking sheet. Bake in 425° (hot) oven, 10 to 15 minutes. Serve with fresh or frozen fruit or jam of choice.

One Serving Without fruit or jam	Total Recipe	
13	77	milligrams sodium
11	63	grams total fat
1	6	grams saturated fat
206	1236	calories

VARIATION

SHORTCAKE: Follow Scone recipe, increasing sugar to 1 tablespoon and baking powder to 1 tablespoon. Or use Baking Powder Biscuit recipe (page 203) increasing sugar to 1 tablespoon.

LOW SATURATED FAT VARIATION

Follow Basic Recipe and Shortcake recipe, except omit egg or substitute 2 egg whites. If no sodium restriction, use regular baking powder and non-fat milk, and add ½ teaspoon salt. *One serving: negligible saturated fat (2 teaspoons vegetable oil).*

SPRING COBBLER
6 Servings

Are you longing for something colorful and just a little bit different in the first days of spring? Why not try rosy rhubarb and tart pineapple in a cobbler?

1 tablespoon vegetable oil	Dash nutmeg
3 tablespoons all-purpose flour	1 cup water
½ cup light brown sugar	½ cup rhubarb, cut in pieces
	1½ cups small pineapple chunks

Blend oil, flour, sugar, nutmeg, and water in saucepan. Cook until thickened, stirring to prevent scorching. Add rhubarb. Cook until rhubarb is just fork-tender. Remove from heat; add pineapple. Pour into ungreased casserole and top with eggless scone batter made into little biscuits (page 232). Bake in 425° (hot) oven about 20 minutes.

One Serving	Total Recipe	
7	39	milligrams sodium
12	73	grams total fat
negligible	negligible	grams saturated fat
347	2081	calories

One serving: 2½ teaspoons vegetable oil.

ZABAGLIONE
4 Servings

If we had to name our most delicious and favorite dessert, we suppose we would choose Zabaglione with little hesitation. Its goodness and delicacy depend upon its ingredients—egg yolks must be fresh; on the making—it must not be overcooked; and on its serving—it must be served immediately in warmed sherbet glasses, or allowed to chill thoroughly if served cold. It does have to be made at the last moment when you elect to serve it hot, but by assembling its few ingredients beforehand, it is no trick to make as you are ready to serve it. *Fortunate are you if you find egg yolk on your allowable list!*

Put into the top part of
a cold double boiler . . .   4 egg yolks
                                 2 tablespoons powdered
                                   sugar

Place over hot water (not boiling) and beat with electric beater or rotary hand beater.

Gradually add . . . . . .   ¼ cup sherry

Beat until thick and fluffy (about 4 to 6 minutes), but remove from heat before any crust forms on sides of pan. Pile into warmed sherbet glasses and serve at once, or chill thoroughly and serve cold.

One Serving	Total Recipe	
16	63	milligrams sodium
5	22	grams total fat
5	22	grams saturated fat
100	401	calories

DESSERT SAUCES

CARAMEL SAUCE
1 Cup

Heat 1 cup sugar in heavy pan over moderate heat until melted and golden brown. Stir constantly. Add 1 cup boiling water gradually. Boil 5 to 6 minutes; cool. Use for custards, and as ice cream topping.

One Tablespoon	Total Recipe	
negligible	negligible	milligrams sodium
negligible	negligible	grams fat
48	770	calories

COFFEE-CARAMEL SAUCE: Substitute ¼ cup strong coffee for ¼ cup water.

CRANBERRY-PINEAPPLE SAUCE
1¼ Cups

Mix ½ can (1-pound size) whole cranberry sauce with ½ cup crushed pineapple (drained). Add ⅛ teaspoon peppermint extract if desired.

One Tablespoon	Total Recipe	
negligible	3	milligrams sodium
negligible	1	grams total fat
negligible	negligible	grams saturated fat
28	552	calories

CURRANT JELLY SAUCE
½ Cup

Beat ½ cup pure currant jelly with fork. Add 2 tablespoons hot water and 2 teaspoons lemon juice and blend. (Jelly may be melted for thinner sauce.)

One Tablespoon	Total Recipe	
2	14	milligrams sodium
negligible	negligible	grams fat
50	403	calories

ORANGE SAUCE
4 Servings

This is another of the fine Sunkist Growers' recipes.

¾ cup sugar
3 tablespoons cornstarch
¾ cup water
½ cup fresh orange juice

3 tablespoons fresh lemon juice
1 teaspoon unsalted butter

Mix sugar and cornstarch in saucepan; stir in water. Heat until mixture boils for 2 minutes, stirring constantly. Remove from heat; add fruit juices and butter. Stir well; cool. Serve over slices of unfrosted cake, snow pudding, or any custard-type pudding where citrus flavor is desired.

One Serving	Total Recipe	
1	5	milligrams sodium
1	4	grams total fat
1	4	grams saturated fat
191	765	calories

LOW SATURATED FAT VARIATION

Follow Basic Recipe, except omit butter. *One serving: negligible saturated fat.*

CAKES

If you like cake, use it as a morale booster in your diet. Perhaps you can remember the World War I days when homemakers were taught to make one-egg and sometimes no-egg cakes. Those cakes weren't as rich and luscious as some of your best recipes, to be sure. But they were cakes; they had some very good ingredients in them—and they were morale boosters.

Now, the situation is somewhat the same in sodium- and fat-restricted cookery. *Eggs must be used sparingly and sometimes not at all* (and only as directed by your physician's instructions). In our recipes or in your own favorites, you may substitute 1 egg white for 1 egg yolk; 2 whites for 1 egg; or 3 whites for 2 eggs (if your sodium count permits). *Ordinary baking powder, corn sirup, dark brown sugar, molasses, and all of the ready mixed cakes, cookies, and some toppings are taboo for you sodium-restricted dieters.* And for many of you the kind and amount of fat will be specified. Within the variety of our recipes there should be some for your special use.

In general, *if you have sodium but no saturated fat restrictions,* you may use recipes with hydrogenated shortenings, unsalted butter or margarine, whole egg or egg yolk (remembering to count them as part of your daily total), and whole low sodium milk. You may want to substitute shortening or unsalted butter for the oil in some of our recipes. (See page 191 for suggestions on substitution.) Using these ingredients, your products will be of finer texture and flavor—more like those before the days of restricted cookery.

If you have saturated fat restrictions, you may need to favor recipes using egg white, non-fat milk, and vegetable oil. Your cakes will be more of a muffin texture—but still mighty delicious and a welcome addition to the restricted dietary. Of course, those of you with saturated fat restrictions but no sodium restrictions may use regular non-fat milk and baking powder and add salt to your recipes.

All of these restrictions narrow the field a good deal,

yet good cakes can be made, velvety in texture, light and fine, and slightly moist on the surface to please you and the family as well. Where you must get every bit of goodness out of your ingredients, a few suggestions may speed you on your way to success for your occasional treats.

1. Read over the recipe before you begin.

2. Assemble your ingredients and equipment before you start any preparation.

3. Measure carefully. Too much is as bad as too little. Too much shortening, sugar, or baking powder may cause your cake to run over the top of pans or fall. Too much flour is apt to result in a dry or tough cake. Too little liquid can have the same effect. Our measurements are level.

4. Prepare baking pans before you do any mixing, and have the right size for the recipe. Lightly oil bottoms of pans with pastry brush and flour lightly, shaking out any extra flour. Or lightly oil and line with paper; or do a combination—whichever you prefer.

5. Bake at correct temperature, and for length of time specified in the recipe. And, of course, let oven preheat while you are mixing ingredients.

6. Test for doneness at minimum time. Press cake lightly with finger tip; if cake is done it will spring back.

7. Remove cake from oven and let stand 10 minutes. Loosen sides with spatula; tip and turn gently, and invert onto rack.

8. Let cake cool, and spread with icing and filling.

BASIC LOW SODIUM TWO-EGG CAKE
12 Servings

2 cups *sifted* cake flour
2 teaspoons low sodium baking powder
1⅓ cups sugar
½ cup vegetable shortening
¾ cup low sodium non-fat milk
1 teaspoon vanilla *or* 2 teaspoons grated lemon rind
2 medium eggs, unbeaten

Mix and sift flour, baking powder, and sugar. Add shortening, milk, and flavoring. Beat for 2 minutes (300 strokes). Add eggs and beat for 2 minutes longer. Bake in 2 lightly greased and floured 8-inch layer pans, at 375° (moderate) oven for 20 to 30 minutes, or until cake springs back when finger-tested. Let cool 10 minutes;

loosen sides with spatula and turn onto rack.

One Serving	Total Recipe	
13	151	milligrams sodium
9	113	grams total fat
9	111	grams saturated fat
238	2858	calories

BASIC LOW SATURATED FAT CAKE
12 Servings

2¼ cups *sifted* cake flour
3 teaspoons low sodium baking powder
1¼ cups sugar
3 medium egg whites

½ cup vegetable oil
¾ cup low sodium non-fat milk
1 teaspoon vanilla *or*
2 teaspoons grated lemon rind

Mix and sift flour, baking powder, and ¾ cup of the sugar. In a large bowl, beat egg whites until foamy; add remaining sugar gradually, beating until mixture forms stiff peaks. Make a well in the dry ingredients and add in order, oil, ½ cup of the milk, and flavoring. Blend; beat 150 strokes (1 minute at medium speed). Add remaining milk and beat an additional 150 strokes (1 minute). Pour batter slowly into the meringue, gently folding until completely blended. Fold, do not stir. Turn batter into 2 lightly oiled and floured 8-inch layer pans. Bake at 375° (moderate) oven for 20 to 30 minutes, or until cake springs back when finger-tested. Let cool 10 minutes; loosen sides with spatula and turn onto rack.

One Serving	Total Recipe	
13	154	milligrams sodium
9	112	grams total fat
negligible	negligible	grams saturated fat
239	2865	calories

One serving: 2 teaspoons vegetable oil.

VARIATIONS FOR BASIC TWO-EGG OR LOW SATURATED FAT CAKE

CUPCAKES OR LOAF CAKE: These Basic Recipes may also be used for cupcakes or loaf cake. Bake cupcakes at 375° (moderate) oven, 15 to 25 minutes; make loaf cake (9 x 9 x 2-inch pan) at 350° (moderate) oven, 45 to 60 minutes.

GLAZED NUT: Bake in 9-inch square pan in 350° (moderate) oven for 45 to 60 minutes or until done. Remove from oven and spread with glaze made from the following ingredients:

2 tablespoons melted, unsalted butter *or* vegetable oil	¼ cup chopped walnuts
	1 teaspoon cake flour
	1 teaspoon water
¼ cup light brown sugar	

Return to oven and bake 5 minutes longer.

ORANGE: Substitute ⅔ cup orange juice for milk in Basic Recipe. Add 1 tablespoon lemon juice to liquids; and 1 tablespoon grated orange peel to dry ingredients. Bake as for Basic Recipe.

PINK AND WHITE: Divide batter in half. Add ¼ teaspoon (or more) red vegetable coloring to one portion. Spoon into 9-inch square pan, alternating white and pink batter. Bake as for Loaf Cake.

PLANTATION MARBLE: Decrease sugar to 1 cup and omit vanilla in Basic Recipe. Divide batter in half. To one portion, add the following ingredients that have been well mixed:

¼ cup light brown sugar	½ teaspoon cloves
	½ teaspoon nutmeg
1 teaspoon cinnamon	

Spoon into 9-inch square loaf pan, alternating white and spice. Bake as outlined for Loaf Cake.

SPICE: Follow Basic Recipe and add to dry ingredients, 1 teaspoon cinnamon, 1 teaspoon ground cloves, and ½ teaspoon allspice. Bake as layer or loaf cake as outlined before.

BASIC ONE-EGG CAKE
9 Servings

1½ cups *sifted* cake flour	vegetable shortening
½ cup sugar	½ cup low sodium non-fat milk
1 tablespoon low sodium baking powder	1 whole egg *or* 2 egg whites
⅓ cup vegetable oil *or*	½ teaspoon vanilla

Mix and sift flour, sugar, and baking powder into large mixing bowl. Make a well and add remaining ingredients. Beat enough to thoroughly blend. Pour and spread batter in lightly oiled and floured 9-inch layer or loaf pan. Bake in 375° (moderate) oven, 20 to 30 minutes. Let cool 10 minutes; loosen sides with spatula and turn onto rack. Serve warm with fresh fruit topping or a fruit sauce (page 242) or divide into halves and frost.

One Serving With egg whites and oil Without sauce or icing	One Serving With whole egg and shortening	
12	9	milligrams sodium
8	6	grams total fat
negligible	6	grams saturated fat
184	166	calories

One serving, with oil: 1¾ teaspoons vegetable oil.

VARIATIONS FOR BASIC ONE-EGG CAKE

APPLE UPSIDE-DOWN CAKE: Arrange 1½ cups thinly sliced apples in a lightly oiled, deep 9-inch pie plate. Sprinkle with ¼ cup sugar mixed with 1 teaspoon of cinnamon or caraway seed. Pour and spread Basic Recipe batter over fruit. Bake in 375° (moderate) oven, 20 to 30 minutes. Allow to cool 10 minutes; then loosen sides of cake with spatula and turn onto serving plate. Serve warm with Whipped Cream" Topping (page 244).

For *Cherry Upside-Down Cake,* use one No. 2 can tart, pitted red cherries (drained). Substitute cherry juice for milk in Basic Recipe and reduce sugar by 1 tablespoon; omit cinnamon.

For *Pineapple Upside-Down Cake,* substitute 1¼ cups crushed pineapple (drained) and sprinkle pineapple with ⅓ cup light brown sugar. Instead of cinnamon, flavor with 5 drops Angostura Aromatic Bitters.

BLUEBERRY CAKE: Pour Basic Recipe batter into pan. Cover with ½ to 1 cup blueberries. Sprinkle with ¼ cup sugar mixed with ½ teaspoon of cinnamon. Bake as for Basic Recipe.

HOT MILK SPONGE CAKE
12 Squares

This sponge cake recipe is simple to make, but has good results. The secret of any sponge cake is beating very well to incorporate just as much air as possible. We have added some baking powder to make up for the decreased amount of eggs. This recipe may be used only by those with whole egg allowance.

2 eggs
1 cup sugar
1 teaspoon vanilla
1 cup *sifted* cake flour
2 teaspoons low sodium baking powder
½ cup hot low-sodium non-fat milk

Beat eggs very well, until thick and light in color. Then beat in sugar and vanilla. Mix and sift flour and baking powder; add, alternately with the hot milk, to the egg mixture.

Bake in lightly oiled 9-inch loaf pan in 350° (moderate) oven for about 30 minutes.

One Serving	Total Recipe	
12	148	milligrams sodium
1	12	grams total fat
1	11	grams saturated fat
111	1332	calories

FROSTINGS AND FILLINGS

BASIC BUTTER FROSTING

This recipe is for those of you who have unsalted butter on your diet lists. Otherwise, use Low Saturated Fat Variation (page 242).

2 cups *sifted* confectioners' sugar
¼ cup soft unsalted butter or unsalted margarine
2 tablespoons low sodium non-fat milk
1 teaspoon vanilla

Blend sugar and butter (have it at room temperature). Stir in milk and flavoring. (Flavoring may be altered to suit.) Stir until smooth.

Total Recipe	
7	milligrams sodium
45 (all saturated fat)	grams total fat
1398	calories

VARIATIONS

BROWNED BUTTER: Follow Basic Recipe except brown butter in skillet before blending with sugar.

COFFEE BUTTER FROSTING: Substitute double-strength coffee for milk in the Basic Recipe.

FRUIT BUTTER FROSTING: Substitute fruit juice for milk.

LOW SATURATED FAT VARIATION

Substitute 1 tablespoon vegetable oil for butter; increase milk to ¼ cup. Or use 2 tablespoons Corn Oil Spread (page 167) with 3 tablespoons low sodium non-fat milk. Adjust to desired thickness by adding a few drops more of milk. *These variations are negligible in saturated fat content.*

APRICOT FILLING AND ICING

1⅓ tablespoons gelatin
½ cup apricot nectar
1½ teaspoons Calcium Sucaryl solution
2 cups cooked apricots, puréed
Dash Angostura Aromatic Bitters
¼ cup low sodium non-fat dry milk powder
⅓ cup cooked apricots, purée and juice
¼ cup lemon juice
6 cooked apricot halves

Put gelatin, nectar, and Sucaryl in top of double boiler and let stand 5 minutes. Then place over low heat, stirring constantly until gelatin mixture is dissolved. Pour into mixing bowl; combine with 2 cups apricot purée and bitters. Chill in refrigerator until just firm enough to spread. Cover one layer of cake with one-half gelatin mixture. Now put ¼ cup milk powder into small mixing bowl; add ⅓ cup apricot purée and lemon juice. Beat with an electric beater until stiff or with a rotary beater until foamy. Fold mixture into remaining gelatine; blend thoroughly but handle lightly. Place the second layer of cake on top of first one. Spread top and sides with gelatin-whip mixture. Chill in refrigerator until set. Decorate with apricot halves at time of serving.

Total Recipe	
54	milligrams sodium
2	grams total fat
negligible	grams saturated fat
848	calories

VARIATION

Substitute ¼ cup sugar for Sucaryl where lower calorie icing is not desired.

FOAMY TOPPING

¼ cup low sodium non-   2 tablespoons sugar
  fat dry milk powder   1 tablespoon lemon
¼ cup water   juice

Combine ingredients in small bowl. Beat vigorously with rotary or electric beater until of a thick, foamy consistency. Combine with fresh or frozen fruit as cake topping.

Total Recipe
Without fruit
        9   milligrams sodium
   negligible   grams fat
      210   calories

VARIATION

Combine with 1 cup cut-up berries, apricots, peaches, or pineapple bits. Fold in ¼ cup chopped walnuts. This is a luscious dessert in itself, but may be used for cake topping too.

Vanilla, 6 drops Angostura Bitters, rum, or almond extract may be added for flavor variation.

LEMON FILLING

1 cup sugar   ¼ cup lemon juice
2½ tablespoons flour   1 egg, slightly beaten
1 tablespoon grated   1 teaspoon unsalted
  lemon rind or lemon   butter
  peel

Mix sugar and flour; add lemon rind and juice, then egg. Melt butter; add mixture and cook, stirring constantly, until it boils. Cool. Orange juice and rind may be substituted for lemon.

Total Recipe
       72   milligrams sodium
       10   grams total fat
        9   grams saturated fat
      958   calories

LOW SATURATED FAT VARIATION

Omit egg, increase flour to 3½ tablespoons, and substitute oil for butter. *Total recipe: negligible saturated fat.*

"WHIPPED CREAM" TOPPING

1 cup double strength low sodium non-fat milk (6 tablespoons powder to 1 cup water)	2 teaspoons gelatin
	1½ tablespoons cold water
	¼ cup sugar
	1 teaspoon vanilla

Scald milk. Soak gelatin in cold water. Combine scalded milk, sugar, and gelatin. Stir until dissolved. Place in refrigerator and allow to jell. Whip with rotary beater until consistency of whipped cream. Add vanilla and whip again. Use as topping for cream pies and puddings as well as spread for cakes.

Total Recipe
16	milligrams sodium
negligible	grams total fat
210	calories

VARIATIONS

One tablespoon sherry may be used in place of vanilla for flavor change.

Imitation banana extract, peppermint, or almond may also be used for flavoring, allowing 1 teaspoon as with vanilla.

COOKIES

In the beginning days of restricted cookery, when you are trying to get used to the many prohibitions, you may wonder if you will ever be able to turn out any of your specialties again, cookies included. The answer is an unequivocal "yes." Your baked goods may go through many changes, to be sure, but you will add adaptations as you feel more at home with the limitations.

There are quite a few good basic cooky recipes which can be made quickly and with few ingredient changes. These are good starters to give a lift to what might otherwise be a pretty drab meal, or for between-meal munching, if allowed.

APPLE-DATE BARS
20 Cookies

When you want a hearty cooky, one that will keep fresh for some time, and a "quickie," try a fruit bar recipe.

First of all, you will want to make your filling, so that it may cool while you are completing the rest of your preparations.

1½ cups cut-up *sun-dried* dates	oil
½ cup applesauce	¼ cup light brown sugar
¼ cup sugar	¾ cup sugar
1 cup water	1½ cups *sifted* all-purpose flour
½ teaspoon caraway or cinnamon	1½ cups rolled oats
3 tablespoons vegetable	

Mix first five ingredients together in saucepan and place over low heat. Stir constantly until mixture is about the consistency of mayonnaise (5 minutes). Set aside to cool. Put oil and sugars into bowl; blend. Stir in flour and oats. Mix so that all are blended. Place ½ mixture in lightly oiled and floured oblong pan. Pat mixture to evenly cover bottom of pan. Spread with cooled filling and cover with other half crumb mixture. Pat lightly and bake in 400° (hot) oven until a golden brown.

One Cooky	Total Recipe	
1	27	milligrams sodium
3	55	grams total fat
negligible	negligible	grams saturated fat
163	3265	calories

One cooky: ½ teaspoon vegetable oil.

BANANA OATMEAL COOKIES
42 Cookies

We are indebted to Miss Grace Fowler, Nutritionist, San Joaquin County Heart Association, for this interesting variation of the standard oatmeal cooky. Hearty, and with-

out egg, it should be a plus contribution to many readers.

½ cup sugar
1½ cups *sifted* all-pur-
    pose flour
¼ teaspoon cinnamon
¼ teaspoon nutmeg
¼ teaspoon mace

¼ cup vegetable oil
⅓ cup water
1 cup mashed bananas
1¾ cups rolled oats
½ cup chopped walnuts

Sift together dry ingredients. Combine oil, water, and mashed bananas; add to dry ingredients. Add rolled oats and walnuts; stir until thoroughly blended. Drop by teaspoonfuls onto lightly oiled baking sheet. Bake in 350° (moderate) oven, 8 to 15 minutes. Allow space on baking sheet for these cookies to spread. (Puréed fruits, as apricots and peaches, may be substituted for the banana.)

One Cooky	Total Recipe	
negligible	11	milligrams sodium
2	101	grams total fat
negligible	negligible	grams saturated fat
59	2492	calories

One cooky: ¼ teaspoon vegetable oil.

BUTTERSCOTCH BROWNIES
16 Squares

A tested recipe from the Home Service Department of Corn Products Refining Company.

1 cup light brown sugar
¼ cup vegetable oil
1 egg (or 2 egg whites)
½ cup chopped walnuts

1 teaspoon vanilla
⅔ cup *sifted* cake flour
1 teaspoon low sodium
    baking powder

Combine sugar and vegetable oil in mixing bowl. Add egg and beat well. Add chopped nuts and vanilla. Fold in mixed and sifted dry ingredients. Bake in lightly oiled pan (8 x 8 x 2 inches) in 350° (moderate) oven, 25 to 35 minutes. Cut into squares while warm.

One Square With whole egg	One Square With egg whites	
8	10	milligrams sodium
6	6	grams total fat
negligible	negligible	grams saturated fat
122	119	calories

One square: ¾ teaspoon vegetable oil.

VARIATIONS

Omit nut meats when plain, chewy brownie is your choice. Substitute ½ cup *sun-dried* raisins for nut meats.

CINNAMON ROUNDS
48 Cookies

⅓ cup egg whites
2 cups confectioners' sugar
½ teaspoon grated lemon rind

½ teaspoon cinnamon
2 cups mixed nuts (walnuts, almonds), ground fine

Beat egg whites until stiff but not dry. Gradually add sugar, blending after each addition. Add lemon rind; continue to beat until completely blended (about 5 minutes). Reserve ¾ cup mixture for filling. Blend together cinnamon and ground nuts; fold into remaining egg white mixture. If batter is too soft to roll, let stand at room temperature until sufficiently stiff to handle. Roll out about ⅛-inch thick on cloth-covered board. (Use confectioners' sugar rubbed on cloth to keep from sticking.) Cut into rounds with cooky cutter. Place ½ teaspoon reserved mixture on center of each round. Bake on lightly oiled baking sheet in 350° (moderate) oven about 12 minutes.

One Cooky	Total Recipe	
3	128	milligrams sodium
3	141	grams total fat
negligible	negligible	grams saturated fat
53	2528	calories

DATE-WALNUT BARS
30 Bars

¾ cup *sifted* all-purpose flour
1 cup sugar
¼ teaspoon low sodium baking powder
½ cup vegetable oil
3 medium egg whites

½ teaspoon vanilla
1 cup (7¼-oz. pkg.) *sun-dried* dates, finely cut
1 cup (or less) chopped walnuts

Mix and sift first three ingredients. Make a well and add in order, vegetable oil, egg whites, and vanilla. Beat until smooth. Add dates and chopped walnuts; mix well. Turn into lightly oiled baking pan (12 x 7 x 2 inches).

Bake in 350° (moderate) oven 20 to 25 minutes. Cut into bars while warm. Dust lightly with confectioners' sugar, if desired.

One Bar	Total Recipe	
5	147	milligrams sodium
6	178	grams total fat
negligible	negligible	grams saturated fat
109	3267	calories

One bar: ¾ teaspoon vegetable oil.

DIETETIC CORN FLAKE DREAMS
50 Cookies

Thanks to Kay Chambers, who was always experimenting for the Buff of this book, we have many delectable conversion recipes. This is a great favorite with dieter and the regulars.

3 medium egg whites
⅞ cup sugar
1 teaspoon lemon extract

1½ cups low sodium dietetic corn flakes
½ cup chopped walnuts

Beat egg whites until stiff; gradually add sugar, a few tablespoons at a time, beating after each addition. Add flavoring and beat. Fold in corn flakes and nut meats. Drop by teaspoonful on lightly oiled baking sheet. Bake in 275° (slow) oven about 25 minutes until golden brown and "set."

One Cooky	Total Recipe	
3	145	milligrams sodium
1	32	grams total fat
negligible	negligible	grams saturated fat
24	1190	calories

EGGLESS FRUIT BARS
18 Bars

¼ cup vegetable oil
½ cup honey
1 teaspoon vanilla
1½ cups *sifted* all-purpose flour
1½ teaspoons low sodium baking powder

1 cup apricot purée
½ cup chopped walnuts
1 teaspoon cinnamon
2 tablespoons confectioners' sugar

Stir together first three ingredients. Sift flour and baking powder. Gradually add to first mixture, alternating with fruit purée. (We use strained baby fruit for quickness.) Mix well after each addition. Stir in nuts. Bake in lightly oiled baking pan (12 x 7 x 2 inches) in 350° (moderate) oven about 30 minutes. Let cool in pan. Cut in bars; then sift over top the blended and sifted cinnamon and confectioners' sugar.

One Bar	Total Recipe	
2	30	milligrams sodium
5	91	grams total fat
negligible	negligible	grams saturated fat
121	2177	calories

One bar: ⅔ teaspoon vegetable oil.

MERINGUE KISSES
36 Kisses

3 egg whites (room temperature)
1 cup sifted sugar

1 teaspoon vinegar
1 teaspoon vanilla

Beat egg whites until they form pointed peaks. Add sugar, 2 tablespoons at a time; beat after each addition. Add vinegar and vanilla and beat until meringue forms stiff peaks.

Lay smooth wrapping paper or aluminum foil on baking sheet; do not oil. Drop mixture onto paper by heaping teaspoonfuls. Bake in 250° (very slow) oven, 25 to 30 minutes, until a pale cream color. Outside will be hard, inside slightly soft; must hold shape. Remove at once from paper and cool on cake rack.

One Meringue Kiss	Total Recipe	
4	141	milligrams sodium
negligible	negligible	grams total fat
23	816	calories

PEANUT COOKIES
36 Cookies

1 egg (or 2 egg whites)
⅔ cup sugar
1 teaspoon water
1 tablespoon all-purpose flour

½ teaspoon low sodium baking powder
1 cup finely ground, unsalted, roasted peanuts

Beat egg until lemon-colored (egg whites until stiff). Gradually beat in sugar and water. Mix flour and baking powder; gently fold into mixture with rubber spatula. Add peanuts, blending gently but thoroughly. Drop by tea-spoonfuls, 2 inches apart, on ungreased wrapping paper or foil on baking sheet. Bake in 325° (slow) oven, 8 to 15 minutes.

One Cooky	Total Recipe	
With	*whole egg*	
2	76	milligrams sodium
2	69	grams total fat
negligible	6	grams saturated fat
40	1423	calories

RYE HAPPIES
36 Cookies

This recipe will be a boon to dieters looking for a goody low in saturated fat. We are indebted to Fisher Flouring Mills Company for permission to adapt.

½ cup rye flour, unsifted
½ cup rolled oats
½ teaspoon low sodium baking powder
¾ cups coarsely chopped walnuts

⅓ cup vegetable oil
½ cup sugar
½ cup light brown sugar, firmly packed
1 teaspoon vanilla
3 egg whites

Mix flour, oats, baking powder, and walnuts. Combine oil, sugars, vanilla, and egg whites in mixing bowl; beat until free from all lumps. Stir in dry ingredients. Bake in lightly oiled 9-inch square pan in 350° (moderate) oven, 30 to 35 minutes. Cool in pan; then cut in squares. You may dust with powdered sugar if desired. Store in covered jar in cool place.

One Cooky	Total Recipe	
5	174	milligrams sodium
4	125	grams total fat
negligible	negligible	grams saturated fat
63	2275	calories

One cooky: ⅓ teaspoon *vegetable oil.*

SPICED WINE COOKIES WITH RAISINS
36 Cookies

We are indebted to the Home Advisory Service of the Wine

Institute, San Francisco, for this delicious cooky.

2 cups *sifted* all-purpose flour	1⅓ cups light brown sugar
2 teaspoons low sodium baking powder	¼ cup vegetable oil
¼ teaspoon cinnamon	¼ cup California muscatel
¼ teaspoon nutmeg	½ cup chopped walnuts
1 egg (or 2 egg whites)	½ cup *sun-dried* raisins

Mix and sift first four ingredients. Beat eggs; add sugar and oil. Stir until well blended. Add sifted dry ingredients to egg mixture alternately with wine. Stir in walnuts and raisins. Drop from teaspoon onto lightly oiled baking sheet. Bake in 400° (hot) oven, 10 to 12 minutes.

One Cooky	Total Recipe	
With whole egg		
5	185	milligrams sodium
3	96	grams total fat
negligible	6	grams saturated fat
86	3096	calories

One cooky: ⅓ teaspoon vegetable oil.

VARIATIONS

White port or sherry may be substituted for muscatel.

One cup unsalted shredded coconut may be substituted for nuts and raisins if saturated fats are not restricted.

SUGAR COOKIES
—GRANDMOTHER'S VARIETY
30 Cookies

1¼ cups *sifted* all-purpose flour	⅓ cup vegetable oil
1 teaspoon low sodium baking powder	½ cup sugar
¼ teaspoon nutmeg (optional)	2 egg whites
	1 teaspoon lemon juice
	½ teaspoon lemon peel

Mix and sift first three ingredients. Combine oil and sugar in mixing bowl. Add unbeaten egg whites, one at a time, beating well after each addition. Add lemon juice and peel. Add sifted dry ingredients all at once; blend well. Shape dough into little balls, about ¾ inch in diameter. Dip balls into granulated sugar. Place balls, sugar side up, 3 inches apart, on lightly oiled baking sheet. Press with a flat-bottom glass covered with a damp cloth until dough is ⅛-

inch thick. Or crisscross with tines of fork. Bake in 375°
(moderate) oven, 8 to 10 minutes. Remove from baking
sheet at once. Cool on cake rack.

One Cooky	Total Recipe	
3	98	milligrams sodium
3	75	grams total fat
negligible	negligible	grams saturated fat
61	1821	calories

One cooky: ½ teaspoon vegetable oil.

VARIATIONS

Sherry may be substituted for lemon juice; vanilla may
also be used as the flavoring.

Balls may be lightly dipped in finely ground nut meats.

Balls may be dipped in cocoa or chocolate if saturated
fats are not restricted.

One egg may be used in place of egg whites if diet allows.

WHEAT GERM DROP COOKIES
36 Cookies

*Another San Joaquin County Heart Association tested
recipe.*

2¼ cups whole wheat flour	½ cup wheat germ
1 teaspoon nutmeg	½ cup honey
1 teaspoon cinnamon	¼ cup vegetable oil
2 teaspoons low sodium baking powder	¾ cup water, less 2 tablespoons

Sift flour, nutmeg, cinnamon, and baking powder. Add
wheat germ and blend. Combine honey, oil, and water. Add
to other ingredients; blend and beat until well mixed. Drop
by teaspoonfuls onto lightly oiled baking sheet. Bake in
350° (moderate) oven, 8 to 15 minutes until golden
brown.

One Cooky	Total Recipe	
1	26	milligrams sodium
2	65	grams total fat
negligible	negligible	grams saturated fat
56	2017	calories

One cooky: ⅓ teaspoon vegetable oil.

PASTRY

You need make no apologies for your pastries. They should be as tender and flaky—and as flavorsome too—as were your products before the restricted dietary.

True, you will not be able to add salt if sodium is restricted, but a little sugar or spice, depending on the flavor of the filling, will help to make your pastry unique. Try a dash of cinnamon or nutmeg with squash, or a little caraway with apple.

Another trick to add flavor to your pastry is to replace some of the liquid with fruit juice. When you make cherry pie, add some cherry juice to your pastry. Ditto for pineapple.

Invest in a deep-dish pie plate, or "flavor saver," as it is sometimes called. Then, the next time you bake an apple pie, after you have sealed the two crusts, make three or four slits around the outer rim, just below the seal. While the pie is baking, some of the flavorsome juices will flow out and give the outer edge of crust the most delicious flavor. The deep plate will protect your oven.

To prevent soaking of lower crusts in custard-type pies, we advise a 400° to 425° (hot) oven.

For a shiny top on your pies, brush lightly with low sodium non-fat milk before baking.

We have included three recipes for pastry—all meeting the requirements of sodium or saturated fat restrictions. Vegetable oil pastry is tender and flaky, and so easy to make—and delicious enough for anyone to enjoy, too.

Of course, you may prefer to use your own recipes for pastry. *Just omit salt, if you are on sodium restriction, and substitute ½ teaspoon sugar. If you are on saturated fat restriction, you will have to omit solid (hydrogenated) shortening and use a vegetable oil pastry.*

Our recipes are for 9-inch pies unless otherwise noted.

VEGETABLE OIL PASTRY
6 Servings
(For 1 two-crust pie)

Vegetable Oil Pastry is a quick pastry method, with no guessing as to cutting in shortening or how much liquid to add.

2 cups *sifted* all-purpose flour	½ cup vegetable oil
½ teaspoon sugar	¼ cup low sodium non-fat milk

Mix flour and sugar; add oil and milk all at once. Stir quickly, until dough "cleans" bowl. Pat into round ball and roll between wax paper squares. Fit to pan, reserving ½ for top crust.

One Serving	Total Recipe	
1	6	milligrams sodium
19	114	grams total fat
negligible	negligible	grams saturated fat
304	1824	calories

One serving: 4 teaspoons vegetable oil.

WHOLE WHEAT PASTRY
6 Servings
(For 1 two-crust pie)

We are indebted to Fisher Flouring Mills Company for this tested recipe, which we have adapted for dietary use.

1½ cups 100 per cent whole wheat flour, unsifted
1 teaspoon low sodium baking powder
½ cup vegetable oil
½ cup low sodium non-fat milk
⅓ cup (more or less) 100 per cent whole wheat flour for pastry board

Mix flour and baking powder. Beat or whip milk and oil together to blend. Add to flour mixture all at once; stir with fork until mixture leaves sides of bowl. Turn onto board sprinkled with ⅓ cup whole wheat flour; press into ball. Divide into 2 pieces; roll out. Or put ball between wax paper squares and roll to desired size.

One Serving	Total Recipe	
1	7	milligrams sodium
19	114	grams total fat
negligible	negligible	grams saturated fat
228	1369	calories

One serving: 4 teaspoons vegetable oil.

CORN FLAKE CRUST
6 Servings
(For 1 crust, 8-inches)

1 cup crushed low sodium dietetic corn flakes
⅓ cup vegetable oil
¼ cup sugar

Roll or grind corn flakes to make generous cupful. Combine with vegetable oil and sugar. Press crust firmly on bottom and sides of pan; chill crust. It is not necessary to bake before filling; it may be chilled in refrigerator for later use. However, you may bake at once in 375° (moderate) oven, 15 minutes. After it is chilled or baked, fill with any previously cooked custard-type filling or fresh or dried fruit filling. Top with meringue if sodium allowance permits. Delicious, too, with a chiffon-type pie.

One Serving	Total Recipe	
	Crust only	
negligible	2	milligrams sodium
12	73	grams total fat
negligible	negligible	grams saturated fat
156	937	calories

One serving: 2⅔ teaspoons vegetable oil.

PIES

APPLE PIE
6 Servings

Vegetable Oil Pastry (page 253)
¾ cup sugar
2 tablespoons flour
1 teaspoon cinnamon
¼ teaspoon nutmeg
6 medium apples, peeled and sliced
3 tablespoons vinegar

Line pie plate with ½ of pastry. Mix sugar, flour, and spices. Alternate layers of sliced apples with sprinkling of sugar-mix, arranging so that apples are piled slightly higher toward center of pan. Sprinkle with vinegar. Wet edges of undercrust, cover with upper crust, and press edges together. Prick several places with fork. Bake in 425° (hot) oven, 45 to 55 minutes.

One Serving	Total Recipe	
2	12	milligrams sodium
20	117	grams total fat
negligible	negligible	grams saturated fat
486	2914	calories

One serving: 4 teaspoons vegetable oil.

APPLE PIE VARIATIONS

Almost as infinite as the imagination of the cook. With highly flavored apples, only a whiff of cinnamon is necessary. But with market-fresh apples, lemon juice and rind may be substituted for vinegar to point up flavor. Caraway may be used in place of cinnamon. And rum or a few drops of Angostura Aromatic Bitters may even be used for extra flavor.

FRESH FRUIT PIE VARIATIONS

Taste-ticklers to be sure, but watch those calories if you have to consider overweight. Follow method outlined in recipe for Apple Pie. Sprinkle flour-sugar mixture over fruit; omit vinegar; add spices if desired. Bake in 425° (hot) oven for 45 to 55 minutes. Reduce baking time 10 minutes if you use canned fruit.

Fruit	Quantity	Sugar	Flour
Apricot	3 cups, sliced	1 cup	2 tablespoons
Berry	3 cups	1 cup	3 tablespoons
Cherry	3 cups, pitted	¾ cup	2 tablespoons
Peach	3 cups, sliced	¾ cup	2 tablespoons
Rhubarb	3 cups, cut	1½ cups	2 tablespoons

CRANBERRY PIE
6 Servings

Put into a saucepan . .   2 cups washed and cleaned cranberries
½ cup sugar
¼ cup water

Cook about 5 minutes until skins begin to burst. Mash through large colander.

Meanwhile, put into a
   measuring cup . . . .   1 tablespoon gelatin
¼ cup cold water

Let stand about 5 minutes until softened. Dissolve by standing cup in bowl of hot water. Now blend cranberry with gelatin.

Add . . . .   2 egg whites, beaten stiff but not dry

Fold these in with . . .   2 teaspoons lemon juice
1 teaspoon lemon rind
¼ cup sugar

Fill a baked 8-inch pie shell and let stand in refrigerator until set. Allow at least 4 hours for this.

One Serving	Total Recipe	
Without pie crust		
17	99	milligrams sodium
negligible	2	grams total fat
negligible	negligible	grams saturated fat
125	752	calories

VARIATIONS

Puréed apricots, peaches, and prunes are other fruits particularly flavorsome in this recipe.

GREEN TOMATO MINCEMEAT
20 Pints

1 peck green tomatoes (8 quarts)
½ peck apples (4 quarts)
½ pound suet (optional)
2 tablespoons cinnamon
6 cups light brown sugar
½ tablespoon cloves
1 tablespoon nutmeg
3 pounds *sun-dried* raisins
¾ cup vinegar

Chop—or put through meat chopper adjusted to coarse knife—tomatoes, apples, and suet. Put in large kettle. Add remaining ingredients. Cook very slowly until tender (about 2 to 3 hours). Bottle in sterilized jars. Allow 1 pint per pie (6 servings). *Omit suet if restricted in saturated fats.*

One Pint	Total Recipe	One Pint	Total Recipe	
Without suet or pie crust		*With suet; without pie crust*		
45	893	50	1005	milligrams sodium
2	35	12	246	grams total fat
neg.	neg.	10	211	grams saturated fat
558	1152	654	13072	calories

MOCK CHERRY PIE
6 Servings

We are indebted to Miss Kathleen Piper of Lynn, Massachusetts, for this recipe. The tart flavor makes it combine well with a bland menu. Serve it once, and we are sure that it will be a favorite with the entire family.

Combine	1 cup cranberries, cut in halves ½ cup seedless *sun-dried* raisins 1 cup sugar 1 tablespoon flour
Mix and add	½ cup water ½ teaspoon almond flavoring

Bake between two crusts, or, for more partylike fashion, with a lattice top. Bake pie on bottom shelf in 425° (hot) oven for 15 minutes. Change to middle shelf and continue cooking until fruit is tender (about 20 to 30 minutes).

One Serving	Total Recipe	
Without pie crust		
4	21	milligrams sodium
negligible	1	gram total fat
negligible	negligible	grams saturated fat
177	1064	calories

PINEAPPLE PIE
6 Servings

2 tablespoons corn-starch	juice
2 tablespoons sugar	1 tablespoon grated lemon rind
2 cups hot, crushed pineapple	Baked pastry shell
1 tablespoon lemon	Meringue (optional)

Mix cornstarch and sugar; add to pineapple. Cook in double boiler 20 minutes, stirring constantly until thickened. Cool; add other ingredients. Fill pie shell. *If sodium count permits,* cover with meringue made of 2 egg whites, ¼ cup sugar, and 1 teaspoon vanilla (add sugar gradually, and continue beating until blended and whites are stiff; add flavoring). Let set, if no meringue is used; if meringue is added, bake in 425° (hot) oven, 4 to 4½ minutes.

One Serving	Total Recipe	
Without meringue or pie crust		
1	4	milligrams sodium
negligible	1	gram total fat
negligible	negligible	grams saturated fat
90	537	calories

SQUASH PIE
6 Servings

¼ cup sugar
½ cup light brown sugar
¼ cup flour
1 teaspoon cinnamon
½ teaspoon ginger

½ teaspoon nutmeg
2 cups cooked, strained squash (unsalted)
1 egg
1½ cups low sodium non-fat milk

Mix sugar, flour, and spice. Add to squash and mix well. Beat egg slightly and add to squash mixture. Add milk gradually. Bake in one crust in 400° (hot) oven, 30 minutes, until knife comes out clean.

One Serving	Total Recipe	
Without pie crust		
18	115	milligrams sodium
1	8	grams total fat
1	6	grams saturated fat
184	1101	calories

LOW SATURATED FAT VARIATION

Follow Basic Recipe except to substitute 2 egg whites for 1 whole egg. If no sodium restriction, use regular non-fat milk and add ½ teaspoon salt. *One serving, without pie crust: negligible saturated fat.*

14. TASTE-TICKLERS

And that's just what they are, taste-ticklers—these morale builders and vitamin boosters and fragrant delicacies of one sort or another. Their primary aim in the diet is to please highly cultivated taste buds, but they can be a plus-value nutritionally and psychologically, too.

Yes, they can make a definite and positive contribution to your emotional climate, if you are on a restricted food program. They represent the "goodies" of eating, and to be able to have at least a few of them may help you to forget or help you to accept the many prohibitions of your sodium- or fat-restricted diet.

If you are on a severely restricted program, your system goes through many changes in adapting from the old to the new food allowances. This is the time to introduce a few "treat times" for nourishment of body and soul. Mid-morning coffee or fruit juice with low sodium toast—afternoon tea with a low sodium cooky or confection—can bolster nutrition and you at the same time.

Afternoon tea is quite a custom, when you come to think of it! Too bad that in the hustle and bustle of everyday living most of us pay it such slight homage. Or—is it a shame, since so few of us brew a really good cup of tea?

Why not begin with tea, then, and go on to other beverages and some of their accompanying delicacies?

BEVERAGES

TEA

The first prerequisite in making a good cup of tea is to buy a tea of good quality. Whether you like the decisiveness of the "black varieties" or the more subtle taste of the green

is a matter of individual taste. Some of the flower blends
are just delightful and are particularly pleasing when
iced tea is to be served.

Bring water to the boiling point, meanwhile scalding out
your teapot. Prepare tea in a china, Pyrex, enamel, or
earthenware pot, allowing 1 teaspoon tea to 1 cup of water.
Put tea leaves in the teapot and pour water over them.
Now steep for 3 to 5 minutes, and strain into another pot,
if you are going to let it stand before serving. We like the
old English custom of muffling this pot in a cozy and let-
ting tea stand quietly until serving time. When serving
tea, have a pitcher of hot water on your tray, so tea may
be diluted to suit individual tastes. Flavor with rose
geranium leaves, thin slices of lemon or orange, preserved
ginger, cloves, or a piece of cinnamon, and serve with low
sodium toast or other goody.

ICED TEA

For a long, cold drink, it's hard to beat a tall glass of iced
tea or lemonade. There are some simple secrets to good
iced tea-making to guarantee a flavorsome result.

Make a tray of tea ice cubes for chilling tea, to preserve both flavor and aroma in your long drink.

Now proceed as outlined above for hot tea. Pour hot tea
in glasses filled with ¾ chopped tea ice or cubes. Sweeten
to taste and garnish as for hot tea, or with any of your
own favorites.

HOW TO MAKE GOOD COFFEE

Some like it strong and some like it weak. All coffee lovers
are agreed they want the full flavor of coffee in their
drink. Whatever the strength for your taste, you will want
your coffee to be clear and completely free of muddiness.

You just can't make good coffee in an unclean pot, so
Principle Number One is a *sparkling clean and scalded
pot.*

Start with fresh, cold water, and for each serving allow 1 standard coffee measure (or its equivalent, 2 level
measuring tablespoons) of fresh coffee to each ¾ cup of
freshly drawn water. (Yes, water does get stale.)

Use only coffee ground for your type of coffee maker.
You can get best results by using your coffee maker at
full capacity. It pays to have a small one for family use
to capitalize upon this point.

Timing is important in the making of coffee and once
you have established it, stick to it and make your coffee

that way, without further experimentation for your taste. Serve immediately after brewing, and serve it hot.

INSTANT ESPRESSO

Unbelievable but at last it's true, you can serve after-dinner coffee with a real deep-roasted, Continental flavor and no more trouble than any other instant coffee. For now espresso is instant, too—Jomar is the brand. By now it should be available in your favorite store, but if you have trouble, write to Martinson's, 190 Franklin Street, New York 13, to find out where.

CAFÉ AU LAIT

Here is your chance to have a gourmet flair to an otherwise simple meal. Serve strong, hot coffee (we like the French Market coffee with chicory for this) with an equal amount of hot low sodium non-fat milk. Pour milk and coffee into cup simultaneously—a pot in each hand. And if you want to be very authentic according to Southern custom, you will use after-dinner coffee cups (*demitasses*) instead of regular size.

ICED COFFEE

For really good iced coffee, make it double strength and pour over iced coffee cubes.

FRUIT BEVERAGES

There is nothing better than a refreshing tall fruit drink on a warm day for a pickup. Minerals, vitamins, and natural sugars of the fruits used, plus the addition of a sweetener, will ensure that energy lift.

FRUIT BEVERAGE SIRUP
1 Cup

Add ¾ cup sugar to ¾ cup boiling water and stir until sugar is dissolved, being careful not to stir sugar onto the sides of the pan, as it will form crystals. Boil over very slow fire for about 10 minutes. Cool and bottle.

One Tablespoon	Total Recipe	
negligible	negligible	milligrams sodium
none	none	grams total fat
35	558	calories

SUGGESTIONS FOR FRUIT BEVERAGES

LEMONADE (6 servings): Combine ¼ cup Fruit Beverage Sirup with ½ cup lemon juice. Add 1 quart cold water. Serve over ice.

PINEAPPLE LEMONADE (12 servings): Combine 1½ cups Fruit Beverage Sirup, ¾ cup lemon juice, and 5 cups ice water. Add 2 cups crushed pineapple. Chill thoroughly in tightly sealed jar. Strain (optional), and serve. If unable to chill, serve over ice cubes.

FRUIT PUNCH (8 servings): Combine 1 cup Fruit Beverage Sirup, 3½ cups ice water, ½ cup lemon juice, 1 cup orange juice, and 1 tablespoon grated lemon or orange rind. Chill thoroughly or serve over ice cubes. The addition of ½ cup lightly crushed berries or ½ cup pineapple chunkies is a delightful variation. Garnish each serving with 1 whole berry.

SPICED HOT CIDER
6 Large Servings

2 quarts apple cider	6 slices orange
1 tablespoon lemon rind	12 cloves
1 small cinnamon stick	

Put cider, lemon rind and cinnamon into a saucepan. Simmer slowly about 15 minutes. Top with orange slices and cloves. Remove cinnamon before serving.

One Serving	Total Recipe	
3	18	milligrams sodium
negligible	negligible	grams total fat
177	1062	calories

MILK BEVERAGES

Chocolate and cocoa may not be used if you have saturated fat restrictions. For the rest of you, make your choices from the low sodium non-fat milk-fruit or coffee combinations. Puréed apricots, peaches, or pineapple, strained berries of choice may be combined with milk and sugar or sirup (page 262) for a nutritious and tasty beverage. If you have a blender, follow directions for any milk-fruit combination of choice, always being careful to check against your list of allowables when you elect to have one of these extras. And be sure to include its count in your daily total.

REDUCER'S COFFEE MILK SHAKE
1 Serving

1 cup low sodium non-fat milk

1 teaspoon instant coffee (100 per cent pure coffee only)

1 ice cube

About ⅛ teaspoon Calcium Sucaryl

Beat in electric blender until creamy.

One Serving

7	milligrams sodium
negligible	grams total fat
87	calories

TREATS TO GO WITH BEVERAGES

Sweet bread, low sodium toast with homemade jam or jelly, toast sprinkled lightly with sugar and orange juice —all of these and other things are good for a mid-morning snack. For tea, try fruit or cinnamon toast, fruit bread or nut, or wee little pastries.

Little pastries are just what their name implies—pies filled with fruit, jam, or custard and handled as for any pie. They can be made in your fluted muffin or 3-inch individual pan, or cut with cooky cutter any desired shape.

Tarts make a particularly nice afternoon sweet, and may appear without top crusting, filled with fruit, jam or a pie filling, or with a gay little top crust in fancy design. If you use individual pudding molds or muffin tins, simply fit pastry over "their backs" and prick to prevent puffing. Put pan upside down on baking sheet and bake in a 450° (very hot) oven for 6 to 8 minutes.

CONFECTIONS

The amount of latitude you have in providing some of these taste-ticklers depends upon your specific diet limitations. Remember that everything eaten must be accounted for, and if you have a "muncher" in your family, you must not neglect to include the "in betweens" in your day's total. Where weight is also a factor, most of the suggestions in this chapter will be of little avail. On the other hand, some of you may be confronted with the problem of having a naturally small eater becoming a smaller eater through dietary restrictions. Your physician may suggest you serve 4 or 5 "meals" during the day rather than the usual 3.

APPLETS
36 Squares

2 cups unsweetened applesauce
2 cups sugar
2 tablespoons unflavored gelatin *softened in*
½ cup cold water

1½ cups mixed nuts (walnuts, pecans, almonds)
Few drops of Angostura Aromatic Bitters
¼ cup confectioners' sugar

Put applesauce through sieve; add sugar and cook until very thick (240°). Remove from heat; add gelatin, and stir thoroughly. Add nuts and flavoring. Pour into oiled pan (8 x 8 inches). Let stand overnight until firm. Cut into squares and roll in sugar.

One Square	Total Recipe	
1	22	milligrams sodium
3	111	grams total fat
negligible	negligible	grams saturated fat
85	3058	calories

FIG-NUT SWEETS
30 Pieces

This is a good candy substitute.

Cover 1 cup *sun-dried* figs with boiling water. Let stand 10 minutes. Drain and cut fine. Mix figs with 1 cup finely cut walnuts. Roll into a long piece, about 1½ inches in diameter, and slice ⅓ inch thick.

For extra richness, make a sirup of ¼ cup water, ½ cup granulated sugar. Boil until it spins a thread (228°). Dip slices into sirup while warm, and roll in ½ cup plain or toasted coconut.

One Serving	Total Recipe	
With coconut		
2	63	milligrams sodium
3	78	grams total fat
negligible	12	grams saturated fat
54	1614	calories

LOW SATURATED FAT VARIATION

Omit coconut; roll in ¼ cup confectioners' sugar.
One piece: negligible saturated fat.

MIXED FRUIT BALLS
20 Balls

A word of warning: Fruit balls are hard to keep on hand.

By this time, you've grasped the idea of using foods only in their natural forms, unless otherwise permitted. This goes for dried fruits, of course, and only the *sun-dried* variety should be used.

½ cup *sun-dried* apricots
½ cup *sun-dried* peaches
½ cup *sun-dried* pears
¼ cup *sun-dried* raisins
½ cup *sun-dried* prunes
¼ cup wheat germ
¼ cup confectioners' sugar

Put all ingredients except wheat germ and sugar through fine cut of meat grinder two times. Blend in wheat germ. Shape with hand into balls the size of a large marble. Roll lightly in ¼ cup sifted confectioners' sugar and put in covered serving bowl in refrigerator to keep cool until time of use.

One Serving	Total Recipe	
3	56	milligrams sodium
negligible	3	grams total fat
negligible	negligible	grams saturated fat
60	1207	calories

GLAZED NUTS
About 30 Pieces

2 cups sugar
1 cup boiling water
⅛ teaspoon cream of
   tartar

2 cups blanched al-
   monds, pecans, or
   walnuts (unsalted)

Cook sugar, water, and cream of tartar to boiling point. From time to time, wipe sides of pan with pastry brush or cloth dipped in cold water to prevent crystallization. Boil without stirring until sirup begins to turn lightly brown at 310° on candy thermometer. Place pan in larger pan of cold water to stop boiling at once. Remove from cold water and set in pan of hot water while dipping nuts into sirup on long pin or skewer. Or add nuts to mixture; stir to cover. Place on oiled baking sheet or waxed paper to dry.

One Serving With walnuts	Total Recipe With pecans	
negligible	2	milligrams sodium
5	158	grams total fat
negligible	negligible	grams saturated fat
95	3044	calories

VARIATIONS

Orange juice may be substituted for water. Omit cream of tartar. Or you may spice your glaze by adding 1 teaspoon cinnamon and ½ teaspoon vanilla extract. Another good variation is double strength coffee boiled with 3 cups light brown sugar to very soft ball stage (234° to 240°). Remove from heat and add 1 teaspoon corn oil; stir. Blend in nuts. Beat and pour onto lightly oiled candy plate. Cut into squares when cold.

CANDIED GRAPEFRUIT PEEL
4 Servings

For a delicious goody, try this easy confection some day soon.

Soak your washed grapefruit peel overnight in a quart of water. Drain and cover with cold water and bring to a boil; let simmer 15 minutes. Then drain and cover with water as before, and repeat the same cooking process four more times. Drain and cut peel in strips 1/4" wide. You will need enough peel to make 1 cup.

Meanwhile, put into a saucepan 1 cup sugar, 1/2 cup water, and a dash of mace. Bring to a boil and add grapefruit peel. Let cook until clear sirup appears. Remove the peel and put out on a platter to cool a little. Roll in 1/2 cup confectioners' sugar and spread on wax paper to dry.

One Serving	Total Recipe	
4	15	milligrams sodium
negligible	negligible	grams total fat
254	1016	calories

PERSIAN DELIGHTS
24 Pieces

2 packages (2 tablespoons) unflavored gelatin	Pure vegetable or fruit juice coloring
1/2 cup cold water	Flavoring
3/4 cup boiling water	1/4 cup confectioners' sugar
2 cups sugar	

Soften gelatin in cold water. Mix boiling water and sugar and stir until dissolved. Bring to a boil and add gelatin, stirring until thoroughly dissolved. Boil mixture slowly about 15 minutes. Remove from heat. Color and flavor as desired. Stir thoroughly, and pour mixture into an oblong pan, 8" x 8" x 2" (rinse in cold water first). Let stand overnight until thoroughly firm. Do not chill in refrigerator. Ease candy from sides of pan with a wet knife and spread, upside down, on a lightly sugared board (confectioners' sugar). Cut into squares and rub all sides in confectioners' sugar. Put cut pieces on a flat serving dish to avoid any stickiness. A delicious Christmas delicacy made in green and red, but delicate and delectable at any season of the year.

One Serving	Total Recipe	
negligible	6	milligrams sodium
none	none	grams total fat
72	1731	calories

PRALINES
8 Pralines

1 cup white sugar	1 cup light brown sugar
½ cup low sodium non-fat milk	1 cup pecan nut meats

Mix first three ingredients together and stir until sugar is dissolved. Cook over medium heat to the soft-ball stage (240°). Set in pan of *ice* water 3 minutes. Beat until mixture becomes slightly cloudy. Now add nut meats. When mixture is shiny, drop by spoonfuls onto greased platter or waxed paper.

One Serving	Total Recipe	
8	60	milligrams sodium
10	79	grams total fat
negligible	negligible	grams saturated fat
297	2379	calories

JELLIES, JAMS, PRESERVES

Jellies, of course, are good taste-ticklers and deserve your attention just as soon as you can get to them. Wine jellies and jams made from frozen fruits make jelly-making an any-month-of-the-year job. If the home jelly is well made, only the *very best* commercial product can compared with it. Jellies on the grocers' shelves often contain sodium citrate as a stabilizer. There might be only a trace of it, to be sure, but you will have to look to your list and your physician's instructions to find out whether or not you may use commercial jellies on your particular diet.

The Farmers' Bulletin No. 1800 of the United States Department of Agriculture, *Homemade Jellies, Jams and Preserves*, has helpful suggestions on basic principles involved in home preservation of fruit with sugar.

To get good jellies—clear, shimmering, and with finest flavor—and good preserves that are clear, tender, and shapely, you will have to work by known principles.

Cook your jellies and jams a minimum amount of time to ensure the most color and flavor. Time will vary with different fruit-sugar combinations, but will have to be sufficient to "concentrate" this sirup—change the texture of the fruit itself.

* From U.S.D.A. Farmers' Bulletin No. 1800, *Homemade Jellies, Jams and Preserves*.

Home economists have worked out many aids in this field and it is wise to follow their suggestions for thin or thick sirups, since firm and soft fruits have different sirup requirements.

You have, no doubt, been using a pectin to set your homemade jellies. Since pectin must be present with acid and sugar to make a jelly which sets successfully, you need to know which fruits are particularly rich in pectin and acid and those which may have to have pectin added. Commercial pectin is fairly high in sodium content, so again, in a very tight diet requirement you may have to make your own pectin (page 271) or use fruits which are high in pectin and acid.

Fruits rich in pectin and acid (to 1 cup juice, use ¾ to 1 cup sugar):

Apples, sour	Grapes (Eastern)
Blackberries, sour	Lemons
Crabapples	Loganberries
Cranberries	Plums (not all varieties)
Currants	Prunes, sour
Gooseberries	Quinces, sour

If you are in doubt about the pectin content, make a simple test by putting 2 teaspoons cooked fruit juice in a glass and adding an equal amount of rubbing alcohol (70 per cent or more). If the juice is high in pectin, you will get a gelatinous material in your glass. If only moderately rich in pectin, you will get a few pieces of this gelatinous material, and if poor in pectin (too poor to make a jelly), you will get only a few flaky pieces.

Now, of course, you can add pectin to your liquid juice in the proportion of 1, 2, 3 or more tablespoons to a cup of juice. You can use your pectin test for this or follow any of the good recipes you have.

Jam- and jelly-making is an easy but an exact form of cookery. You must (1) wash, scald, and drain glasses and tin covers; (2) bring mixture to boil, reduce heat, cover, and simmer when recipe specifies simmering time; (3) mix a little water with pulp in jelly bag and squeeze again if there is a slight shortage of juice; (4) be sure to measure accurately, using the same measuring cup for both dry and liquid ingredients; (5) be sure you have a full rolling boil that cannot be stirred down; (6) fill jelly glasses to ½ inch of top so there will be space between the paraffin, and cover to prevent seepage; (7) use only new paraffin. Pour ⅛ inch layer of it over jellies and jams and cover glasses with tin or tightly pasted paper covers; (8) store in cool, dry place.

HOMEMADE APPLE PECTIN EXTRACT*

Summer apples do not have sufficient pectin for such use. Sound culls or apples with surface blemishes are usable. Scrub the apples and cut out the imperfect spots, then slice thin, retaining ends and cores. For each 4 pounds of prepared apples, use 4½ pints of water for the first extraction.

Place 4 pounds apples and the water in a large pan so as to allow rapid boiling. Cover and boil for 20 minutes. Strain through 4 thicknesses of cheesecloth until the juice stops dripping.

Repeat the process, adding the same quantity of water, boiling and straining as before. The two extractions should amount to about 3 quarts. A little lemon juice may be added to the water in order to increase the amount of pectin obtained.

Boil this juice in a pan large enough so that the liquid will be 2 inches deep. Boil rapidly until the juice is reduced to ¼ of its original volume. This usually requires from 30 to 40 minutes. There should be 1½ pints of the concentrated apple juice or pectin extract. If the extract is not to be used at once, pour it while hot into hot sterilized half-pint jars, partially seal, and process on a rack in a boiling water bath for 20 minutes. Complete the seal and store in a cool dry place. Once the canned extract is open, it must be used immediately as it will not keep.

One Pint	Total Recipe	
4	12	milligrams sodium
2	6	grams total fat
negligible	negligible	grams saturated fat
309	928	calories

PORT WINE JELLY
5 6-Ounce Glasses

Wine jellies are delicious with meats, as a spread on low sodium toast, or as a garnish (to be eaten) on a huge fruit salad platter.

Simply combine 2 cups port with 3 cups sugar in a saucepan, and cook over briskly boiling water 2 minutes, until wine and sugar are thoroughly heated. Stir constantly. Now mix in ½ bottle commercial liquid pectin

*From U.S.D.A. Farmers' Bulletin No. 1800, *Homemade Jellies, Jams and Preserves.*

or ½ cup homemade pectin. Pour immediately into 5 6-ounce sterilized glasses, and seal with paraffin.

One Tablespoon	One Glass	Total Recipe	
With homemade pectin			
1	9	45	milligrams sodium
negligible	negligible	1	gram total fat
53	630	3148	calories

Burgundy, sherry, and sauterne may also be used in this recipe.

STRAWBERRY PRESERVES
1½ pints

4 cups whole washed, drained, and hulled strawberries	2 cups sugar
	2 tablespoons water
	1 teaspoon lemon juice

Combine sugar, water, and lemon juice in a 2-quart saucepan and place over low heat, bringing to a boil, stirring constantly. Add berries. Stir just enough to combine thoroughly with the sirup mixture. Bring to a rolling boil and boil just 4 minutes—be sure to time this, for good results. Remove from heat and skim carefully. Pour preserves into a shallow platter. Allow to stand a full day. (This is the real secret of this recipe.)

When the preserves are of the proper consistency, ladle into hot, sterilized jars and seal.

One Tablespoon	One-half Pint	Total Recipe	
negligible	3	8	milligrams sodium
negligible	1	3	grams total fat
negligible	negligible	negligible	grams saturated fat
37	586	1757	calories

RHUBARB PRESERVES
3 pints

2½ pounds rhubarb (about 6 cups)	1½ small unpeeled oranges, sliced
1⅓ cups crushed pineapple	1½ cups walnut meats, broken into small pieces
3½ cups sugar	

Wash rhubarb and cut into ½-inch pieces. Combine with remaining ingredients in saucepan and bring to boil, stirring occasionally. Now reduce heat and simmer, uncovered, over low heat about 1½ hours, or until like a conserve in consistency. Stir only as needed the first hour, but more frequently during last period of cooking to prevent any scorching. Remove from heat. Pour into hot, sterilized jars and seal.

One Tablespoon	One-half Pint	Total Recipe	
negligible	3	15	milligrams sodium
1	16	98	grams total fat
negligible	negligible	negligible	grams saturated fat
43	689	4136	calories

CALIFORNIAN MARMALADE
2 Pints

2 medium-sized oranges	2 cups *sun-dried* apricots
5½ cups water	3 cups granulated sugar
1 lemon	

Slice one unpeeled orange very thin. Add 2½ cups water and grated rind from lemon. Boil 1 hour. Wash apricots thoroughly. Cover with 3 cups water and boil until tender. Beat to a pulp. Add sugar, cooked orange slices, juice from second orange, and lemon juice. Boil slowly until very thick (about 1 hour). Stir frequently to prevent scorching. Pour into hot, sterilized glasses and seal with paraffin. Makes 2 pints of beautiful golden, lemon-orange-colored marmalade.

One Tablespoon	One-half Pint	Total Recipe	
1	9	35	milligrams sodium
negligible	negligible	2	grams total fat
51	814	3256	calories

RELISHES

Use cranberry jelly, sauces, and relishes for occasions other than "turkey times," when chicken, veal, and mixed dishes are your selection. Orange and cranberry have a natural affinity for each other, as you will discover in relishes, sauces, salad molds, and frozen desserts.

UNCOOKED CRANBERRY—ORANGE RELISH

Wash 1 quart cranberries. Wash and cut up 1 large orange, being sure to remove the seeds. Grind both fruits coarsely and stir in 1½ cups granulated sugar. Let stand, stirring occasionally, until sugar is dissolved, then cover loosely and keep in refrigerator. Makes 2 pints of relish.

One Tablespoon	One-half Pint	Total Recipe	
negligible	2	7	milligrams sodium
negligible	1	4	grams total fat
negligible	negligible	negligible	grams saturated fat
23	367	1477	calories

SAUCES

For an added bit of pleasurable eating, try these sauces on your menus.

COLD ORANGE SAUCE

4 Servings

This is a great favorite with lamb and duck and can be used with veal, too.

Put into a mixing bowl .	6 tablespoons pure currant jelly
	3 tablespoons sugar
	Grated rind 2 oranges
Beat about 5 minutes until ingredients are thoroughly blended.	
Add	2 tablespoons California port
	2 tablespoons orange juice
	2 tablespoons lemon juice
	Dash cayenne

Stir all together until well blended. Chill and serve.

One Serving	Total Recipe	
2	9	milligrams sodium
negligible	negligible	grams total fat
129	514	calories

CUMBERLAND SAUCE
6 Servings

"Dee-licious," with any chicken dish, veal, or duck.

6 tablespoons pure red currant jelly
4 tablespoons port
4 tablespoons orange juice
2 tablespoons mustard powder

1 teaspoon paprika
½ teaspoon ground ginger
1 teaspoon cornstarch
2 tablespoons grated orange rind

Stir jelly over low heat until melted. Blend other ingredients, add to jelly and bring to boil. Then simmer, stirring constantly, for 5 minutes. Let stand at least 1 hour before serving.

One Serving	Total Recipe	
3	16	milligrams sodium
negligible	negligible	grams total fat
72	433	calories

15. THE HOME FREEZER CONTRIBUTES TOO

The large freezing section of your refrigerator, or your home freezer, can be a real bonanza in diet cookery. It makes it possible to do in-season buying for out-of-season use. So utilized, it can make a real contribution to that fast-diminishing food dollar, and at the same time provide you with a larger selection of foods all the way around the calendar. Such foods as roasted meats, poultry, and mixed dishes can be prepared in large quantities, packaged in one-meal portions, and kept in the freezer. This gives you food insurance—a guarantee of always having on hand low sodium or low fat foods for special needs.

Imagine having melon balls for Thanksgiving or New Year's Day dinner; sliced cucumbers, dressed in vinegar, in January; corn on the cob all year long; home-grown cherries in November; chicken every month of the year at spring prices; whole dinners to take out of the freezer at a moment's notice. All of these things and more are possible—if you put your freezer to work for you in creating interesting and unusual meals. You do the planning and let it give its yield.

If you have the large storage space that a home freezer affords, or even the lesser space of a modern refrigerator cold section, try to use your energy and effort in that once-a-week extra cooking and baking to provide supplies for freezer packaging, too.

In the chapter on breads, you may remember that the suggestion was made to make enough dough in one mixing for different purposes and for use even at different times. The same principle is involved in planning, marketing, and preparing ahead to get the best use out of other foods for freezer use. If you are going to have pie for dinner, make an extra one to freeze. Or, convert the extra pastry into tart shells or four individual pies, each with a different filling. Similarly with soups and casserole dishes—double the recipes and have a substantial part of a meal "ahead." The extra effort involved in increasing a recipe is very little in comparison with the dividend you get in variety and delicacies at a later date.

Your freezer is also an asset and economizer in the wise use of leftovers. That "smidge" of soup or sauce adds special flavor to your dieter's menu when saved for future use. Of course, leftovers do require a little special care. You cannot freeze them with safety if they have been allowed to stand around for some time after initial preparation. Wrap and freeze leftover meat the day of preparation—or make it into a vegetable-meat soup, croquettes, hash, or a casserole dish. Label and freeze. And, in general, it is best not to refreeze foods.

Let your freezer simplify your shopping, too. Quantity buying can save you money and effort. You never run short, once you get the frozen food habit. Even an inexperienced cook can have a feeling of confidence with a supply of frozen foods and meals on hand. Stock up on frozen vegetables and fruits when they are offered at bargain prices, to add to your homemade foods. Frozen fruits and vegetables are clean and uniform and are halfway prepared when they come out of the freezer, so they save precious minutes at meal preparation time.

One of the problems in getting use out of frozen foods is to know just how long they may safely be stored. In the first place, try to budget your food storage and plan menus from frozen food stocks so that foods are used within the recommended storage period. Remember that long storage impairs quality. Use first the food that has been stored longest.

The following storage times are a guide for foods stored at zero Fahrenheit:

Beef, veal, and poultry—9 to 12 months
Ground meat—1 to 3 months
Cakes, angel, sponge, chiffon, baked—4 to 6 months
Cakes, shortened—2 to 6 months
Cooked meats—2 to 4 months
Fruits and vegetables—12 months
Pies:
  Chiffon with gelatin base—1 month
  Fruit—6 months
  Pumpkin—1 to 3 weeks
Pork, fish, and lamb—3 to 6 months
Sandwiches—2 to 4 weeks
  Open-face—1 to 2 weeks

In general, baked goods with any kind of filling and sandwich fillings have the shortest storage periods. Water ices and sherbets will keep indefinitely, but both flavor and texture begin to deteriorate after one month, and they may develop icy crystals if kept too long.

Fish may be kept up to 6 months but fatty fish should not be stored longer than 3 to 4 months. Lake trout gives finest flavor if used within 2 to 3 months.

Prepare and freeze chickens during the spring season, spacing your freezing so that you guarantee chicken around the calendar at spring's low prices.

If you have had your home freezer for some time you have already experimented and know about its most effective use for your own needs. No two families are exactly the same in what they want their freezers to do for them. One family may want the most economical purchasing of food to be the prime consideration; another may want it for special occasion delicacies or for hard-to-make dishes ahead of use. One use that almost everyone will agree upon is the storage of the makings of a complete dinner. However, for home use it is recommended that the foods be stored separately, not together on a tray. What a lifesaver this can be for the sodium- and fat-restricted dieter and for you, too, on the kitchen end of things! Consult your manufacturer's directions for best results from your home freezer. And above all remember that the food you take from it can only be as good as the food you put into the freezer.

FREEZE-EASY DINNER I

Suppose for one dinner for six you want to serve Tuna and Mushroom Casserole, Peas, Stuffed Baked Potatoes, Frozen Fruit Salad, Dinner Rolls, and Cherry Pie.

To prepare the dinner for freezing:

TUNA AND MUSHROOM CASSEROLE

6 Servings

Place in a lightly oiled casserole alternate layers of dietetic low sodium tuna (2 cans, 6½ oz. each) and sliced broiled mushrooms (about 1 cup slices). Cover with 2 cups low sodium Medium White Sauce (page 137) seasoned with ½ teaspoon dill, 1 teaspoon low sodium Worcestershire sauce, and dash of paprika. Top with ½ cup crumbled or

rolled dietetic low sodium corn flakes. Bake in a 350°
(moderate) oven 30 to 60 minutes, but do not overbrown
topping.

LOW SATURATED FAT VARIATION

Use Low Fat Medium White Sauce (page 137). If no sodium restriction, use regular tuna fish, regular Worcestershire sauce and corn flakes, and add 1 teaspoon salt.

STUFFED BAKED POTATOES
6 Servings

Follow recipe given on page 160. Fill one shell for the
dieter; add salt to taste for the regulars. Put a toothpick
in the special one to designate it when you take it from
the freezer. Wrap all for freezing.

PEAS

Put 1½ packages frozen peas into a single carton for the
regulars. Plan to use fresh or approved-brand dietetic
canned peas without added sodium for the sodium-restricted dieter.

FROZEN FRUIT SALAD
6 Servings

Make Basic Recipe for Molded Salad (page 177), using ¼
cup sherry in place of that amount of liquid in the recipe.
Spoon into individual molds, and wrap for freezing.

DINNER ROLLS
12 Rolls

Take ½ dough from 2-loaf Basic Bread Recipe (page
194-95) and make into a long roll. Cut into 12 slices.
Shape as desired or keep as cut. Lightly bake as directed
(page 194). Cool on rack. Put onto baking sheet or special
freezer pie plate. Wrap for freezing.

CHERRY PIE
6 Servings

Follow directions for making Cherry Pie (page 257-58),
lightly bake; cool, wrap for freezing.

Assemble the complete meal on a cooky tray if you

choose, but wrap items separately, and label (being sure
to include sodium or fat content); freeze.

To cook the dinner:

Unwrap potatoes. Arrange on a cooky sheet and place
on top shelf of oven, with Tuna and Mushroom Casserole.
Bake in 350° (moderate) oven; bake 45 minutes, or until
thoroughly heated. Serve at once. (Do not reheat or refreeze.) Place unwrapped pie and rolls (let them stand
at room temperature for 1½ hours first) on bottom shelf
of oven. Boil peas for the regulars in ¼ cup salted water
until fork-tender (8 to 20 minutes); cook fresh peas for
those with sodium restrictions. Just before serving, unmold salads on beds of lettuce greens. Garnish as desired.
For a crunchy addition, serve a plate of raw vegetable
sticks to round out this meal.

FREEZE-EASY DINNER II

Another freezer meal might consist of Soup, Meat Patties,
Corn on the Cob, Mixed Fruit Cup, Basic Cake, frosted.

To prepare the dinner for freezing:

SOUP

Bottle leftover low sodium or low fat soup in special
freezer container, and freeze.

MEAT PATTIES

Make individual Beef Patties (page 89), separating each
one with a round of laminated paper to prevent sticking.
Wrap for freezing.

CORN ON THE COB

Corn on the Cob is easily prepared for freezing. Follow
directions for your freezer for parboiling corn. Cool
quickly, and pack in freezer bags. These come in various
sizes, permitting you to freeze a single ear, 2 or 4 ears
in combination. From the standpoint of most efficient use
of space, it seems unwise to store more than 4 ears to a
package.

MIXED FRUIT CUP

For 4 servings, allow 2 cups blended fresh or combined
fresh and frozen fruits. To give flavor and texture delight

be sure to include at least 1 crunchy fruit, such as apple or pineapple. Use orange juice, apricot nectar, or liquid of choice to moisten. Sugar (or not) to taste. Pack fruits, cut in edible sizes, in a large-necked jar, especially put out for freezer storage. Pour liquid over all and cover.

BASIC CAKE

See recipe on page 237 or 238. If you want to bake and frost cake, be sure to set it in your cold section *unwrapped* for 1 hour to allow frosting to partly freeze so it will stay in place and not run. Remove from freezer, wrap, label, and put in freezer.

Now wrap other items in separate wraps, label, and put in freezer. By labeling, we mean the complete story—food name; amount and number of servings; sodium and fat content; date. Make this inventory in duplicate so you will have a copy near your work center for planning purposes.

To cook the dinner:

Let corn thaw before cooking.

Set soup container in a pan of water to speed thawing. Turn into pan to heat as soon as thawing permits. Now put meat patties on broiling rack of oven and broil at 400° until brown on one side. Turn and brown on other side. Salt the patties for the regulars. Boil the thawed corn 5 to 8 minutes, adding a *pinch* of sugar if you want to emphasize its sweetness. Let fruit cup and cake stand at room temperature to thaw. Add a beverage, low sodium bread, and unsalted butter—and your meal is ready to be served.

Before leaving these dinner meals, we want to remind you that with marked meal packages listing the menu, number of servings, and instructions for reheating, you have an entire precooked meal package and can arrange one you later put unwrapped on a shallow pan (to catch drips), and heat it in the oven, with little fuss.

Generally speaking, you will want to allow 30 to 45 minutes longer cooking time for meals right out of the freezer than for thawed food. Thawed food should be ready to eat in about 30 minutes. You will have to figure your time by the meat you are going to serve, rather than by the vegetables.

To thaw most packaged meals, allow 6 to 8 hours in the refrigerator, or 2 to 3 hours at room temperature.

Work out some kind of inventory (and usually it has to be in duplicate so that one copy can be at the freezer location and one in the kitchen for meal planning) so that you use your frozen food to best advantage.

OTHER FOODS

All kinds of goodies can be made and stored for treats and menu enrichment. Some of the foods we have found particularly adaptable are:

Low sodium low fat ice cream: Store in container and scoop out portions 20 to 30 minutes before serving time. Can also be used in an ice cream pie by softening ice cream and filling baked low sodium pie shell. Wrap and return to freezer until ready to use. A fruit sauce may be served with this if desired.

Lunch sandwiches: Make a different sandwich for each of 5 days, using such fillings as meat; low sodium cheese (if no fat restrictions); blended peanut butter (unsalted for sodium restriction; non-hydrogenated for saturated fat restriction); and pure fruit jelly; tuna (canned without added sodium for sodium restriction); ground date mix. Spread on low sodium bread, lightly "buttered" with unsalted margarine or butter, or oil spread. Sprinkle the meat sandwich with a little Bakon Yeast for gourmet flavoring. Place sandwiches in plastic boxes or sandwich bags, label, and freeze.

Sunday-night treat: Serve frozen "creamed" asparagus on low sodium toast topped with low sodium heated dietetic cheese sauce if cheese spread is allowed. *Not for* fat-restricted dieters. Truly delectable for the regulars, as well as for the dieter.

Baked apples: Bake apples as usual. Cool and set in paper cups; seal, freeze.

Apple pie: Nothing so very new about apple pies in the larder or freezer in this case. Remember the accounts of old Colonial days when the winter's supply of apple pies was baked and frozen? For longest use, bake, cool, freeze; then wrap and store.

Meat balls: Prepare your favorite way in sauce. Cool and fill freezer container.

Leftovers: Freeze the extra soup, chicken à la king, sandwich spreads, leftover turkey. They will taste wonderful next month, and the family will thank you for their spaced reappearance.

Or, combine that leftover chicken with dietetic peas

canned without added sodium, thin semolina spaghetti, and a medium low sodium white sauce. At time of serving, sprinkle each portion with 1 tablespoon low sodium grated cheese if allowed.

FACTS FOR FREEZING

1. Only the finest fruits and vegetables should be frozen and they must be fresh if you want tasteful results. *Freezing retains the quality of the food, but cannot improve it.*

2. Learn about the foods that freeze best. Some give better results than others.

3. Follow the directions for your freezer for best results. Scalding before packaging is necessary for vegetables to inactivate the enzymes that turn food dark and contribute to flavor loss, too. Fruits are usually frozen with cold sirup or crushed and coated with dry sugar.

4. Always freeze immediately after packaging. Leave packages in cold compartment (quick freeze) until solid, with every package touching a side or coil.

5. Use only recommended packaging materials if you want fine results. Wrappings must be moisture- and vapor-proof if foods are to be stored for more than one month. Cellophane, Pliofilm, aluminum or heavy laminated paper, and waxed locker paper—all fulfill this requirement. A double wrap is usually recommended for meats, fish, and poultry. Use rigid containers for fruits and other somewhat liquid foods. The large-necked jars, plastic boxes with interliners, waxed tubs—all meet the requirement here. Vegetables are usually packed in rectangular containers, with interliners of Cellophane or laminated paper. The liners are heat-sealed with a hand iron before packaging.

6. Protect all packaging materials from dust and insects.

7. If packaging material becomes brittle in the heat, place in a refrigerator for 48 hours before using.

8. Freezing jars must be clean and in perfect condition for getting best results from your frozen food.

9. A word of caution about frozen baked goods with frostings. If you want to frost any kind of baked goods before freezing (the alternative would be to frost just before use), use a confectioners' sugar or so-called "fancy type" frosting. *Don't use seven-minute or egg-white types.* They become spongy and somewhat disintegrated during storage period. No frosted cake holds up any too well in freezing, so plan to use within 3 to 4 weeks from freezing

date for best results. On the other hand, unfrosted cakes hold up very well in a freezer and may be kept for several months as indicated.

POSTSCRIPT

Consider your freezer a bank. Deposit every bit of surplus that you can manage to save. Withdraw that surplus as you have need. So conceived, the freezer can be one of the best aids available to you in restricted cookery—to provide variety in your meals, extra dollars in your pocket, and energy and smiles in your disposition.

16. YOU CAN TAKE IT WITH YOU

Many of you on sodium- and fat-restricted programs will elect to take lunch to work with you rather than put up with the frustrations of restaurant eating at peak hours. Of course, the fine restaurants in almost every city have à la carte service which can meet your need—if you have the time to wait for such service and can pay the price.

If you have decided to pack your own, you are, no doubt, considering sandwiches first of all. They are the good old stand-by of lunch boxes and make a good foundation for an adequate luncheon meal. You may remember that starches produce energy—and it is the energy-producing carbohydrates that are important for a midday meal, particularly if you are in an active occupation.

Well, what can you use? You have various breads (sodium-restricted for those with sodium restrictions, fat-restricted for those with fat restrictions) to offer variety—so let's take a look at fillings for sandwiches from the standpoint of allowables, palatability, and contribution to good nutrition.

BUTTERS AND THEIR SUBSTITUTES

If unsalted butter or margarine are on your allowable list, remember to let them stand at room temperature to make most usable. If you are restricted in saturated fats, simply substitute your Oil Spread (page 167) or special margarine, if allowed, and use as you would a butter spread. For an interesting tang, try any of the following in combination with your allowable fat: dry mustard, lemon juice and grated lemon peel; fruit juice and grated grapefruit peel; minced green bell pepper or chives; onion juice or minced onions; dried or green herbs, such as parsley, marjoram, thyme; dry wine, such as claret; or Bakon Yeast for that smoky bacon flavor; a chopped clove of garlic, or pure garlic powder; chopped onion, or pure onion powder; dill, oregano, or tarragon (allow about ¼ to 1 teaspoon herb to 4 tablespoons spread). You may want to add a half teaspoon of white wine vinegar or lemon juice to some of the herb spreads to sharpen their flavor. You will have to test-taste for these combinations as the base spread will alter the additions possible.

MEAT SANDWICHES

If you are packing a lunch for a man, it's hard to improve on a plain bread, butter, or Oil Spread, and meat sandwich. The meat allowance, it must be remembered, will have to be relatively small if you are planning to serve meat again at the evening meal. You can include it in the daily lunch box, if you are on a severe restriction program, only with the consent of your physician. In some instances, it can be substituted for an egg or other high sodium or fat food in the day's menu.

ROAST BEEF

Sliced sirloin of beef is tasty if spread with Bakon Yeast and a "butter" combination.

When you want something other than plain roast beef sandwiches, try combining one of the following with your meat:

Thin slices of onion, with a sprinkling of medium-grained fresh pepper. Delicious on 100 per cent whole wheat bread with one of basic spreads

Thin slices of cucumber, with a sprinkling of medium-grained black pepper, dry mustard, and vinegar

Very thin slices of tomatoes, in the same way as cucumbers

Some of your specially prepared pickled fruits (without salt for sodium restriction) as a topping to meat filler

A little chopped green bell pepper

Crisp leaf of your favorite lettuce

A thin spread of mustard (low sodium dietetic for sodium-restricted dieters)

LAMB AND VEAL

Pure fruit currant and cranberry jelly combine well with lamb or veal—spread with plain unsalted butter or margarine, lemon butter, or Oil Spread.

Spiced fruit also combines nicely with veal.

Sprinkle meat with Bakon Yeast for a barbecued flavor.

PORK

Chop raisins or prunes in low sodium French dressing as a topping for thin slices of pork.

Use a firm applesauce topping for pork sandwiches.

Grind the end of your pork roast, and mix with a little dry mustard and Bakon Yeast.

Spread with lemon butter, or Oil Spread.

Spread with herb or wine butter, or Oil Spread.

OTHER SANDWICH FILLINGS

Spread bread with one of the basic spreads, and fill with:

Sliced breast of chicken or turkey, plain or with cranberry relish or jelly (must be paper-thin)

Flaked white fish, marinated in low sodium French dressing for extra flavor

Raison-nut spread

Mashed avocado blended with low sodium French dressing

Low sodium tomato aspic combined with paper-thin cucumber slices

Deviled egg, plain or with Bakon Yeast added, mixed with low sodium mayonnaise or with curry powder and a dash of dry mustard

Ground meats, with high seasonings or slivers of onion; or sliced low sodium meat loaf (but not in hot weather unless sandwich is to be eaten soon after preparation)

Low sodium peanut butter with wine jelly (non-hydrogenated peanut butter for saturated fat restriction)

Dietetic tuna, shrimp, or salmon with lettuce

Low sodium cheese, plain or with sprinkling of Bakon Yeast; low-sodium dietetic cheese spread

(not for saturated fat restriction)

Succulent, paper-thin slices of onion, with herbs; or yoghurt with lemon, garlic, or herb spread

Low sodium cottage cheese with pure fruit jelly

Chopped ginger with honey

Alternating slices of light and dark bread may be used with any of the above combinations.

GROUND FILLERS

The good old food grinder can be worked overtime in making tasty sandwich fillers. This is a good way to use tag-end meats and vegetables, too. Combined with other ingredients, they make some of the best sandwich spreads. Blend them with one of the special butters or low saturated fat spreads for high flavor.

For planning ground fillers, try:

One-half cup orange marmalade combined with ¼ cup ground nut kernels

Combined equal amounts of chopped dried dates with chopped walnuts, or filberts (use lemon butter as spread for bread)

Dry roasted peanuts (unsalted, of course for those with sodium restrictions)—a good source of Vitamin B complex and lending themselves to many sandwich fillings, combined with spreads, vegetables, or fruits

Combined in equal amounts, low sodium peanut butter with ground *sun-dried* dates moistened in orange juice (non-hydrogenated peanut butter for saturated fat restriction)

For something on the exotic side, and if it's a man you're pleasing, try sprinkling your buttered bread with ground peanuts and top with thin slices of Bermuda onion.

Or you may want to try a salad filling for bread or rolls:

I.

¼ cup shredded cabbage

¼ cup low sodium peanut butter (non-hydrogenated for saturated fat restriction)

1 tablespoon finely minced parsley

Orange juice

Black pepper

II.

½ cup minced low sodium dietetic shrimps

Dash dill

Lemon juice

ROLLED SANDWICHES

The rolled sandwich is a real lunch-box treat in appearance and taste and is a space saver, too.

Many people think of rolled sandwiches as lots of extra work and consequently use them only for special occasions. They are quite the opposite—and one of their special values is that they may be made ahead of use. They store well in the freezer, too. You do have to be a little more careful in rolling low sodium bread than with regular bread, but it handles well with reasonable care.

All you have to do, to make a delectable rolled sandwich, is to slice bread lengthwise in desired thinness, spread the slices with a seasoned butter or spread, and add filling. Once your slices are spread with their fillers, let stand for a few minutes. Then roll as for jelly roll. Seal edges with unsalted butter, margarine, or low saturated spread, wrap in wax-paper rolls and store.

When ready to use, unwrap roll, and slice. Such sandwiches make wonderful additions to the lunch box and give it a festive air.

SUGGESTED FILLINGS FOR ROLLED SANDWICHES

Paper-thin slices of meat, chicken, or turkey

Dietetic-pack tuna, chicken, shrimps, or salmon with shredded lettuce

Low sodium dietetic peanut butter (non-hydrogenated for those with saturated fat restrictions) with pure fruit jelly

Low sodium dietetic cheese or cheese spread (not for those with fat restrictions)

Ground cauliflower and tomato and yellow turnip mixture

Paper-thin slices of cucumber on low sodium peanut-butter spread (non-hydrogenated for those with fat restrictions), or with Bakon Yeast butter spread

Mashed kidney beans (low sodium, prepared) with garlic butter

SANDWICH ACCOMPANIMENTS

Now the next thing to ask yourself is, "What to put into the lunch box to combine with the sandwiches?" For one thing, raw vegetables for color and texture contrast and for good nutrition. Use the crunchy varieties, such as yellow turnip strips, cauliflower flowerets, slices of green peppers, or wedges of lettuce. A whole tomato, although lacking in texture contrast, is juicy and colorful and a welcome supplement, particularly in warm weather.

Make it Rule Number One to include a raw vegetable in some form in every packed lunch. Select from your allowable list.

Fruits are more universally used in traditional lunch boxes than are vegetables—and they are good for our purpose, too. Vary the usual orange, apple, banana treatment with berries in season—and for fun's sake, try leaving them stemmed, including a small carton of sugar for dunking purposes. The rolled dried fruits (page 266) are a fine goody when your box calls for a rich dessert or confection. Wedges of fresh pineapple, melon in season, and fruit cup, all make good additions to sandwiches when fruit is the choice.

SANDWICH SUBSTITUTES
OR SUPPLEMENTS

Salad

There will be times when you want the heartiness and freshness of a salad in place of sandwiches or to supplement them. Look over the chapter on Salads pages 168-87) and line up the "carrying ones." Salads can be very tempting and refreshing *if* sufficiently chilled before packing, and properly insulated. The best way to ensure this is to pack them well. Use a paper container for a new type of insulator. The paper cup with cover type is good for this purpose—the cup itself is a fairly good insulator.

What do we suggest to put in the container? First of all, there are the vegetable and fruit-vegetable slaws. Cabbage slaw, in its many variations, is one of the best carrying salads. Try it with apple, yoghurt, pineapple, berries, fresh pears or peaches, or any of your own favorites.

Potato salad holds up well, too, for lunch-box purposes. Remember to use parsley and a little extra vinegar to give it a lift without benefit of salt. You may like a dash of curry powder, Bakon Yeast, or extra dry mustard for flavor change. We like a little wine vinegar for extra tanginess.

Then there are vegetables to stuff. A good, firm tomato is all right, if properly drained before stuffing, so that it is not leaky and mushy by the time it is to be eaten. Left-over meat, chicken, fish, or vegetables can be used alone or in combination as a stuffing. Don't overlook crunchy raw vegetables for their pleasant blending qualities. You may even want to use your egg allowance by hard-boiling it for the tomato filler.

Avocado is also good for any of the above stuffings. It is a little bland and sweet, so needs the sharpness of vinegar and oil to give it character.

There are, also, the gelatin salads—the molded salads, which may be used occasionally if the weather is not too hot, and if packing conditions and "equipment" are favorable. Salads molded with fruits or fish seem particularly appropriate for the lunch box. *Make your selections only from your allowables.* A tiny little covered container for liquid dressing is a must. These are available in paper or plastic, or you may use well-washed discards from your bathroom shelf.

Casseroles

Indeed they do have a place in the lunch box, if your dieter has a place to warm anything or is fortunate enough to have one of the new cup-shaped insulators just big enough for such an addition. Any of your low sodium or low fat leftovers can go into this—tuna-mushrooms; minestrone; stew with vegetables; rice-turkey or chicken; ground meat casseroles; mock tamale casseroles—in fact, almost any flavorsome *made dish.*

But do not include dishes made with milk sauces or eggs unless they can be refrigerated.

Desserts

Fresh fruit has been mentioned already. It is certainly one of the best desserts for the meal to be taken—from the standpoint of its carrying qualities and its taste appeal. But it should not be considered the only dessert, by any means.

There are the tiny pastries; the tarts; the deep pies; fruit turnovers; scones; low sodium or low saturated fat cakes, cookies, and pies; puddings galore—surely your dieter will not want for a dessert sweet in some allowable form. Don't forget some of the taste-ticklers pages 265-69). There are the fruit balls, rich desserts in themselves; the dipped walnuts; the pralines—and ever so many other goodies to add a surprise element to the lunch box, providing calories and other restrictions allow them.

PACKAGING AND
PACKING THE LUNCH

Second only to the lunch itself is the packing of it. First of all, you will need a box large enough to do the job well. Many shapes and varieties are now being shown in the stores. There are even plastic lunch boxes available. Light to carry, they make attractive food servers. The lunch-box liner fits inside a standard lunch box, makes it easy to pack a lunch the night before to keep in the refrigerator. Two covered compartments have ample space for salads, casseroles, fruits, vegetables, or pudding. The large compartment is planned for sandwiches, pastry, and fruit. A plastic box with alligator finish, equipped with wallet and compact accessories, may even be found—to satisfy milady's whim if she is the dieter.

You will probably want two Thermos bottles—if you hope to put out a balanced and complete lunch. The regular size (1 or 2 cup) will do very nicely for soup or beverage, but you will also want to add one of the new squat-shaped kind of insulator for salad, casserole, gelatin, or dessert.

Package your various foods carefully and attractively. Use enough wax paper to do the job required. There is nothing a man so dislikes in a lunch box, they tell us, as leaky foods. Wrap sandwiches separately. (This goes for vegetable sticks, too.) Don't let them rub against other foods, but protect them with their own wrappings. Think of the order of eating as you put your packages in their place. Relatedness is a factor here as in general food planning and preparation.

Let your freezer or the cold compartment of your refrigerator work for you. Make up sandwiches a week ahead (page 282) so that some of your early morning energy can be spent on careful packaging. Oh, yes, just one last word—for eye appeal, put a gay paper napkin on the very top of all the wrappings to greet the dieter when he or she "opens up."

17. TIPS ON TRIPS
AND EATING OUT

Life (as far as eating is concerned) need not be lived within the four walls of your home just because you happen to have a restricted sodium or fat dieter in your midst. There are ways to manage the mechanics of eating out and even taking trips, once you have mastered the limitations and opportunities of your program.

You may be quite content to depend upon home fare in the beginning—whether you are preparing it or consuming it. There is a time at first when the patient must learn to conform to his new and radically different diet and when the homemaker must learn not only the sodium or fat content of foods allowed, but to use her cooking skills to make food without salt or the usual fats taste good. Both tasks call for mature acceptance of responsibility. While all of this is taking place, home base may seem particularly attractive.

But the day will come when you are tired of planning, ordering, and preparing or eating home meals and when you will want that "first" meal out. That time may come quite by accident and on the spur of the moment. If such is the case, you may forget to take with you some of your sodium-restricted items, such as unsalted butter, salt substitute, low-sodium bread, or other requirements of your dietary. Your dieter may get a pretty slim meal. So what? There is always the refrigerator from which to forage when you get home—and the pleasure of the change may have more than compensated for the slimness of the meal.

FOR THE SODIUM-
RESTRICTED DIETER

Once the plunge is made, you will begin to realize that with a little care in the ordering end of things you can eat out as frequently as your inclination and pocketbook will allow. You will have to choose restaurants having à la carte service, of course, one where dishes may be cooked to order. And you will have to learn to be very specific in your ordering. It will not be enough to say, "I can't have vegetables with salt." You might be served canned vegetables to which no salt had been added, it is true, but which were salted as they were processed for canning.

Nor can you order, "Fried chicken without salt," for dinner. The chef, who may know nothing of the low sodium diet, might fry your chicken in butter or some other frying agent not on your list. No, you will have to be absolutely *specific as to what you want and how you want it prepared.* If you learn to do this, you will learn that the restaurant yield is quite varied.

A good STARTER for restaurant dining is *fruit juice* or an acid fruit, such as grapefruit, chilled or broiled.

FOR THE MAIN COURSE, plain broiled meats offer you considerable choice—chops, steaks, hamburgers. Inside cuts of roasts and poultry may also be ordered providing you trim one-fourth inch off edge and do not eat skin. No gravy. Meats should be prepared without salt or seasonings, except lemon juice and pepper. If herbs are to be added, why not sprinkle them on when served for extra precaution?

BAKED POTATOES, without dressing, are usually available, and once in a while French-fried potatoes (if you know the frying agent).

SALADS offer you a broad selection. Head lettuce, *fresh* unsalted vegetables (raw or cooked), a tossed salad of greens, or fruit, abound on à la carte menus. Avoid all molded salads. Specify no dressing; use lemon juice, vinegar, vegetable oils, and herbs of your choice, but do not use *herb salts* or parsley flakes.

FOR DESSERT—fresh or frozen fruits or ices, not sherbets, as they are often made of milk. One of the best (and most healthful) luncheon meals can be centered around a large salad "without dressing." Perhaps you will unashamedly (why not?) take from your pocket or purse a piece of unsalted matzoth as its accompaniment. Select a beverage, and you have rounded out that lunch with friends, family, or colleagues. Or build your meal around your egg allowance, if your diet list specifies one medium egg soft-boiled or poached in unsalted water.

Unless you live and work in a community where there is a very active Heart Association, you may not find low sodium bread, unsalted butter, or salt substitute in the restaurants of your choice. These are the three indispensables of the severely restricted sodium diet that you will have to carry with you for meals away from home. Of course, if you are on the 500 milligram diet, a glass of milk broadens your selection base. And for you lucky ones with a sodium allowance of 1,000 milligrams or more, perhaps a slice of regular bread and a pat of butter (if fat is not restricted) and ever so many other choices await you. Your problems are small indeed.

The sodium-restricted dieter soon learns to carry his own equipment. For this try a small basket and stock with salt-substitutes, a French dressing, matzoth, and unsalted butter—the latter put in at the very last moment for each sojourn away from home. Such a carrier might even harbor delicacies for picnics and nibbling "en route." One day it might produce sandwiches (low-sodium bread and fillers, of course); another, fried chicken; and still another, salad mixings, or cocktail goodies, or cookies.

FOR THE LOW SATURATED FAT DIETER (WITHOUT SODIUM RESTRICTIONS)

FOR THE MAIN COURSE, broiled sirloin steak or ground top round, fish, or breast of chicken are your best choices. Veal roasted or in a made dish if not loaded with a butter sauce may also be selected. Here seasoning is not a problem for those of you without sodium restrictions, so specify as to your preference. Avoid gravy. Vegetables may be ordered with abandon—your only restrictions here would be vegetables in milk or cream sauce, dressed with butter, or prepared with salt pork.

POTATOES without dressing may be the accompaniment.

SALADS, too, are no problem if you specify no dressing; use only vegetable oil and lemon juice or vinegar to dress.

BREADS: Muffins, hot breads, and even plain yeast breads may be off the severely restricted fat diet list. It may be necessary to carry your homemade products which use only allowable items.

DESSERTS: Fresh or frozen fruits or ices offer many choices. Avoid all commercial desserts made with chocolate, coconut, whole egg, butter, margarine, whole milk fancy sauces. This means that baked goods such as pastries and cake will be tabooed, as well as puddings, pies, ice creams, sherbets, and confections.

BEVERAGES: Carbonated as allowed, cider, coffee, fruit juices, buttermilk, non-fat milk, and tea offer you many choices.

The exciting thing about eating out is that it shows both the dieter and the homemaker that it is possible to have well-rounded meals, wherever you decide to eat.

To be able to go anywhere any time and eat at any place means just one thing—always having some low sodium or low fat specialties on hand. (Another good argument for that once-a-week cookfest.)

You can even go to formal banquets (if you want to) and keep within your restrictions. For such occasions, you will have to find out ahead of time something about the menu and duplicate it at home, as far as practicable, with an eye for restraints. It's impossible to impose upon a hostess at such times the requirements of a special dietary or expect a large kitchen staff to make special provisions, if it is set up to cater a special meal. So you will have to make the meal and carry it in a vacuum ice (hot) bucket. A bucket can be bought for around six dollars up or in fine sterling, depending upon your need and wishes or those of your dieter.

How use it? Well, it's as simple as this: Prepare chicken or turkey parts (yes, you can buy them), or steak, cook a vegetable, and bake a potato in your own kitchen. Add a carton of homemade salad, low sodium or low fat roll and unsalted butter or Oil Spread, and salt-substitute. You now have a good start on a well-rounded meal. Add an individual fruit pie or turnover—and it's a meal fit for the finest.

You and the ice bucket can arrive at your destination with the ice bucket making a quick delivery to hostess or steward. When dinner is served, few if any guests, and sometimes not even the dieter, will remember that his meal was specially prepared and so different in some details from the other dinners. A word of caution: the unsalted butter or Oil Spread won't carry well in the bucket with hot dishes. You had better pack it separately to slip in pocket or purse for those meals away from home.

Picnics or outdoor meals in your own garden or patio are good beginning experiences in preparation for the more formalized ones of restaurant eating. If your dieter is a man and if you can get that man interested in outdoor cookery, you can make even restricted meals seem attractive to him.

There is something about the anticipation of a meal in its preparation and actual cooking out of doors that makes good food taste better. Barbecued corn or potatoes with flavorsome meats seem to rate high with most men. Perhaps it's the informality of the setting; perhaps it's the open air; perhaps it is the flavor of the food, specially prepared. At any rate, such service lends variety and pleasure to home meals.

If you don't have a barbecue or don't particularly like to eat in your garden, why not plan an occasional informal meal around casserole cookery? With a seasoned earthenware casserole (garlic and vegetable oil), it is easy to duplicate the distinctive European cookery. A fish or vegetable chowder, a wonderful Italian minestrone; whole broiling chickens with fresh mushrooms; veal with wine, vegetable oil, and herbal seasonings—or even a thick vegetable stew with fresh garden vegetables redundant with pungent spices—could form the basis of such a meal.

Work out at least one casserole dish that is uniquely your own. Build it around a starch, perhaps—such as one of the noodle or spaghetti pastas or rice, brown or white.

It is but an additional step to move from these special occasion meals at home and restaurant meals to an overnight trip. Your physician may not encourage this at the beginning, until you have been on the low sodium or fat program for some months. It takes a lot of know-how to get away from your own kitchen—when the health of a person is so dependent upon the products of that kitchen. But travel-minded we Americans certainly are, and you can be right in that throng whenever your physician gives you the green light. Now every major transportation system, whether it be train, plane, or ship can take care of your special diet needs if you specify them in advance to your travel agent or reservation clerk. We have found by actual trial and error that it is much more satisfactory to *list individual requirements in writing.* These may include non-fat or low sodium non-fat milk, unsalted butter or margarine, low sodium bread, vegetable oil other than olive, fresh vegetables cooked without salt, or special canned dietetic low sodium ones (specify string beans, peas, et cetera). Major hotels are also set up to serve you. Here too, an advance letter with your requirements will bring you quite often some special goodie. The Parker House in Boston has been known to make Parker House rolls low in sodium, New York hotels have bought delicious little low sodium dietetic muffins for their dieting guests, and the maître d' will always see that your food is specially prepared (particularly so if you pass one of those green bills over his palm).

Your task will be simpler when you elect to travel by automobile. You can take some of your diet items with you or have them shipped to your principal stopover points.

Don't start out expecting to find all the items that line your grocer's shelves. We found unsalted butter particularly hard to get in the South. In Baton Rouge, one creamery insisted that sweet-cream butter was the same as unsalted butter, although the butter had a definite salty flavor. We located it through the Louisiana Heart Association in New Orleans.

How can you transport food items, if you travel by automobile? Simply store diet items in a shallow carton in the trunk compartment where you can get to them easily. For hotel or roadside eating, try a wicker basket, a carrying kit, a covered can, such as a fruit-cake tin or a large substitute milk powder tin, for the daily basics.

For summer travel, some kind of refrigeration for perishables is a must. Portable coolers and ice boxes are available in stores carrying camping equipment. Be sure to watch those casserole and egg dishes when the mercury soars. For the bacteria that cause food poisoning, life begins at 40 and ceases at 140 degrees Fahrenheit. Keep hot foods hot and cold foods cold when you are on the road.

For snacks or roadside picnics, shop for the junior-size carrying containers that are just right for two. One smart container we saw in a plaid tartan covering includes two Thermos bottles—a regular one for beverages and a wide-necked one for soups and casserole dishes. A large center section with a plastic box and cover is ample for sandwiches, fruit or salad. And there is space to tuck in eating utensils.

There is one more thing for the traveler with a low sodium diet to consider. It is the public water supply.* The sodium content of the water supply of most cities is low enough to be ignored; but in some areas certain supplies are entirely unsuited to sodium-restricted diets. Under these circumstances, the doctor may suggest a change in destination or tell you to get accommodations where diet meals can be cooked with distilled water.

---

*See "Sodium-Restricted Diets"—Food and Nutrition Board, the National Research Council. Publication 325, July 1954, pp. 27-29; 59-70. Or check with local Heart Association or local purveyor of water.

Here is a final admonition about travel and restricted diets for the heart patient. *If you have to be on a restricted food program, stick to it wherever you are.*

Diet is not the only consideration in planning a trip. Before the heart patient leaves the doctor's supervision, he should know enough about his ailment to function effectively while traveling.

Uncertainties should be cleared up, and time should be taken to review the Don't list. Discuss these with your doctor when you go in for a travel checkup.

Often the doctor wants the patient to travel with a medical report, in case medical care is needed away from home. Such a report is ease-of-mind insurance, and provides any doctor with important information for evaluating the emergency situation. This report usually includes the latest electrocardiogram. If you are departing on a long trip and your doctor does not offer you a medical report, ask him to prepare one for you.

There is the matter of medicine. Some of the new drugs are hard to get. Your doctor may decide it is wise for you to travel with enough of the precious pills to last your stay. Also, carry a copy of all prescriptions in case of change of travel plans or loss of baggage.

"The biggest block to travel," one San Francisco cardiologist told us, "is the patient's concern about getting a doctor away from home." Today medical care is as near you as the nearest telephone in any of the cities and communities stretching from Maine to California. Sponsored by the Council on Medical Services of the American Medical Association in 1948, county medical societies have been developing this medical plan, known as the Emergency Call Plan.

If you're away from home and need a doctor, all you have to do is to pick up a telephone and ask the operator to get you a doctor. Give her a statement about your illness and whether your prefer a general practitioner or specialist. In many cases, it will hasten medical care if you have a number to call, such as the local medical society or hospital. Turn to the classified section of the telephone directory and see if an emergency call service is included with the listing of physicians and surgeons.

In large cities the operator will refer your call to a special switchboard operated by or in cooperation with one of the local health societies. Increasingly, this is on a round-the-clock basis seven days a week. In smaller communities, a shut-in may fill the role of the PBX operator of the large city, and the call may be referred to the local hospital, police or other public agency ready to contact and speed medical assistance when needed.

Your doctor may give you the names of a few doctors he knows along your route. He may suggest a person-to-person call to him by the emergency physician, if he thinks it is important.

What does this all add up to, if you have had some form of heart or blood vessel disease and want to travel?

1. In the first place, the doctor is the core of any travel plan. He alone can tell you the when, where, and how long.

2. Advance planning is essential for both safe and pleasurable traveling.

3. A checkup is a must.

4. In this checkup, do the following:

. . . clear up any uncertainties about your ailment

. . . know what orders you must follow and how they are to be carried out

. . . get a copy of all prescriptions and plan for enough medicines to last the trip

. . . ask for a medical report, including the last electro-cardiogram

. . . understand your diet program and whether you must consider the sodium content of public water supplies in making your plans

. . . know how to get emergency medical care away from home and whether your doctor is to be notified.

5. If you must be on a restricted diet, stick to it. And for greater flexibility in eating, carry some diet items with you when you are to be away from home. And remember that the more severe your restrictions, the better advance planning you must do.

18. UNFINISHED BUSINESS

You know that "woman's work is never done" if you want to be an alert and competent homemaker. So many labor-saving devices and foods wearing new faces appear on the market these days that it is hard to keep up with them all.

We find ourselves confronted with exactly the same problem in completing this book. It is amazing how much has been made available to improve variety and flavor in restricted diets during the time we have been working on this project.

So we have decided to add this chapter—to include some new products, a few late discoveries, and to share recipes which were insufficient in number to warrant a chapter by themselves.

EGGS

We just can't leave them out, even if they must be used so sparingly. If you are permitted the whole egg, your physician will have specified your allowance, whether one a day or three a week, or you will be told what part of the egg is best for your particular diet needs. As was pointed out earlier, you will have to choose, on the planning end of things, how that egg allowance is to be used. If you use it in cooking, of course you will have to forego serving it otherwise on the same day.

So special is it in these diets that it deserves special care and preparation. Unfortunately, the egg is carelessly handled all too often in many kitchens—it may not be kept fresh to yield its best flavor; it may be improperly cooked with too high heat, and toughened; it may be poorly seasoned, and often is; it may be used without imagination, poor thing, and lose its wonderful versatility. Let's try to get maximum goodness from it when it is such a precious commodity in restricted cookery.

HOW TO FLAVOR THE EGG

1. Line egg cup with a sprinkling of thyme or sweet basil for a completely new savor.
2. Be imaginative in your flavoring of eggs. Try:

Minced parsley, with sweet basil and chives

Thyme with a few grains of cayenne

Marjoram and minced garlic

Low sodium dietetic cheese or spread sprinkled over top of omelet and lightly browned under broiler for those without saturated fat restrictions

Port wine jelly (1 tablespoon for each serving) spread on puffy omelet, before folding; if jelly is very stiff, set in pan of hot water or heat slightly to encourage easy spreading

Vegetable of choice, or combination of vegetables for omelet filler

Divide omelet in 2 sections and spread with herb-flavored, tomato sauce canned without added sodium; top with other half of omelet

The addition of a little sherry or dry white wine to scrambled eggs or omelet in place of some of the other liquid—with or without herbs, a wonderful delicacy (but whatever you do, don't overdo this)

A *sprinkling* of Bakon Yeast for a bacon flavor that is bound to earn you the gratitude of your dieter

HOW TO USE EGGS IN
LOW-SODIUM COOKERY

Batter: Combine with flour, low sodium baking powder, and low sodium milk

Cake: Combine with flour, low sodium baking powder, low sodium milk, sugar, and seasonings

Custard: Boil, steam, or bake with low sodium milk

Dessert: Combine with other food ingredients

Macaroons: Egg white(s) combined with sugar, flavoring, coconut or nuts

Meringue: Egg white(s) combined with sugar and lemon juice

Mayonnaise: Beat with oil and vinegar—seasonings added to taste

Pancakes: Beat with flour, low sodium milk, low sodium baking powder, and cook on special grill

Sandwiches: Scrambled, fried, or hard boiled make good fillers

Sauces: Combined with flour, liquid, and seasonings for special use

Sherbert: Beat whites raw with fruit juice or combine with puréed fruit and freeze

Soufflé: Beat, mix with low sodium milk sauce, low sodium cheese, and seasonings, and bake

Rarebit: Combine with low sodium cheese, beer, or low sodium white sauce, and seasonings—for a rich rarebit

Torte: Beat whole and combine with other ingredients, the base of which will be sugar, nuts, and flavoring(s)

Waffle: Special low sodium batter cooked on special irons

HOW TO USE EGGS IN SATURATED FAT-RESTRICTED COOKERY

If egg yolk is restricted, use two egg whites for each whole egg in our recipes and in adapting your own favorites

Do not use regular butter or margarine; instead use vegetable oil for pan treatment in all egg cookery

If you use an egg in cooking, remember that you must count it in your daily or weekly allowance

For egg in your meal of choice, use one of the following methods of cooking:

bake	soft boil
coddle	hard boil
poach	scramble

BASIC OMELET
3 Servings

½ cup low sodium non-fat milk	½ teaspoon sweet basil
1 tablespoon flour	⅛ teaspoon white pepper
2 tablespoons low sodium non-fat milk powder	Yellow food coloring
	4 fresh egg whites
½ teaspoon minced parsley	¼ cup chopped fresh mushrooms
	1 teaspoon vegetable oil

Put milk into a jar with flour, low sodium non-fat milk powder, seasonings, and food coloring. Cover and shake to blend. Pour into a saucepan and heat over slow heat, stirring constantly until thickened. Put egg whites into large bowl, beat until they stand in rounded peaks. Fold in the thickened sauce (the substitute egg yolk). Add mushrooms sautéed in 1 teaspoon oil. Lightly oil sides and bottom of medium-sized skillet. Pour the egg white mixture into the skillet and cook over moderate heat until mixture is puffy and a golden brown on the under side. Then place in broiler to lightly brown the top. Add ½ teaspoon salt if sodium is not restricted.

One Serving	Total Recipe	
Without salt		
66	199	milligrams sodium
2	5	grams total fat
negligible	negligible	grams saturated fat
69	206	calories

One serving: ⅓ teaspoon vegetable oil.

VARIATIONS

Regular non-fat dry milk powder may be substituted for low sodium non-fat milk and powder when sodium is not restricted.

Parsley (about 2 tablespoonfuls), or a few drops of Angostura Aromatic Bitters, or 1 teaspoon white dinner wine may be substituted for the mushrooms in this and scrambled egg recipes.

Instant potato (about 2 teaspoonfuls) may be added to white sauce blend if sodium is not restricted, for added body to egg dishes.

SCRAMBLED YELLOW EGG WHITES
3 Servings

The yellow coloring is very important in egg white recipes as it makes your dishes look like the real thing, and taste more like it, too.

½ cup low sodium non-fat milk

1 tablespoon low sodium non-fat dry milk powder

Dash marjoram

⅛ teaspoon freshly ground black pepper

Dash thyme

1 drop yellow coloring

1 teaspoon chopped chives

1 teaspoon chopped parsley

5 egg whites

Parsley sprigs

Combine and mix all ingredients except egg whites. Add to egg whites. Beat lightly with fork. Lightly oil sides and bottom of skillet with vegetable oil. Warm and add egg white mixture. Heat, stirring constantly with fork. Serve onto warm plates and garnish with parsley sprigs. Portion very carefully if your dieter has to be on strict sodium restriction. Salt for those without sodium restriction as you serve.

One Serving	Total Recipe	
81	242	milligrams sodium
negligible	negligible	grams total fat
45	134	calories

VARIATIONS

Regular non-fat dry milk and powder may be used if sodium is not restricted. See variations for Basic Omelet (page 303).

DIETETIC CHEESES
AND WAYS TO USE THEM

For Sodium-Restriction:

Now that several companies manufacture low sodium cheese and spreads you can adapt some of your favorite recipes to restricted dishes simply by substituting dietetic low sodium cheese for regular, omitting the addition of salt, and using the kind of milk specified on your diet list. Tillamook Dietetic Low Sodium Cheddar-type Cheese* is sharp and as easy to use as regular cheddar cheese. Similarly with Cellu Dietetic Low Sodium Cheese.† This cheese, of medium hard texture, has only 3 milligrams sodium in 1 ounce and is sold in ½-pound and 1-pound loaf sizes. We have used this for quite a few years in our experimental cookery and have had excellent results with it as well as with some of the newer dietetic cheeses. The Cellu Dietetic Cheese Spread has 20 per cent fat and can be used in all the ways you usually enjoy cheese. It is particularly tasty in a rarebit or as a topping for asparagus or cauliflower. Use only in amounts specified on your diet list.

* Tillamook Cheese Company, Tillamook, Oregon.

† The Chicago Dietetic Supply House, Inc., 1750 West Van Buren Street, Chicago 12, Illinois.

The Danish Cheese Company* also manufactures a diet cheese known as a "Gouda Type." And Swift & Company † distributes a low sodium dietetic cheese (Imitation Colby Cheese) under the Gold Crest label which contains 3.5 milligrams sodium in 1 ounce. These are only a few of the many dietetic low sodium items on the market in this food class.

For Low Saturated Fat Restriction:

The Kaukauna Dairy Company ‡ manufactures an excellent low calorie, low fat cheese specialty, Kaukauna Diet Treat (but check with your dietitian to find out if you may use it). Easy to spread and very tangy, this is an excellent spread for sandwiches, topping for vegetables or casseroles, and a flavor-aid to white sauces.

The fat content of cheese spreads in general, while somewhat lower than the fat content of processed cheese and natural cheese, is still high enough to require special care in use, if they are allowed at all. Some of the Scandinavian types of cheese are made from skim milk and whey and therefore have a very low fat content. Sapsago, Geska brand,§ is a Swiss green cheese and contains only about 1 per cent fat. It is a grating-type cheese and can be used on this diet for flavor additions. The only fat-free cheese easily available is the uncreamed curds of cottage cheese, which may be obtained from your local dairy.

Low fat cheeses for the most part are not restricted in sodium content so are only for those of you on the low saturated fat diet without sodium restriction. Oh yes, and lest we forget, there is Dairy Diet * and Cheese Whiz,† the former having 2.4 grams fat per tablespoon of spread, the latter having 3.8 grams of fat per tablespoon, and Koch

---

* Nisqually, Washington.

† Chicago, Illinois.

‡Kaukauna, Wisconsin.

§ Local food specialty store, mail order food store as S. S. Pierce Co., Boston, Mass., or write to distributor Otto Roth & Co., Inc., 177-179 Duane Street, New York 13, New York.

*Calumet Cheese Company, Inc., Hilbert, Wisconsin.

†Kraft Foods Division of the National Dairy Products Corporation, 500 North Peshtigo, Chicago, Illinois.

Kaese ‡ which is less than 2 per cent fat.

For low saturated fat dieters wishing a grated cheese topping, Sapsago cheese may be your only choice. This hard green cheese made from skim milk and herbs comes in both solid cones and in grated form. For easy grating, put cone through meat grinder. Store in covered jar in refrigerator. Its fat content is approximately 0.3 grams per ounce.

CHEESE TOAST
1 Serving

Spread one piece of low sodium bread with a slice of dietetic low sodium cheese (1 ounce) or with 1½ tablespoons low sodium dietetic cheese spread. Sprinkle with paprika. Place under broiler and cook until cheese bubbles and begins to brown. Serve at once.

One Slice
(with cheese slice)

4	milligrams sodium
10	grams total fat
9	grams saturated fat
210	calories

LOW SATURATED FAT VARIATION

If not restricted in sodium, and diet allows low fat cheese, use low fat rye bread and 1½ tablespoons Dairy Diet. *One serving: 4 grams saturated fat.*

SAVORY MACARONI-CHEESE
4 Servings

2 cups cooked macaroni
1 cup grated low sodium dietetic cheese
1 cup low sodium die-
tetic tomato juice
Pinch sweet basil
White pepper

Lightly oil a 1½ quart casserole; arrange macaroni to layer bottom. Top with grated cheese. Repeat layer of

‡Sheboygan Falls Creamery Company, 837 Buffalo Street, Sheboygan Falls, Wisconsin.

macaroni and cheese. Measure tomato juice and add seasonings; blend. Pour over macaroni mixture. Cover and bake in 350° (moderate) oven, 25 to 30 minutes. Uncover for last 10 minutes of baking for golden, crunchy top.

One Serving	Total Recipe	
6	23	milligrams sodium
9	36	grams total fat
9	34	grams saturated fat
229	916	calories

VARIATIONS

Low sodium non-fat milk (thickened or not with 2 tablespoons flour) may be substituted for tomato juice in equal amount. One tablespoon white dinner wine may be added to milk to heighten flavor and for a piquant flavor use ¼ teaspoon dill weed. Sprinkle paprika over top before baking.

For extra richness, simmer ½ cup sliced fresh mushrooms in ¼ cup white dinner wine and blend with each layer.

LOW SATURATED FAT VARIATION

As pointed out, cheese dishes in general are not your best choice and must be used in very small amounts *if allowed at all*. If not restricted in sodium, substitute a low fat cheese for the low sodium dietetic cheese and use regular tomato juice or non-fat milk. Add ½ teaspoon salt.

WELSH RAREBIT WITH BEER
2 Servings

1 5-ounce jar Cellu Low Sodium Cheese Spread	1 teaspoon dry mustard
	Few grains cayenne
	Dash sweet basil
1 tablespoon vegetable oil	½ cup beer (about)
	Paprika
1 teaspoon cornstarch	

Blend all ingredients together except beer and paprika and put into heavy duty skillet or in top of double boiler. Melt cheese slowly over very low heat, stirring constantly to avoid scorching or lumping. Add beer and continue to stir until first bubbles appear at rim of pan. Serve at once on slices of low sodium toast. Sprinkle paprika over each serving.

> *One Serving*
> *Without toast*

15	milligrams sodium
21	grams total fat
14	grams saturated fat
270	calories

One serving: 1½ teaspoons vegetable oil.

VARIATIONS

1 cup lightly grated low sodium dietetic cheese may be substituted for the cheese spread.

Brick cheese (low sodium, of course) may be cut into small cubes and melted over slow heat.

LOW SATURATED FAT VARIATION

Again, concentrated cheese dishes are not for you except for a rare treat indeed, and then only if such allowance appears on your diet list. If this is the case, if you have no sodium restrictions, substitute any one of the low fat spreads and use as in the Basic Recipe; add ¼ teaspoon salt.

CASSEROLE DE LUXE
8 Servings

Now here's a dish to carry you back to some of the specialties you used to make before taking over restricted cookery. The extra special thing about this casserole is that it is better each time you reheat it—and, as if that were not enough, it freezes beautifully. (Be careful to package in small container for freezing, because cheese dries out quickly, once it has thawed.)

4 cups cooked elbow macaroni
2 tablespoons vegetable oil
½ cup chopped onion
1 tablespoon minced parsley
¼ cup sliced fresh mushrooms
1 pound *lean* ground beef
Dash allspice
¼ teaspoon thyme
½ teaspoon freshly ground pepper
¾ cup low sodium dietetic tomato juice
¼ cup white table wine
1 can Number Two dietetic cream-style corn, canned without added sodium
1 cup low sodium dietetic grated cheese
Paprika

Measure macaroni and set aside. Put oil into heavy duty skillet and sauté onions, parsley, and mushrooms until light golden brown. Crumble meat into small pieces and add to onion mixture. Sprinkle with seasonings. Stir to blend, and cook over low heat until meat is lightly browned on all sides. Add tomato juice, macaroni, wine, and corn; stir to blend. Stir in ¾ cup low sodium cheese. Remove from heat and pour into lightly oiled 2-quart casserole. Sprinkle remaining cheese over top and garnish with paprika. Cover and bake in 350° (moderate) oven 30 minutes, or until mixture bubbles. Uncover for last 10 minutes of baking for a colorful, crunchy top. Add salt for those without sodium restrictions.

One Serving
(1½ oz. meat,
cooked weight)

46	milligrams sodium
15	grams total fat
11	grams saturated fat
368	calories

VARIATIONS

With this Basic Recipe, you may alter flavors and seasonings to suit.

LOW SATURATED FAT VARIATION

If total fat is not limited, sauté onions, parsley, and mushrooms as in Basic Recipe. Brown meat under broiler until lightly browned. Add to onion mixture and follow Basic Recipe, but be sure to use ground top round steak (trimmed of all visible fat) for the meat; omit cheese. *One serving: 3 grams saturated fat (¾ teaspoon vegetable oil).*

CHILE CON CARNE
8 Servings

½ pound red kidney beans
Water
2 tablespoons vegetable oil
¼ cup chopped onions
1 pound *lean* ground meat
1 chopped clove of garlic
½ teaspoon freshly ground pepper

2 cups fresh tomatoes, cut in small pieces
1 teaspoon curry powder
4 dried red peppers
Dash cayenne
1 tablespoon wine vinegar
Dash sugar
2 tablespoons grated low sodium dietetic cheese

Soak beans overnight. In the morning cook in same water until skins split and beans are tender. Meanwhile, put into a heavy-duty skillet 2 tablespoons vegetable oil. Heat and add onions. Sauté 5 minutes. Add crumbled ground meat and garlic. Brown lightly; add to beans. Add remaining ingredients except cheese, breaking peppers into small bits if desired. Cook over low heat about 1 to 1½ hours. Watch for scorching last half hour and add water if necessary. About 10 minutes before serving, add 2 tablespoons grated cheese. Stir to blend and to avoid scorching. Add salt for those without sodium restrictions at time of serving.

One Serving
(1½ oz. meat,
cooked weight)

44	milligrams sodium
11	grams total fat
7	grams saturated fat
268	calories

LOW SATURATED FAT VARIATION

Brown meat (using top round, trimmed of all visible fat) under broiler heat and proceed as in Basic Recipe. Add salt if there are no sodium restrictions. Omit addition of cheese. Chill dieter's portion in refrigerator and remove any solid fat; reheat. *One serving: 3 grams saturated fat (¾ teaspoon vegetable oil).*

YOGHURT

Yoghurt has been a connoisseur's food through the centuries, although it has only rather recently become popular in this country. With such a historical background as it enjoys, you may be sure it has passed the taste-test and is a fit delicacy for your table. It has a subtle, tangy flavor, a custardlike texture, and a fragrancy uniquely its own. However, it is a cultured milk product, so will have to be used with discretion because of its sodium content of 49 milligrams per ½ cup. And it is not for you with saturated fat restrictions, unless your dairy has yoghurt made with non-fat milk.

Many people enjoy eating it plain, but it does combine pleasantly with many foods. Combining it with other foods, you get the yoghurt flavor without running up the sodium content too high.

Here are a few suggestions as a starting point:

Use as topping for puddings or desserts

Use as topping for fruits or blended with cheese

Combine with low sodium salad dressing for flavor change

Beat and combine with fruit juices for refreshing and unusual beverages

Spread lightly over fish before baking

SPECIAL NEWS

CASEC

Quite often it is necessary to increase the protein content of the low sodium dietary, but still keep the sodium count at a minimum level. You can see at a glance how difficult this might be.

First of all—think of our protein foods. Meat, poultry, fish, eggs, milk, cheese—all high in protein but also high in sodium. Increasing the amount of protein with these foods means increasing the amount of sodium, too.

True, you do have low sodium milk, which will certainly be helpful. But there is a limit to the amount of milk you can serve, regardless of how ingenious you may be in the kitchen. Once again, the laboratory has stepped in to assist you by supplying Casec.

Casec is a powder obtained from milk. It is almost pure protein (88 per cent), furnishing 4 grams of protein for each tablespoon used. Better still, one tablespoon contains only an average of 0.9 milligram of sodium.

Just think what this means to you in the kitchen. By adding 3 tablespoons of Casec to one cup of custard, for example, you are able to up the protein content the equivalent of almost two eggs. But such a difference in the sodium count!

Casec can be a cooking aid even if you have to keep one eye on the fat count, too. With an almost negligible fat content per tablespoon (0.1 gram), the problem of a high protein, low sodium, low fat diet is easily solved.

Casec offers little resistance to use in your favorite recipe. It is almost tasteless, so is unnoticeable in even the most delicate flavors. It blends readily, too, so can be combined with most foods, with little difficulty.

From the laboratory of Mead Johnson come the following suggestions for using Casec:

Include in meat, egg, and cheese dishes
Add to gravies, sauces, and salad dressings used with meats and vegetables
Stir into cooked cereals, mashed potato, squash
Mix with milk, eggs, and flavorings in beverages to be served hot or cold
Incorporate in custards and other simple desserts

With these suggestions as a guide, plus a little imagination, there are endless opportunities for you to increase the protein content of your menus, yet still serve meals with taste and eye appeal. Just let yourself go, remembering that Casec may be added to foods by any of the following methods:

Beat into eggs or milk
Combine with water to make thin paste
Sift with dry ingredients
Mix with ground meats

CALCIUM SUCARYL

Good news for those of you who must be both sodium and calorie conscious. It comes to you from the Abbott Laboratories in the form of Calcium Sucaryl—a sugar substitute with no calories and no sodium.

If you possess that proverbial sweet tooth, here is a true lifesaver provided your doctor supervises its use. With it, you can add a natural sugarlike flavor to your beverages, fruits, and other foods, yet avoid the excess calories that real sugar entails.

Better still, it can be used in cooked, baked, canned, and frozen foods with no unpleasant, bitter aftertaste.

Calcium Sucaryl may be purchased as a sweetening solution or in tablets. One tablet, or ⅛ teaspoon solution, is equal to about one level teaspoon of sugar. (You will have to designate *Calcium* Sucaryl when purchasing, as a sodium form is also available. Sodium Sucaryl or saccharin may be used only if you have no sodium restrictions.)

If tablets are your choice, be sure that they are completely dissolved. It is best to crush them to a powder and then dissolve in water, fruit juice, or other liquid. Or, they can be crushed and then sprinkled dry over the food to be sweetened if you are careful to distribute evenly. Remember, like sugar, they dissolve more readily in hot liquids and foods.

A word of caution: Calcium Sucaryl is a good helpmate, but like so many other things that are worthwhile, it must be used with care and should be taken *only under medical supervision*.

SUGGESTED MENUS FOR SPECIAL OCCASIONS

There are always those special occasions in family living which in their very nature invite special foods. You don't have to give up all of your pleasures in good eating just because you are on a highly restricted diet. A few special menus, worked out with respect to the count and palate, can simplify company dinners and special occasion meals and enhance your reputation as a cook, restrictions or not.

Here are some of the things you will have to consider:

1. Do your planning so that you stay within the prescribed limitations.

2. Strive for at least *one* unusual flavor or dish in every special meal. *Let it be the center of interest. Keep other dishes simple.*

3. Work out some combinations which do not require too much last-minute kitchen work. No one wants to be in the kitchen any more than necessary after the guests have arrived. *Plan ahead and work ahead (preferably the day before you are to entertain.)*

4. If you are responsible for your own service—and most of us are these days—combine courses or otherwise simplify your meals so that you are not eternally serving the meal. After all, it is not the number of courses or the variety (in numbers) that spells the meal a success or failure. It is rather the appropriateness of the foods selected —the blending qualities, and the skillful food preparation which will win you your laurels.

MENUS

SUNDAY-NIGHT SUPPERS

I.

Welsh Rarebit * (*Made the day before and reheated in double boiler*)

Lettuce wedges

Low sodium Bread Sticks * (*Made on weekly baking day and stored in refrigerator or freezer*)

* See Index for recipe.

Apple Pandowdy * (*Made the day before and reheated while assembling meal*)
Beverage

LOW SATURATED FAT VARIATION

Use this meal only if low fat cheese appears on your diet list.

II.

Casserole de Luxe * (*Made at least one day before use: better with each reheating*)
Tossed green salad
100 per cent Whole Wheat Rolls * (*Made on baking day and brought from freezer in time to let rise*)
Orange-Prune-Walnut Whip *
Beverage

LOW SATURATED FAT VARIATION

Use the variation suggested for the Casserole de Luxe (page 310).

BIRTHDAY DINNERS

I.

Basic Tossed Salad * (*Made at table and served with meal*)
Sirloin of Beef * (*As directed in recipe in this book*)
Potatoes (*Roasted with meat*)
Broccoli * (*Prepared just before serving*)
Homemade Standard Rolls * (*Prepared on baking day and thawed and cooked as directed*)
Raspberry Ice Cream * (*Made about 6 hours before use*)
Basic Low Sodium Two-egg Birthday Cake * (*Made in morning or day before use or taken from a home freezer*)
Beverage

LOW SATURATED FAT VARIATION

Use baked potato for dieter or roast potato lightly brushed with vegetable oil, and cooked in separate pan.

* See Index for recipe.

Substitute Basic Low Saturated Fat Cake * for the Basic
Low Sodium Two-Egg Cake.

II.
Outdoor Celebration, Western Style

Tossed green salad (*Made in a large wooden bowl and
tossed for all to see*)

Chicken Pilau * (*Of course, you have some slices of
chicken stored in the home freezer. Prepare this
dish early in the day, or take from freezer*)

Corn on the cob (*Barbecued or boiled before serving
—used in place of bread for a change*)

Watermelon compote (*Scooped out watermelon filled
with fresh fruit of choice—elegant with fresh
peaches aged a half-day in a sweet dinner wine, or
assorted melon balls—fresh and appetizing on a
scorching day*)

Basic Low Sodium Two-Egg Birthday Cake * (*Made
ahead; perhaps frozen until day of use*)

Beverage

LOW SATURATED FAT VARIATION

Use only white of chicken. Substitute Basic Low Saturated
Fat Cake.*

THANKSGIVING DINNER

Take a look at the sodium content of turkey and do your
planning so the dieter may have a little extra portion for
this special eating occasion. It is the day of days for good
food, for it has held first place throughout our Nation's
history on the family dinner table.

Apple Cider Ring * (*Made the day before*)

Turkey stuffed with Low Sodium Dressing * (*Made at
least the day before the big day if you have a
freezer or refrigerator; but do not stuff the bird
until time to roast. Garnish platter with boiled,
buttered (unsalted) pearl onions—enough for
individual servings, of course; gravy if you omit
the giblets for the dieter and include the count*)

Sweet Potatoes (or yams) * mashed with orange
juice (*Try adding ¼ cup crushed pineapple for
each person to be served—all done the day before,
of course, and stored in your refrigerator*)

* See Index for recipe.

Fresh or Frozen String Beans *
Uncooked Cranberry-Orange Relish * (*If you want a change*)
Parker House Rolls * (*Made ahead of time, of course*)
Pumpkin Ice Cream * (*Substitute 1 cup pumpkin for fruit. This dessert is a particularly good choice if the young generation is to be present—eliminates the necessity of making 2 desserts; pumpkin pie may be substituted if you feel you must have your holiday pie. Let the youngsters have the "filling" for their portions*)

LOW SATURATED FAT VARIATIONS

Refer to Low Saturated Fat Variations of various recipes.

CHRISTMAS DINNER

The automobile has brought with it many changes in the ways of family celebrations so that there are apt to be several family dinners during Christmas week. Why not show a little originality in your menus and get away from too many turkey dinners all at once? If there is to be a big family gathering Christmas Eve, why not have cold chicken or some specialty for family billing Christmas day? You could even plan to serve buffet style, if the gathering is too large, and have a casserole dish as an accompaniment. To keep you out of the kitchen, here's a suggestion or two:

I.

Stuffed cabbage salad with apples, walnut meats, shredded cabbage (*Outer side of cabbage may be decorated with toyon berries by piercing berries with pins. Fill cabbage with unpeeled apple cubes, sprinkled with lemon juice, shredded cabbage, and 1 cup broken walnut meats for 8 servings. Blend and dress with your favorite salad dressing. Beautiful to look at and so-o good*)
Cold roast chicken (*Cooked at least the day before; a week before if you have a home freezer. Use white meat only for saturated-fat restriction*)
Spanish Rice with Wine *
Cranberry jelly, pure fruit
Peas (*Do not use frozen for those with sodium restrictions; peas canned without added sodium may be used for them*)
Clover-leaf Rolls *

* See Index for recipe.

Cranberry Pie * (*The beauty of a gelatin dessert is that it can be made ahead of use*)
Beverage

II.
A change for the Day of Days

A tray of raw vegetables—radishes, cauliflower flowerets, tomato wedges (*If you live in the Far West*)
Homemade chicken soup (*Without salt for those with sodium restrictions*)
Tamale Pie * (*Made ahead of time and stored in freezer*)
White pearl onions with unsalted butter
Toasted Herb Bread * buttered with unsalted butter
Green Tomato Mince Meat Pie *
Beverage

LOW SATURATED FAT VARIATIONS

Omit butter from onions; substitute 1 tablespoon vegetable oil if desired, or sprinkle lightly with a few grains of nutmeg.

Refer to Low Saturated Fat Variations for individual recipes.

* See Index for recipe.

19. RECIPE HINTS FOR CONTROLLING FAT

To prepare meals with a gourmet flair when the fat must be controlled presents a great challenge to you. You have read about the whys and wherefores of your diet in Chapter 2, so we will emphasize cooking methods here. Very briefly, in review, there are two commonly used diets for controlling fat. Each is very different—and only your physician can decide which is best for you.

One diet limits all types of fat—both animal and vegetable. And as most of the specified fat is used by meat, fish, and egg allowances for the day, the remainder of your food and cooking must be relatively fat-free.

The second diet restricts the amount of saturated fat (mainly animal fat) and allows specified use of vegetable oils. This diet is sometimes called a *Vegetable Oil Diet.*

As you can readily see, cooking methods will be quite different for these diets. If the diet is *restricted in total fat,* select recipes that can be *prepared without the addition of fat.* If the diet is *restricted in saturated fat,* you must learn to *substitute the allowed oils* for butter, margarine, hydrogenated shortenings, and some of the other more familiar table and cooking fats.

There are, however, certain basic principles that must be followed whether total fat or just saturated fat is limited:

For browning of meat or poultry: The usual methods of flouring and browning meats and poultry before cooking will have to be omitted (even if you have an oil allowance). Remember that even well-trimmed meat contains *invisible* fat which collects in the pan during browning and is partly absorbed by the flour. You want this fat to drip away, so meat must be either browned in the broiler or in a ribbed-bottom skillet. Drippings that accumulate are to be discarded, or chilled, and solid fat removed before use.

For browning vegetables: If you have an oil allowance, vegetables may be sautéed in vegetable oil before adding to soup or casserole; those of you on total fat restriction will need to forego pan-browning. Instead, simmer vegetables in a small amount of wine and herbs or other liquid until tender, then add to soup or casserole.

For roasting or braising: Whenever possible, meat should be cooked on rack so that fat drips way. Drippings should be discarded; or, if allowed, chilled and solid fat removed before use. Drippings should not be used for basting while meat is cooking.

For removing fat from gravies and soups: For most complete removal of fat, cook food ahead and chill in refrigerator until fat comes to top and solidifies; remove and discard. For quick use, add cube of ice to gravy to solidify fat; then skim with spoon, lettuce leaf, or paper towel.

For thickening gravy, soup, and sauce: If you have an oil allowance, just mix the oil and flour before adding liquid; when total fat is restricted, combine flour with a small amount of cold liquid. Stir to remove all lumps, then add remaining hot liquid gradually.

For oiling cooking and baking pans: The number of grams of fat supplied by oiling pans or casseroles has not been included in our recipe calculations, but you will note that we use it sparingly. When total fat is severely restricted, it should be taken into consideration. To make a little oil go a long way, brush on pan lightly with pastry brush. Use paper liners for baking whenever possible. Or use one of the new pan applications which make it possible to cook without the addition of any oil or fat.

A second look at restricted foods might prove helpful before you read the chapter suggestions.

For saturated fat restriction, do not use:

Butter, coconut oil, hydrogenated shortenings, lard, margarine (except special margarine if on diet list), or meat fats

Cheese (except Sapsago low fat and dry cottage)

Coconut, chocolate, or hydrogenated peanut butter

Cream

Meats and poultry excepting kinds and amounts specified on your diet list

Oil in excess of your daily allowance

Whole egg or egg yolk (unless specified on your diet list)

Whole milk (including condensed, dried, or evaporated)

Commercial or homemade foods containing any of the above

For total fat restriction, do not use:

Cheese (except Sapsago low fat and dry cottage)

Coconut, chocolate, olives, avocado, nuts, and peanut butter

Cream

Fats, oils, and shortenings (except in amounts specified on your diet list)

Meats, poultry, and fish (except in kinds and amounts specified on your diet list)

Whole milk (including condensed, dried, and evaporated)

Whole egg or egg yolk (except in amounts specified on your list)

Commercial or homemade foods containing any of the above

SOME POINTS ON RECIPES

And now for the recipes. Probably you can make all of the necessary changes without any help from us. But to get you started, we will give each of the chapters in miniature —including hints mainly on how to adapt the recipes for total fat restriction. Variations for saturated fat restriction are included with the recipes in the main chapters.

Remember our recipes state low sodium non-fat milk, but you may substitute whatever milk your physician prescribes. If you have no sodium restrictions, you may also use regular baking powder, canned foods, and add salt to taste.

Remember, too, to subtract any of your restricted foods used in cooking from your total for the day.

START THE MEAL WITH SOUP

Soup is a must on your menus, too. And flavorsome soups are possible in spite of the limitations of your diet.

With a few changes, you may use most of the recipes

given for the sodium-restricted diet. You will have to forego the browning of meats in fat, but they can be lightly browned in broiler. Mushrooms, onions, green peppers, and other like vegetables should be simmered in wine and then added to soup.

Use low fat variation for cream soup, and just omit butter or oil from ingredient listing for other soups. Substitute Sapsago low fat cheese (if it is on your diet list) for topping Vegetable Chowder.

And if you have no sodium restriction, you may add shellfish (oyster, crab, or lobster) for even greater variation when soup is on the menu.

MEAT'S SPECIAL ROLE

Take heed of the kitchen-proven hints in Chapter 7. They can guarantee your success in the dining-room—whether you are serving Sirloin Roast, carved with an air at the table, or the more lowly (but so delicious) Beef Stew.

Your own diet list will tell you whether you can plan to use all meats—and in amounts indicated in our recipes. Because of fat content, some of you may be restricted to certain cuts of meat. For example, you may be only allowed top round of beef for roasts or steaks. If this be the case, use a meat tenderizer to assure fork-tender results.

Since you won't be able to pan-brown your meats for flavor richness, you will have to depend on wines and herbs or other liquids, such as tomato juice. In any event, remember to trim meat of all visible fat before cooking. Do not use drippings for basting. Be certain, too, that all fat is removed from the drippings before using these for gravy. And use only if allowed.

One more point—if you elect pan-broiling as a cooking method, use only a ribbed-bottom skillet, and pour off the fat before serving.

CHICKEN EVERY SUNDAY

Chicken will be a special occasion delicacy on your menus. And because it will be such a welcome treat, you will want to select your method of cooking with care—so as to enhance its flavorsome goodness.

The suggestions given in Chapter 8 are for you, too. Of course, you will need to close your eyes and ears to those tips about adding flavor in the form of oils and unsalted butter, and frying as a choice of cooking, but savory dishes can still be yours.

Choose fryers for your chicken cookery because of their lower fat content. As with meats, trim off fat before cooking, and chill drippings and remove solid fat before using for gravy (if gravy is allowed on your diet list).

You have the herbs and wines, and you can broil, roast, or braise. With these to choose from, monotony need never be the password at your table. With braising, remember to forego the initial browning in oil; instead brown lightly in broiler.

One more reminder—white meat is the choice for your dieter because it is lower in fat. And, of course, your dieter will discard the skin.

TRICKS WITH FISH

Again you will want to glean the introductory material for every hint for tasty fish menus.

Low in total fat content (and all fat unsaturated), fish should appear often on your fat-controlled menus. Pan-broiled, oven-broiled, baked, steamed, or boiled, fish can be presented in a variety of ways. And if you have no sodium restriction, shellfish may be added to the long list of fish choices.

Sauces (low fat variety) can add their bit of flavor to your meals, too. Make them without fat. Instead, add cold liquid *gradually* to flour, blending to remove all lumps.

A PARADE OF VEGETABLES

Here is where you can really shine. With little fat, and a wide selection, vegetables can abound on your table. And, properly cooked, they will be welcomed by your family and dieter alike.

With a few exceptions, all of the cooking tricks to bring out the natural flavors of vegetables can be yours, too. As always, you will desist from the use of butter—adding vegetable oils depending upon your allotment of fat. For this reason, do not choose frying as your cooking method. But with steaming, boiling, baking, pressure cooking, and broiling to select from, you will not be at a loss for variety in your menus.

WITH A CRUET IN EACH HAND

A treat, too, is the succulent salad for the person on the sodium- and fat-restricted diet. Perhaps, for you, this chapter should read "With a Cruet in One Hand"—because your fat restriction may add certain limitations along this line.

Your tossed salad will have to forego that dribbling with oil—at least for your dieter. Instead, choose one of the readymade dressing recipes listed in Chapter 10, in which the oil content is kept at a minimum.

In spite of this, you can still whip up refreshing salads that will be welcomed by your dieter.

THE STAFF OF LIFE

Homemade breads and rolls will be welcomed with high favor at the dining table. Hot breakfast muffins or crunchy bread sticks can be just the thing to give that partylike air to an otherwise everyday meal.

Restrictions are few with yeast breads even when cholesterol and fat must be counted. Choose the crisp-crust variety rather than brush on the added fat necessary for a shiny top. But many families prefer that crispness when biting into bread or rolls.

There will be the limitations of egg yolk or increased fat content of the sweet yeast breads, and quick breads. However, as you will see, many breads can be made with just egg white. We will get you started with a few, knowing that you can add to ours with experimentation in your own kitchen. Follow the directions in the Low Saturated Fat Variations for muffins and quick breads.

Insofar as fat is concerned, only your daily allotment can tell if and how often you may serve these breads. They are higher in fat content and are apt to be on your Don't list. If allowed, try to include occasionally for variety's sake.

DESSERTS FOR EVERY OCCASION

Desserts, too, take their place on your menus. Perhaps many of your old favorites will be out because of the egg or fat content, but many delicious recipes can still be yours.

There are always fruits, whips, gelatins, and sherbets. And then using non-fat milk, you can make low fat ice cream and low fat puddings such as blancmange or rice. Fruit tapiocas, too, can add their bit to round out your menus.

If saturated fat is your concern, you will discover that some of your cake and cooky recipes give very satisfactory results when two egg whites are substituted for one whole egg and vegetable oil is used as the shortening agent. Remember to avoid recipes with cocoa, chocolate, or coconut. But you may favor nuts. (In this book, follow the Low Saturated Fat Variations in the dessert chapter.) Pastry is no problem with delicious Vegetable Oil Pastry. We always use this recipe in our homes when making pie.

If total fat must be restricted—well, let's face it. Most cakes and cookies are just too high in fat content to be used. Not only do they contain large amounts of oils or other fats, they often include chocolate or nuts. You will have to content yourself with a meringue type cooky (without nuts) such as Meringue Kisses, or angel cake (if you are not restricted in sodium).

TASTE-TICKLERS

These morale boosters should be a part of your everyday living. Learn to include that between meal snack, or keep a dish of confections close at hand. They will pay dividends in enjoyment to your special dieter.

Avoid confections with nuts if total fat is restricted. Nuts are high in fat content.

THE DEEP FREEZE CONTRIBUTES TOO

If utilized to best advantage, it can both subtract from your efforts in the kitchen, and multiply your success in the dining room. So study all of the suggestions made in Chapter 15 to see if your freezer is really working its hardest. Remember, of course, that the menus given were meant to be used as guides. You will have to make the substitutions as your diet list demands.

YOU CAN TAKE IT WITH YOU

Yes indeed, we do mean this literally. You can take an attractive and appetizing lunch with you. It is not necessary to pack a dull and tasteless lunch box because you have to abide by the restrictions of a special diet. Chapter 16 will tell you how to cure the "slumps" of a humdrum lunch pail. True, you will need to adapt the suggestions to your specific needs. Perhaps the "butter" spreads or "oil" spreads will have no place in your diet. Again, you may have a small fat allowance and elect to use it here. In any case, there is no excuse for unpalatable, monotonous lunches.

TIPS ON TRIPS AND EATING OUT

It is not necessary to eat all of your meals in your own home just because you are the victim of a special dietary. Read Chapter 17 to see just what we mean. It may mean a little more planning and a little more work, but it is well repaid in pleasurable living. Again, you will need to make the necessary substitutions or changes that your dietary entails.

UNFINISHED BUSINESS

Here, too, are some late discoveries for you. As with the other chapters, you will find some limitations due to total and saturated fat restrictions, but there are still many ideas to round out variety and flavor in your menus.

Eggs: Or should we say *egg whites?* True, you are denied some of the suggestions offered in this section because you may be required to omit egg yolk. However, you will discover that egg white does pretty well on its own when used in batters, cakes, cookies, and the like. You will have to keep a close eye on the sodium count, though, because as you learned in Chapter 1, most of the sodium is concentrated in the egg white.

Bakon Yeast: This is one flavoring (negligible in fat

content) that you will use often when you want to add a smoked, barbecued flavor to your foods.

Low Sodium Cheese: Unfortunately, this product, too, must be added to your lengthy Don't list. High in both total and saturated fat content, it will rarely be found on this type of diet list. Chapter 18 does offer suggestions for low fat cheese that you may be able to use if your diet is not restricted in sodium.

Yoghurt: Yoghurt made from skim or fat-free milk contains negligible fat. However, like whole milk yoghurt, it is high in sodium content (49 milligrams per ½ cup) and will have to be used with discretion. Refer to your diet list to see if it is among your allowables.

Casec: The problem of a diet high in protein yet low in sodium and fat can also be readily solved with the use of Casec. As you read in Chapter 18, Casec is low in sodium and fat. So, if your diet must be high in protein, read—and use—all of the suggestions made in this section.

Calcium Sucaryl: Calcium Sucaryl can also help to satisfy your sweet tooth if you must restrict calories. But remember, it should be used only with medical supervision.

MENUS FOR SPECIAL OCCASIONS

Special occasions with their special foods should be a part of your family living. The general suggestions should prove helpful on the planning end. The menus will need to be adapted to your particular needs. For example, you might choose Leftover Chicken in Curry Sauce and Fruit Gelatin in place of Cheese Rarebit and Apple Pandowdy. Water Ices, and Low Saturated Fat Cake or angel cake (if you are not restricted in sodium) are excellent for birthday dinners. And so on—with a little imagination, countless combinations are possible. Do remember that your dieters need these Special Occasions with their food treats more than ever before.

APPENDICES

1. SODIUM, SATURATED FAT,* AND CALORIE CONTENT OF COMMON FOODS AND MISCELLANY†

Item	Measure	Milligrams Sodium	Grams High Saturated Fat	Grams Low Saturated Fat	Calories
Ala Fisher's, dry	1 cup	5		1	600
Anchovy paste	1 tsp.	686		1	14
Apples, raw	1 medium	1		1	76
Cider	½ cup	1		none	62
Frozen	½ cup, sliced	80		1	91
Sauce, canned	½ cup	3		negligible	92
Apricots, raw	3 medium	1		negligible	54
Canned, unpeeled	4 halves	5		negligible	97
Dried	5 halves	2		negligible	49
Frozen	4 halves	5		negligible	82
Arrowroot	1 tbsp.	negligible		none	29
Artichoke, globe	1 large	41		negligible	51
Asparagus, raw	6 stalks	3		negligible	21
Canned	6 stalks	394		negligible	22
Canned without added sodium	6 stalks	4		negligible	22
Frozen, uncooked	6 stalks	3		negligible	21
Avocado	½ small	3		30	279
Bacon, raw, cured	1 long strip	140	13		126
Fried crisp	2 slices	384	9		97
Baking powder, regular	1 tsp.	378		none	none
Low sodium	1 tsp.	1		none	none
Baking soda	1 tsp.	1232		none	none
Bananas	1 medium	1		negligible	88
Barley, pearled, dry	½ cup	3		1	354
Beans, Baked, Heinz, with pork and tomato sauce, canned	½ cup	629	3		148
Beans, dry (navy, pea, etc.)	½ cup, scant	1		2	321

* The grams of high saturated fat and low saturated fat are based on the total grams of fat contained in a food generally classified as highly saturated (mainly the animal fats) and low saturated (see Appendix IV, page 351, for general classification). For fatty acid content, see Appendix V, page 356.

† Sources for the calculations are given in the Acknowledgments, page 6.

Item	Measure	Milligrams Sodium	Grams High Saturated Fat	Grams Low Saturated Fat	Calories
Beans, Lima, raw	½ cup	1		1	128
Canned	½ cup	248		negligible	76
Canned without added sodium	½ cup	2		negligible	76
Frozen, uncooked	3 rd. tbsp.	variable		1	109
Beans, snap, green and yellow wax, raw	½ cup	1		negligible	18
Canned	½ cup	258		negligible	14
Canned without added sodium	½ cup	1		negligible	14
Frozen, uncooked	½ cup	2		negligible	35
Bean sprouts, raw	1 cup	6		negligible	49
Beef, raw, lean	1 oz.	20	2 (cooked)		65 (cooked)
Corned, medium fat, raw	1 oz.	369	7		83
Dried	1 oz.	1219	2		58
Heart, raw	1 oz.	24	1		31
Kidney, raw	1 oz.	57	2		40
Koshered, lean, raw	1 oz.	454	3		52
Liver, raw	1 oz.	37	1		39
Suet	1 oz.	14	26		240
Thymus, raw	1 oz.	27	4		52
Tongue, raw, unsmoked	1 oz.	23	4		56
Beets, raw	½ cup, diced	40		negligible	28
Canned without added sodium	½ cup	33		negligible	34
Greens, fresh, cooked	½ cup	130		negligible	20
Beverages (average)					
Beer	1 cup	17		none	112
Soft drinks (Cola drinks, fruit sodas, ginger ale, root beer, etc.)	1 cup	16		none	107
Wine (see page 349	1 cup	17		none	varies

Item	Measure	Milligrams Sodium	Grams High Saturated Fat	Grams Low Saturated Fat	Calories
Blackberries, raw	½ cup	1		1	41
Canned	½ cup	1		negligible	108
Blueberries, raw	½ cup	1		negligible	43
Canned	½ cup	1		1	123
Frozen	½ cup	1		1	61
Bouillon cube	1 cube	960		negligible	2
Boysenberries, frozen	½ cup	1		negligible	113
Brandy, Schenley's	1 jigger	1		none	110
Bread					
Boston brown, with raisins	1 slice, 3" diam. × ¾"	134	1		105
Rye, with salt	1 slice	138	negligible		57
Unsalted	1 slice	7	negligible		57
White, with salt	1 slice	138	1		63
Unsalted	1 slice	7	1		63
Whole wheat, with salt	1 slice	138	1		55
Unsalted	1 slice	7	1		55
Broccoli, raw	1 stalk, 5½" long	15		negligible	29
Frozen, un-cooked	1 stalk, 5½" long	15		negligible	23
Brussels sprouts	9 medium	12		1	47
Frozen, un-cooked	9 medium	12		1	47
Butter					
Salted	1 tsp.	50	4		33
	1 tbsp.	140	11		100
	1 cup	2240	181		1604
Unsalted	1 tsp.	1	4		33
	1 tbsp.	1	11		100
	1 cup	22	181		1604
Buttermilk, cultured	1 cup	317	negligible		86
Cabbage, raw	½ cup	8		negligible	12
Candy					
Bar, Baby Ruth	1 5c bar	67	9		290
Bar, Milky Way	1 5c bar	86	2		121
Bar, Oh Henry	1 5c bar	29	9		290
Gum drop	8 small	4		none	33
Marshmallow	1 average	3		none	25
Milk chocolate	1 5c Hershey	21	8		143
Necco wafers	1 5c package	2		none	unknown
Peppermint patty, Schrafft's	1 5c patty	3	5		125
Sweet chocolate	1 oz.	10	8		143

Item	Measure	Milligrams Sodium	Grams High Saturated Fat	Grams Low Saturated Fat	Calories
Cantaloupe	½ cup, diced	9		negligible	15
Carrots, raw	½ cup,				
	grated	28		negligible	23
	1 large	25		negligible	21
Canned	½ cup	204		negligible	22
Canned without added sodium	½ cup	26		negligible	22
Casec powder	1 tbsp.	1	negligible		17
	1 cup	15	2		272
Catchup, tomato	1 tbsp.	221		negligible	17
Cauliflower, raw	½ cup	10		negligible	13
Frozen, uncooked	½ cup	20		negligible	25
Caviar, salmon, canned	1 rd. tsp.	220		2	30
Celery	3 sm. inner, 5" long	50		negligible	9
Cereals					
All-Bran	½ cup	392		1	73
Bran, crude, unsalted	1 cup	9		2	145
Corn flakes	1 cup	165		negligible	96
Corn flakes, unsalted	1 cup	2		negligible	96
Cream of Rice	½ cup, cooked	negligible		negligible	68
Cream of Wheat, plain	½ cup, cooked	negligible		negligible	67
Cream of Wheat, quick-cooking, enriched	½ cup, cooked	17		negligible	67
Farina, unsalted	½ cup, cooked	4		negligible	67
Grape-Nuts	¼ cup	187		negligible	110
Instant Ralston	½ cup, cooked	negligible		negligible	71
Maltex	½ cup, cooked	1		negligible	77
Muffets	1 average	1		negligible	83
Pabena	6 tbsp., dry	91		negligible	68
Pablum	6 tbsp., dry	88		1	53
Pettijohns	½ cup, cooked	negligible		negligible	75
Rice flakes	1 cup	216		negligible	118
Rice flakes, unsalted	1 cup	2		negligible	118
Rice, puffed	1 cup	negligible		negligible	55
Rolled oats	½ cup, cooked	negligible		1	74
	1 cup, dry	2		6	312

Item	Measure	Milligrams Sodium	Grams High Saturated Fat	Grams Low Saturated Fat	Calories
Wheat, cracked	½ cup, cooked	negligible		1	69
Wheat flakes	¾ cup	341		1	88
Wheat flakes, unsalted	¾ cup	1		1	88
Wheat germ, malt-flavored, Zing	1 tbsp.	negligible		negligible	15
Wheat, puffed	1 cup	negligible		negligible	43
Wheat, shredded	1 biscuit	1		1	102
Wheatena	½ cup, cooked	negligible		negligible	76
Certo (pectin solution)	1 cup	36		unknown	unknown
Chard, fresh, cooked	½ cup	100		negligible	15
Cheese					
Cheddar, salted	1 oz.	198	9		113
Cheddar, un-salted	1 tbsp., grated	1	2		28
	1 cup, grated	11	34		446
	1 oz.	3	9		113
Cottage, salted	½ cup	328	1		108
Cottage, un-salted	½ cup	23	1		108
Cream, Phila-delphia	2 tbsp.	75	11		112
Process	1 oz.	425	9		105
Swiss, domestic	1 oz.	198	8		105
Whey, Velveeta	1 oz.	454	7		90
Cherries, raw	15 large	2		1	61
Canned, sour	½ cup	2		negligible	61
Frozen, sour	½ cup	2		negligible	55
Chicken, fryer, raw	1 oz.	21	1		65
Chives	1 tbsp., chopped	1		negligible	unknown
Chocolate, bitter	1 square (1 oz.)	3	15		142
Semisweet bits	1 oz.	4	8		150
Citron, candied	1 oz.	54		negligible	89
Cocoa, Dutch process	1 tbsp.	4	2		21
Plain, Hershey	1 tbsp.	negligible	2		21
	1 cup	6	27		329
Coconut, raw	1 piece, 2" × 2" × ½"	14	16		161
Dry, shredded	1 tbsp.	1	2		22
	1 cup	11	24		344
Milk	½ cup	95	1		30
Cod-liver oil	1 tsp.	negligible		4	33

Item	Measure	Milligrams Sodium	Grams High Saturated Fat	Grams Low Saturated Fat	Calories
Coffee, instant					
Nescafé, dry	1 tsp.	1		none	none
Roasted, dry	1 tbsp.	negligible		none	none
Sanka	1 tbsp.	negligible		none	none
Collard greens, frozen	½ cup	18		negligible	37
Corn, popcorn, popped, un-salted	1 cup	negligible		1	54
Popcorn, popped and salted	1 cup	280		1	54
Sweet, raw	½ cup	2		1	70
	1 medium ear	2		1	92
Sweet, canned	½ cup	170		1	70
Sweet, canned without added sodium	½ cup	2		1	70
Sweet, frozen	½ cup	2		1	77
Corn meal	½ cup, cooked	negligible		negligible	60
Raw	1 cup	3		2	264
Cornstarch	1 tbsp.	negligible		negligible	29
	1 cup	3		negligible	464
Cowpeas, fresh, uncooked	½ cup	2		1	87
Crackers					
Graham	2, 2½" square	99	1		55
Matzoth					
American style, salted	1 piece	94	unknown		unknown
Egg	1 piece	4	unknown		unknown
Passover	1 piece	negligible		negligible	78
Plain	1 piece	negligible	negligible		78
Poppy seed	1 piece	70	unknown		unknown
Thin tea	1 piece	negligible	unknown		unknown
Whole wheat	1 piece	56	unknown		unknown
Ry-Crisp	1 wafer	93	negligible		47
Soda	2 crackers	121	1		
Cranberries, raw	1 cup	1		1	54
Sauce, canned	1 tbsp.	negligible		negligible	34
Cream, heavy, 32 per cent fat	1 tbsp.	6	5		49
Cucumber, raw	½ medium	7		negligible	13
Currants, raw	½ cup	1		negligible	30
Dried	½ cup	20		1	268
Dandelion greens, fresh, cooked	½ cup	76		1	40
Dates	4 pitted	negligible		negligible	85
	1 cup pitted	2		1	505

Item	Measure	Milligrams Sodium	Grams High Saturated Fat	Grams Low Saturated Fat	Calories
Dextrose	1 tbsp.	negligible		none	45
Duck, raw	1 oz.	24	8		92
Egg, whole	1 medium	70	6		77
White only	1 medium	47	none		15
Yolk only	1 medium	14	5		61
Eggplant, raw	½ cup, diced	2		negligible	24
Endive greens, fresh	4 long leaves	3		negligible	5
Figs, raw	3 small	2		1	90
Canned	3 figs	2		negligible	129
Dried	1 large	7		negligible	57
Fish					
Albacore tuna, raw	1 oz.	10		3	unknown
Bass, raw	1 oz.	19		5 (baked)	72 (cooked)
Bluefish, raw	1 oz.	19		1	35
Buffalo fish, raw	1 oz.	14		1	29
Carp, raw	1 oz.	14		2	38
Catfish, raw	1 oz.	17		1	unknown
Codfish, raw	1 oz.	22		negligible	21
Frozen fillets	1 oz.	113		negligible	21
Salted, dried	1 oz.	2296		1	106
Crab, boiled	⅝ cup	370		3	104
Canned	⅝ cup	1000		3	104
Flounder, raw	1 oz.	16		negligible	19
Haddock, raw	1 oz.	17		negligible	22
Halibut, raw	1 oz.	15		2	36
Herring, lake, raw	1 oz.	16		2	40
Lingcod, raw	1 oz.	18		1	20
Lobster, boiled	⅔ cup	250		1	92
Mackerel, Atlantic, raw	1 oz.	14		3	53
Mackerel, Pacific, (Spanish), raw	1 oz.	25		3 (canned)	51 (canned)
Mullet, fresh water, raw	1 oz.	15		unknown	unknown
Mullet, salt water, raw	1 oz.	23		unknown	unknown
Oysters, raw	1 cup	variable		5	200
Perch, fresh water, raw	1 oz.	19		negligible	25
Perch, salt water, raw	1 oz.	22		negligible	25
Pike, yellow, raw	1 oz.	15		1	29
Pollack, raw	1 oz.	14		negligible	20

Item	Measure	Milligrams Sodium	Grams High Saturated Fat	Grams Low Saturated Fat	Calories
Porgy or scup, raw	1 oz.	18		unknown	unknown
Red snapper, raw	1 oz.	20		unknown	unknown
Rockfish, raw	1 oz.	19		negligible	20
Salmon, raw	1 oz.	22		5	63
Canned, red	½ cup	405		7	130
Canned without added sodium	½ cup	45		7	85
Sand dab, raw	1 oz.	35		negligible	unknown
Sardines, canned	2 small	550		11	214
Scallop, frozen	2 to 3 pieces	150		negligible	78
Shad, raw	1 oz.	15		3	48
Sheepshead lake, raw	1 oz.	24		2	38
Sheepshead, river, raw	1 oz.	17		2	38
Shrimp, raw	4 to 6	70		1	64
Canned without added sodium	4 to 6	35		1	64
Sole, raw	1 oz.	26		1	29
Swordfish, raw	1 oz.	22		1	33
Trout, lake, raw	1 oz.	15		1	29
Trout, sea, raw	1 oz.	17		unknown	unknown
Tuna, canned with oil	⅝ cup	800		8	198
Canned without added sodium	½ cup	40		1	121
Whitefish, raw	1 oz.	15		2	47
Whiting, raw	1 oz.	18		unknown	unknown
Flour, bleached, enriched; whole wheat; rye; etc.	1 tbsp.	negligible		negligible	25
	1 cup	2		2	401
Flour, self-rising	1 cup	1650		1	385
Fruit cocktail, canned	½ cup	6		1	90
Garlic	1 clove	negligible		negligible	2
Gelatin, plain	1 tbsp.	3		none	34
Dessert flavored	1 box	281		none	324
Flavored, without added sodium	1 serving	5		none	13

Item	Measure	Milligrams Sodium	Grams High Saturated Fat	Grams Low Saturated Fat	Calories
Gin	1 jigger	negligible		none	105
Ginger, preserved	1 oz.	negligible		negligible	97
Goose, raw	1 oz.	23	9		100
Liver, raw	1 oz.	40	3		34
Gooseberries, raw	½ cup	1		negligible	30
Frozen	½ cup	2		negligible	unknown
Grape juice, sweetened	½ cup	1		negligible	85
Frozen	½ cup, diluted	1		negligible	64
Grapefruit, raw	½ medium	2		negligible	75
Canned	½ cup	3		negligible	125
Frozen	½ cup	6		negligible	unknown
Juice, canned sweetened	½ cup	3		negligible	66
Frozen	½ cup, diluted	negligible		negligible	50
Grapes, raw (Concord, Emperor, Tokay)	22 to 23 grapes	2		1	70
Thompson, seedless	60 grapes	2		1	66
Gravy flavoring (Kitchen Bouquet)	1 tsp.	4	none		none
Gum, chewing, spearmint	1 stick	1		none	unknown
Ham, cured, raw	1 oz.	312	9		98
Canned, low sodium (Cellu)	1 oz.	14	2		42
Hash, corned beef, canned	½ cup	540	6		141
Hominy, canned	1 cup	605		negligible	122
Honey	1 tbsp.	2		none	62
Ice cream	⅛ quart	64	9		146
Jam	1 tbsp.	1		negligible	55
Jelly	1 tbsp.	1		none	50
Kale, fresh, cooked	½ cup	40		negligible	23
Frozen	½ cup	32		1	40
Kumquat	6 medium	7		negligible	65
Lamb, lean, raw	1 oz.	26	2 (cooked)		55 (cooked)
Leeks	1 leek, 5" long	4		negligible	unknown
Lemon, peel, candied	1 large piece	5		negligible	11
Peel, fresh	1 tsp., grated	negligible		negligible	unknown
Pulp and juice	½ cup	1		1	30
Frozen	½ cup, diluted	2		1	26

Item	Measure	Milligrams Sodium	Grams High Saturated Fat	Grams Low Saturated Fat	Calories
Lemonade, frozen	1 cup, diluted	1		negligible	104
Lentils, dry	½ cup, scant	3		1	338
Lettuce, head	1 small leaf	2		negligible	3
	⅙ head	11		negligible	11
Lettuce, leaf	1 small leaf	1		negligible	3
Lime, pulp and juice	½ cup	1		negligible	29
Liver, beef, raw	1 oz.	37	1		40
Goose, raw	1 oz.	40	3		40
Pork, raw	1 oz.	23	1		38
Turkey, raw	1 oz.	14	1		40
Macaroni, plain	½ cup, cooked	1		negligible	105
	1 cup, dry	6		2	463
Margarine, salted	1 tsp.	55	4		34
Unsalted	1 tsp.	1	4		34
	1 tbsp.	1	11		101
	1 cup	22	181		1613
Marmalade, orange	1 tbsp.	3		negligible	55
Mayonnaise, salted	1 tbsp.	77		10	92
Without added sodium	1 tbsp.	3		10	92
Meat extract, flavored	1 tsp.	550	unknown		unknown
Milk					
Cow's					
Buttermilk, cultured	1 cup	317	negligible		86
Condensed, sweetened	1 tbsp.	27	2		61
Evaporated	½ cup	126	10		173
Skim, fresh	1 cup	123	negligible	negligible	87
Dried milk powder	1 tbsp.	39	negligible	negligible	28
Whole, fresh	1 cup	123	10		166
Goat's	1 cup	83	10		164
Low sodium					
Cellu, dried	1 tbsp.	2	negligible		28
	1 cup	36	1		434
Liquified	1 cup	7	negligible		87
Lonalac, dried	1 tbsp.	1	2		39
Liquified	1 cup	4	8		166
Low-Sodium, fresh	1 cup	12	10		166
Malted, dry	1 tbsp.	40	1		35
Mixed vegetables, frozen	½ cup	71		negligible	79
Molasses, cane	1 tbsp.	8		none	50
Mulberries	½ cup	1		1	42

Item	Measure	Milligrams Sodium	Grams High Saturated Fat	Grams Low Saturated Fat	Calories
Mushrooms, raw	10 small	5		negligible	16
Canned	½ cup	488		1	14
Canned without added sodium	½ cup	4		1	14
Mustard greens, fresh					
Cooked	½ cup	41		negligible	16
Frozen	½ cup	12		negligible	20
Nectarines, raw	2 medium	2		negligible	60
Noodles, egg	½ cup, cooked	3	1		54
Nuts					
Almonds, raw	1 cup	4		77	848
Roasted in oil, salted	14 nuts	24		unknown	unknown
Brazil, raw	2 medium	negligible		6	56
Roasted in oil, salted	2 medium	29		unknown	unknown
Cashew nuts, raw	7 medium	2		7	88
roasted in oil, salted	7 medium	30		unknown	unknown
Chestnuts	3 small	negligible		negligible	28
Filberts (hazel nuts)	11 medium	negligible		9	95
Litchi, dried	6 nuts	1		negligible	45
Peanuts, raw	16 nuts	1		7	84
Roasted, dry	16 nuts	1		7	84
Roasted in oil, salted	16 nuts	69		unknown	unknown
Pecans, raw	1 cup	1		79	752
Walnuts, black	9 halves	1		9	94
English	1 cup	2		64	654
Oil, coconut	1 cup	negligible	220		1945
Oils, corn, cottonseed, olive, peanut, etc.	1 tbsp.	negligible		14	124
	1 cup	negligible		220	1945
Okra, raw	8 pods	1		negligible	28
Frozen	8 pods	2		negligible	39
Olives, green, pickled	1 large	156		1	7
Ripe, pickled	2 small	64		1	11
Stuffed, pickled	2 small	182		1	7
Onions, raw	1 tbsp., chopped	1		negligible	4
	1 onion, 2½" diam.	11		negligible	49

Item	Measure	Milligrams Sodium	Grams High Saturated Fat	Grams Low Saturated Fat	Calories
Orange and grapefruit juice, frozen	½ cup, diluted	1		negligible	49
Oranges, raw	1 medium	2		negligible	70
Juice, canned, sweetened	½ cup	1		1	68
Frozen, Birdseye	½ cup, diluted	2		negligible	50
Peel, fresh	1 tsp., grated	negligible		negligible	unknown
Pulp and juice	½ cup	1		negligible	54
Temple	1 orange	7		1	106
Parsley, raw	1 sprig	negligible		negligible	1
	1 tbsp., chopped	1		negligible	1
Parsnip, raw	½ large	8		1	78
Peaches, raw	1 medium	1		negligible	46
Canned	2 halves	2		negligible	79
Dried	6 halves	5		negligible	133
Frozen	½ cup, scant	3		negligible	89
Peanut butter, with salt, hydrogenated	1 tbsp.	19	8		92
Without added sodium, hydrogenated	1 tbsp.	1	8		92
Peanut butter, with salt, non-hydrogenated	1 tbsp.	19		8	92
Without added sodium, non-hydrogenated	1 tbsp.	1		8	92
Pears, raw	1 medium	3		1	63
Canned	2 halves	2		negligible	79
Dried	2 halves	8		negligible	unknown
Peas, raw	½ cup	1		negligible	65
Canned	½ cup	216		1	73
Canned without added sodium	½ cup	2		1	73
Dried split	1 cup	40		2	689
Frozen, unsalted	½ cup	variable		negligible	75
Peppers, green, raw	1 tbsp., chopped	negligible		negligible	3
	1 shell	1		negligible	16
Red, dried	1 pepper	1		unknown	unknown
Persimmon, wild	1	1		negligible	78
Pickle, dill	1 large	1890		negligible	15
Pineapple, raw	½ cup	1		negligible	37

Item	Measure	Milligrams Sodium	Grams High Saturated Fat	Grams Low Saturated Fat	Calories
Canned	1 large slice	1		negligible	95
	½ cup, crushed	1		negligible	102
Frozen	½ cup, scant	1		negligible	97
Juice, canned	½ cup	1		negligible	61
Frozen	½ cup, diluted	1		negligible	60
Plums, raw	2 medium	1		negligible	58
Canned in sirup	2 medium	1		negligible	62
Pomegranate	1 medium	negligible		1	90
Pork, lean, raw	1 oz.	16	3 (cooked)		71 (cooked)
Liver, raw	1 oz.	23	1		38
Pancreas, raw	1 oz.	16	4		52
Salt	1 oz.	510	24		222
Postum, cereal beverage, dry	1 tbsp.	2		negligible	unknown
Instant, dry	1 tsp.	1		negligible	4
Potatoes, chips	10 pieces	68	7		108
Sweet, raw	1 small	10		1	123
Canned	½ cup, scant	48		negligible	117
White, raw	1 potato, 2¼" diam.	3		negligible	83
	½ cup, diced	3		negligible	83
Canned	3 very small	497		negligible	118
Pretzels	5 small	85	negligible		18
Prunes, raw	2 medium	1		negligible	58
Canned	3 prunes	4		negligible	92
Dried	6 medium	2		negligible	110
Juice	½ cup, scant	2		negligible	85
Pumpkin, raw	½ cup, cubed	1		negligible	unknown
Canned	½ cup	2		negligible	38
Quail, raw	1 oz.	12	2		48
Rabbit, raw	1 oz.	11	2		35
Radish	1 small	1		negligible	1
Raisins	1 tbsp.	3		negligible	26
	1 cup	40		1	429
Raspberries, raw	½ cup	1		1	70
Canned	½ cup, scant	2		negligible	101
Frozen	½ cup	1		negligible	84
Rennet tablet (Junket)	1 tablet	38		unknown	unknown
Rhubarb, raw	1 cup	1		negligible	19
Frozen	½ cup, scant	2		negligible	138
Rice, brown	½ cup, cooked	2		negligible	68
	1 cup, raw	19		4	748
Minute rice	½ cup, cooked	negligible		negligible	81
	1 cup, raw	2		negligible	420

Item	Measure	Milligrams Sodium	Grams High Saturated Fat	Grams Low Saturated Fat	Calories
Polished and coated	½ cup, cooked	negligible		negligible	101
	1 cup, raw	4		1	692
Vitaminized	½ cup, cooked	1		negligible	101
Wild	½ cup, cooked	1		negligible	78
	1 cup, raw	11		1	593
Rum, Puerto Rican Bacardi	1 jigger	1		none	105
Rutabaga, fresh, cooked	½ cup, scant	5		negligible	38
Sauerkraut, canned	⅔ cup	650		negligible	22
Sausage, bologna	1 slice, 4½″ × ⅛″	390	5		66
Frankfurter, raw	2 average	1100	20		248
Pork, raw	1 small	240	13		94 (cooked)
Seasonings				All extracts, herbs and spices used in small quantities may be considered negligible in fat and calories.	
Allspice, ground	1 tsp.	2			
Allspice, whole	4	negligible			
Almond extract	1 tsp.	negligible			
Anise seed	1 tsp.	negligible			
Banana extract	1 tsp.	negligible			
Basil	1 tsp.	negligible			
Bay leaf	1 leaf	negligible			
Bouquet Garni for beef	1 tsp.	1			
Bouquet Garni for soup	1 tsp.	5			
Caraway seed	1 tsp.	1			
Cardamon, ground	1 tsp.	negligible			
Cardamon, seed	1 tsp.	negligible			
Cassia, cracked	1 tsp.	1			
Celery flakes	1 tsp.	115			
Celery salt	1 tsp.	840			
Celery seed, ground	1 tsp.	2			
Celery seed, whole	1 tsp.	4			
Chervil	1 tsp.	1			
Chili con carne seasoning powder	1 tsp.	1			

Item	Measure	Milligrams Sodium	Grams High Saturated Fat	Grams Low Saturated Fat	Calories
Chili pequins	1 pod	negligible			
Chili powder	1 tsp.	57			
Cinnamon, ground	1 tsp.	negligible			
cinnamon, whole	¼" stick	negligible			
Cloves, ground	1 tsp.	1			
Cloves, whole	1 clove	negligible			
Coriander, ground	1 tsp.	1			
Coriander seed	1 tsp.	1			
Cream of tartar	1 tsp.	8			
Cumin, ground	1 tsp.	negligible			
Cumin seed	1 tsp.	negligible			
Curry powder	1 tsp.	1			
Dill seed	1 tsp.	negligible			
Dill weed	1 tsp.	negligible			
Fennel seed	1 tsp.	1			
Fenugreek seed	1 tsp.	1			
Fines herbes	1 tsp.	1	All extracts, herbs and spices used in small quantities may be considered negligible in fat and calories.		
Garlic	1 clove	negligible			
Garlic chips	1 tsp.	1			
Garlic powder	1 tsp.	1			
Ginger, ground	1 tsp.	1			
Ginger, whole	1 piece	1			
Gumbo file	1 tsp.	1			
Horseradish	1 tsp.	1			
Juniper berries	1 berry	negligible			
Lemon peel	1 tsp.	1			
Mace, ground	1 tsp.	2			
Mace, whole	1 tsp.	2			
Marjoram	1 tsp.	negligible			
Mint flakes	1 tsp.	negligible			
Mushroom, powdered	1 tsp.	1			
Mustard, ground	1 tsp.	negligible			
Mustard, prepared	1 tsp.	65			
Mustard, prepared without added sodium	1 tsp.	2			
Mustard seed	1 tsp.	negligible			
Nutmeg, ground	1 tsp.	1			
Nutmeg, whole	1 nut	1			
Onion, instant minced	1 tsp.	2			
Onion powder	1 tsp.	2			

Item	Measure	Milligrams Sodium	Grams High Saturated Fat	Grams Low Saturated Fat	Calories
Onion, shredded green	1 tsp.	11			
Orange peel	1 tsp.	1			
Oregano leaf	1 tsp.	negligible			
Paprika	1 tsp.	2			
Parsley, fresh	1 tbsp.	1			
	1 sprig	negligible			
Parsley flakes	1 tsp.	29			
Pepper, black	1 tsp.	negligible			
Pepper, Nepal	1 tsp.	1			
Pepper, red	1 tsp.	1			
Pepper, white	1 tsp.	negligible			
Peppercorns	4	negligible			
Peppermint extract	1 tsp.	negligible			
Peppermint (spice)	1 tsp.	3			
Pickling spice	1 tsp.	1			
Poppy seed	1 tsp.	negligible			
Poultry seasoning	1 tsp.	1			
Pumpkin pie spice	1 tsp.	negligible			
Rosemary leaves	1 tsp.	negligible			
Saffron, Spanish	1 tsp.	1			
Sage	1 tsp.	negligible			
Salad herbs	1 tsp.	negligible			
Salt	1 tsp.	2361			
Savory, powdered	1 tsp.	negligible			
Sesame seed	1 tsp.	2			
Spearmint	1 tsp.	2			
Spice Parisienne	1 tsp.	1			
Tarragon	1 tsp.	negligible			
Thyme	1 tsp.	1			
Turmeric	1 tsp.	1			
Vanilla extract	1 tsp.	negligible			
Vinegar, cider and distilled	1 tbsp.	negligible		negligible	2
	1 cup	2		negligible	29
Vinegar, wine, red	1 tbsp.	4		negligible	2
	1 cup	70		negligible	29
Vinegar, wine, white	1 tbsp.	5		negligible	2
	1 cup	84		negligible	29
Worcestershire sauce	1 tbsp.	315		unknown	unknown

Item	Measure	Milligrams Sodium	Grams High Saturated Fat	Grams Low Saturated Fat	Calories
Worcestershire sauce, prepared without added sodium	1 tbsp.	4		unknown	unknown
Semolina	½ cup, cooked	negligible		unknown	unknown
Shortenings, Crisco, Spry, etc.	1 tbsp.	negligible	13		110
	1 cup	negligible	200		1768
Lard	1 tbsp.	negligible	14		126
	1 cup	negligible	220		1984
Sirup, chocolate, Hershey	1 tbsp.	12	negligible		42
Karo	1 tbsp.	14		none	57
Maple	1 tbsp.	3		none	50
Sorghum	1 tbsp.	8		none	52
Table blends	1 tbsp.	12		none	57
Soft drinks, see Beverages					
Soup, beef, canned	⅓ can, diluted	426	2		82
Tomato, canned	⅓ can, diluted	377	2		73
Vegetable, canned	⅓ can, diluted	395		1 (no meat)	64
Soy beans, dry	½ cup	4		19	348
Flour, solvent-extracted	1 cup	1		1	230
Spaghetti, plain	½ cup, cooked	1		negligible	109
	1 cup, raw	5		1	354
Spices, see Seasonings					
Spinach, fresh, cooked	½ cup	75		negligible	22
Canned	½ cup	288		1	23
Canned without added sodium	½ cup	45		1	23
Frozen, cooked	½ cup	70		negligible	20
Squab, raw	1 oz.	59	6		unknown
Squash, raw, all types	½ cup	1		negligible	17 (summer) 48 (winter)
Frozen, cooked	½ cup	6		negligible	16 (summer)

Item	Measure	Milligrams Sodium	Grams High Saturated Fat	Grams Low Saturated Fat	Calories
Strawberries, raw	10 large	1		1	54
Canned	½ cup, scant	1		negligible	unknown
Frozen	½ cup, scant	2		negligible	90
Suet, beef	1 oz.	14	26		240
Sugar, light brown	1 tbsp.	4		none	51
	1 cup	55		none	813
Powdered	1 tbsp.	negligible		none	31
	1 cup	negligible		none	493
White	1 tbsp.	negligible		none	48
	1 cup	negligible		none	770
Tangerines, raw	1 medium	1		negligible	35
Juice, canned	½ cup	1		negligible	48
Tapioca, dry	1 tbsp.	negligible		negligible	34
	1 cup	6		negligible	547
Tea, blend, dry	1 tsp.	negligible		none	none
Tomatoes, raw	1 small	3		negligible	22
Canned	½ cup	22		negligible	23
Canned without added sodium	½ cup	4		negligible	23
Catchup	1 tbsp.	221		negligible	17
Juice, canned	½ cup	278		negligible	25
Canned without added sodium	½ cup	4		negligible	25
Toothpastes					
Amident	1 gram	2			
Pepsodent	1 gram	65			
Squibb	1 gram	2			
Tooth powders					
Colgate	1 gram	5			
Dentrix	1 gram	8			
Tripe, pickled	1 oz.	13	1		28
Turkey, raw	1 oz.	18	2 (cooked)		57 (cooked)
Gizzard, raw	1 oz.	16	3		unknown
Heart, raw	1 oz.	20	2		45
Liver, raw	1 oz.	14	1		40
Turnip, leaves, fresh, cooked	½ cup	10		negligible	22
Frozen	½ cup	23		negligible	23
White, raw	½ cup, diced	26		negligible	22
Yellow (rutabaga), fresh, cooked	½ cup, scant	5		negligible	38
Veal, raw, lean	1 oz.	28	1 (cooked)		57 (cooked)
Vinegar, see Seasonings					

Item	Measure	Milligrams Sodium	Grams High Saturated Fat	Grams Low Saturated Fat	Calories
Water, distilled	1 cup	none		none	none
Watermelon, pink part	½ cup	1		negligible	28
Whiskey, blended (Seagram's Bonded)	1 jigger	negligible		none	119
Wine, see Beverages and page 349					
Yeast, compressed	1 cake	negligible		negligible	24
Cultured, dry	1 tbsp.	variable		negligible	22
Yoghurt, fat-free	1 cup	98	negligible		unknown
Regular	1 cup	98	7		207
Zwieback	1 piece	19	1		31

2. AVAILABLE COMMERCIAL PRODUCTS RESTRICTED IN SODIUM CONTENT*

Check with your neighborhood grocer, specialty shop, or health store for the products listed below.

Food	Brand	Household Measure	Milligrams Sodium per Household Measure
Asparagus	Average	6 stalks	4
Baking powder	Average	1 teaspoon	1
Beans, Lima	Average	½ cup	2
Beans, snap, green and yellow, wax	Average	½ cup	1
Beans, soy, green	Cellu	½ cup	5
Beets	Average	½ cup	33
Bouillon cube			
Beef flavor	Cellu	1 cube	33
Chicken flavor	Cellu	1 cube	10
Bread, canned			
Rye	Horlamus	½ inch slice	1
White	Cellu White Wheat	½ inch slice	2
	Horlamus	½ inch slice	negligible
Whole wheat	Horlamus	½ inch slice	1
Bread, fresh, white, whole wheat, and rye	Average	½ inch slice	7
	Oroweat	½ inch slice	1
Bread, Melba toast	Cellu	4 slices	3

Food	Brand	Household Measure	Milligrams Sodium per Household Measure
	Devonsheer	1 slice	negligible
Bread, Italian, sticks	Stella D'oro	1 stick	2
Candy			
Chocolate bar	Estee Dietetic	1 square	4
Filbert praline	Estee Dietetic	1 bar (¾ oz.)	20
Hard	Cellu	1 roll	2
Licorice Wonder Jets	Be Leave	1 piece	3
Marzipan	Scandia Maid	1 bar	26
Milk chocolates, assorted	Estee Dietetic	1 piece	8
Thin mints	Estee Dietetic	1 piece	5
Cake, canned	Cellu	½ inch slice	5
Cake, honey fruit	Holland	½ inch slice	10
Cake mix	Cellu	⅙ cake	6
Carrot juice	Nutradiet	½ cup	70
Carrots	Average	½ cup	26
Cereals			
Cornflakes	Van Brode Dietetic	1 cup	2
Rice flakes	Battle Creek	¾ cup	2
	Van Brode Dietetic	1 cup	2
Wheat flakes	Average	¾ cup	1
Zo	Battle Creek	⅔ oz.	2
Cheese, cheddar	Cellu Dietetic	1 tablespoon, grated	1
		1 cup, grated	11
		1 oz.	3
Cheese, cottage	Average	½ cup	23
Cheese spread	Cellu Dietetic	1 oz.	4
Cookies, rice	Cellu	4 cookies	3
Corn	Average	½ cup	2
Crackers			
Protein wafers	Devonsheer	1 wafer	negligible
Rice wafers	Cellu	6 wafers	1
Wheat wafers (salt-free)	Venus	1 cracker	8
Dressings			
French dressing	Cellu	1 tablespoon	negligible
French dressing, Type V	Diafoods	1 tablespoon	2
Type Y	Diafoods	1 tablespoon	1
Fruit dressing	Cellu	1 tablespoon	1
Mayonnaise	Average	1 tablespoon	3
Soyamaise	Cellu	1 tablespoon	2
Superb dressing	Diamel	1 teaspoon	3
Tangy dressing	Diamel	1 tablespoon	12
Gelatin dessert	Average	1 tablespoon	1
Margarine	Average	1 teaspoon	1
		1 tablespoon	1
		1 cup	22
Meats			

* Sodium values for food items listed as average were calculated from Table 2, Publication 325, *Sodium Restricted Diets, The Rationale, Complications, and Practical Aspects of Their Use*, National Academy of Sciences—National Research Council.

Food	Brand	Household Measure	Milligrams Sodium per Household Measure
Beef and mushroom sauce	Swift	1 can (6 oz.)	91
Beef steak and sauce	Swift	1 can (6 oz.)	92
Beef steaks, chopped	Swift	1 can (6 oz.)	122
Beef stew	Overland	1 can (6 oz.)	48
Chicken, boned	Cellu	1 oz.	11
	Overland	1 oz.	13
Chicken cacciatore	Swift	1 can (6 oz.)	54
Ham	Cellu	1 oz.	14
Lamb and mint sauce	Swift	1 can (6 oz.)	94
Liver and creole sauce	Swift	1 can (6 oz.)	109
Pork steaks and barbecue sauce	Swift	1 can (6 oz.)	75
Roast beef hash	Swift	1 can (6 oz.)	103
Milk, dry, non-fat	Cellu	1 cup, dry	36
		1 cup, liquefied	7
Milk, fresh	Lo-Sodium	1 cup	12
Mixed vegetables	Cellu	½ cup	22
Mushrooms	Average	½ cup	4
Peanut butter	Average	1 tablespoon	1
Peas	Average	½ cup	2
Puddings, Danish Dessert	Junket	¼ package	16
Puddings, Type J	Diafoods		
Butterscotch		½ cup	3
Caramel		½ cup	8
Chocolate		½ cup	3
Coconut		½ cup	1
Koffymaple		½ cup	4
Vanilla		½ cup	2
Relishes, sauces, and flavorings			
Catsup	Cellu	1 tablespoon	2
Chili sauce	Cellu	1 tablespoon	1
Cucumber pickles	Cellu	1 serving	2
Diazest	Diafoods	4 drops	negligible
Dill sauce, Type W	Diafoods	1 tablespoon	1
Mustard	Plantation	1 teaspoon	1
Vegetable relish	Cellu	1 tablespoon	6
Worcestershire sauce	Plantation	1 tablespoon	4
Salmon	Average	½ cup	45
Shrimp	Cellu	4 to 6	35
Soup Stock Mix			
Beef flavor	Cellu	1 serving	1
Chicken flavor	Cellu	1 serving	negligible
Soups (diluted)			
Beef soup base, Type M	Diafoods	¾ cup	13
Chicken broth	Cellu	1 cup	60
	Claybourne	1 cup	23
Chicken soup base, Type L	Diafoods	¾ cup	1
Consommé, jellied, Type R	Diafoods	½ cup	1
Consommé, Type O	Diafoods	¾ cup	1
Cream of mushroom	Claybourne	1 cup	35
Mushroom broth	Cellu	1 cup	10
Pea, condensed	Claybourne	1 cup	23
Tomato, condensed	Claybourne	1 cup	35

Food	Brand	Household Measure	Milligrams Sodium per Household Measure
Type P	Diafoods	¾ cup	6
Tomato-rice	Cellu	1 cup	29
Vegetable, condensed	Claybourne	1 cup	46
Soynuts	Cellu	¼ cup	1
Spinach	Average	½ cup	45
Tomato juice	Average	½ cup	4
Tomato paste	Average	½ cup	4
Tomatoes	Cellu	⅓ cup	30
Tuna	Average	½ cup	40

3. SODIUM CONTENT OF TABLE WINES *
(Milligrams per cup)

Type	No. of Samples	Minimum	Maximum	Average
Red wines				
California wines (total)	82	2	35	13
Barbera	3	10	12	11
Barenblut	1			14
Burgundy	23	6	35	14
Cabernet Sauvignon	9	3	24	10
Chianti	2	6	12	9
Claret	5	13	17	14
Gamay	3	11	29	18
"Grape wine"	2	18	23	20
Miscellaneous table wines	7	9	19	13
Pinot Noir	6	5	27	11
Rosé	10	2	28	16
Zinfandel	11	3	25	12
French wines (total)	5	4	58	19
Chambertin '06	1			4
Château Haut Brion #1	1			7
Château Haut Brion #2	1			9
La Tâche '33	1			58
Pommard '26	1			16
Totals, red wines	87	2	58	14

* Source of data: "Dietary Sodium and Potassium in California Wines" by Salvatore P. Lucia, M.D., and Marjorie L. Hunt, M.P.H. (with the technical assistance of Edith Feis), American Journal of Digestive Diseases, 2:26, January, 1957.

Type	No. of Samples	Minimum	Maximum	Average
White wines				
California wines (total)	73	3	41	13
Chablis	9	3	26	13
Champagne	1			20
Chateau (3 wineries)	3	5	30	14
Colombard	1			19
Folle Blanche	2	4	4	4
"Grape wine"	1			16
Pinot Blanc	8	4	27	9
Pinot Chardonnay	2	6	10	8
Rhine	2	5	13	9
Riesling	9	4	23	12
Sauterne	28	4	41	15
Sauvignon Blanc	2	6	14	10
Sylvaner	2	6	6	6
Traminer	3	15	20	18
Foreign wines (total)	4	3	9	6
Chablis Les Clos	1			4
Champagne—Louis Roederer	1			3
French: Champagne— Möet	1			7
German: Dom Avelsbacher	1			9
Totals, white wines	77	3	41	13
Totals, red and white table wines	164	2	58	13

SODIUM CONTENT OF CALIFORNIA DESSERT WINES

Type	No. of Samples	Minimum	Maximum	Average
Angelica	2	6	17	11
Black Muscat	1			12
Muscat de Frontignan	2	7	14	10
Muscatel	15	5	61	23
Port	31	5	22	17
Ruby	16	6	29	16
Tawny	4	13	30	22
White	11	5	33	16
Sherry (includes cream, dry, pale-dry, and miscellaneous sherries)	36	6	48	16
Cream	8	10	48	21

Type	No. of Samples	Minimum	Maximum	Average
Dry and pale-dry	12	6	29	15
Tokay	14	4	24	15
Vermouth	3	26	28	27
Total	104	4	61	17

4. (A) COMMON FOODS LOW IN SATURATED FATS

Beverages
  Alcoholic (ale, beer, brandy, whiskey, wine)
  Carbonated (Coca-Cola, ginger ale, root beer, etc.)
  Cider
  Coffee, black
  Fruit juices
  Lemonade
  Milk, buttermilk
  Milk, non-fat
  Postum
  Tea

Bread and Bread Products
  Commercial
    Italian
    Rye
  Homemade (with vegetable oil, non-fat milk, egg white)
    Baking powder biscuits (curry, herb, orange, parsley)
    Coffee cake
    Muffins (apple, blueberry, cornmeal, fruit, graham, nut)
    Orange bread
    Prune bread
    Sweet yeast (cinnamon buns, rolls, and twists; orange)
    Yeast breads and rolls
    (cracked wheat, date, graham, herb, potato, water, white, whole wheat)

Cereals and Cereal Products
  Barley
  Bran
  Bran flakes
  Corn flakes
  Cornmeal
  Cream of Wheat
  Grape-Nuts
  Macaroni
  Maltex
  Muffets
  Oats
  Pettijohns
  Popcorn (without butter or margarine)
  Ralston
  Rice
  Spaghetti
  Tapioca
  Wheat (flakes and puffed)
  Wheat, Shredded

Crackers
  Matzoth (unsalted)

Dairy Products
  Cheese (cottage)
  Egg white
  Milk, buttermilk

Milk, dried skim
Milk, non-fat

Desserts
Angel cake
Cakes and cookies, home-
made with vegetable oil;
without whole milk, egg
yolk, chocolate, coconut
Gelatin
Ices, plain
Pies, homemade with vege-
table oil; without cream,
egg yolk, whole milk
Puddings, homemade with-
out whole eggs, whole
milk

Fats and Oils
Vegetable oils (corn, cottonseed, olive, peanut, saf-
flower, soybean, sunflower)

Fish (canned, fresh, or frozen)
Bass
Bluefish
Butterfish
Cod
Flounder
Haddock
Halibut
Herring
Mackerel
Perch
Porgy
Salmon
Sardines
Shellfish
Swordfish
Tuna
Whiting

Flours and Flour Products
Barley
Cake (not mixes)
Cornstarch
Gluten
Graham

Rice
Rye
Wheat
Whole wheat

Fruit (canned, fresh, or frozen)
Apples
Apricots
Avocado
Bananas
Berries
Cherries
Cranberries
Dates
Figs
Grapefruit
Grapes
Lemons
Limes
Melon
Oranges
Peaches
Pears
Pineapple
Plums
Prunes
Rhubarb
Tangerines

Nuts (plain or with vegetable
oil)
Almonds
Brazil nuts
Butternuts
Cashew nuts
Peanut butter (non-hydro-
genated)
Peanuts
Pecans
Walnuts

Sauces
Homemade with vegetable
oil, non-fat milk, egg
white

Sirups and Sugars
Corn sirup

Honey
Maple sirup
Molasses
Sugar (brown, powdered, granulated)
Table sirup

Soups (see page 67)
Bouillon
Chowders (homemade with non-fat milk, vegetable oil; without butter, meat)
Consommé
Cream soups (homemade with vegetable oil, non-fat milk)

Sweets
Candy (homemade without butter, margarine, whole milk)
Gum drops
Jams
Jelly beans
Jellies
Marmalades
Marshmallow
Mints, cream
Necco wafers

Vegetables (canned, fresh, or frozen)

Artichoke
Asparagus
Bean sprouts
Beans (dried, green, Lima, snap)
Beets
Broccoli
Cabbage
Cauliflower
Celery
Corn
Cucumber
Eggplant
Garlic
Greens (chicory, dandelion, escarole, kale, spinach, etc.)
Leeks
Lettuce
Mushrooms
Onions
Peppers
Potatoes
Pumpkin
Radish
Rutabaga
Squash (all types)
Sweet potatoes
Tomatoes
Turnip
Yams

4. (B) COMMON FOODS HIGH IN SATURATED FATS

Beverages
Chocolate milk
Cocoa
Eggnog
Milk shakes
Milk, whole
Soda, ice cream

Bread and Bread Products
Boston brown bread
Bran, raisin bread
Commercial (with butter, hydrogenated shortening, lard, whole egg, whole milk)

Coffee cake
Corn bread
Danish pastry
Doughnuts
Homemade (with butter, hydrogenated shortening, lard, margarine, whole egg, whole milk)
  Baking powder biscuit
  Banana bread
  Corn bread
  Date bread
  Muffins (all kinds)
  Yeast breads and rolls (all kinds)
Muffins (all kinds)
Yeast breads and rolls (cracked wheat, French, raisin, white, whole wheat)

Cereal Products
Egg noodles
Macaroni and cheese
Spaghetti with meat sauce

Crackers (with lard or hydrogenated shortenings)
Cheese
Graham
Pretzel
Saltines
Soda
Wheat

Dairy Products
Butter
Cheese, (cheddar, cream Edam, Limburger, Parmesan, Roquefort, spreads, Swiss, Velveeta)
Cream
Eggs (whole and yolk)
Ice cream
Milk, chocolate
Milk, condensed
Milk, dried whole
Milk, evaporated

Milk, goat's
Milk, malted
Milk, whole
Yoghurt, from whole milk

Desserts (except homemade with vegetable oils; without whole egg, whole milk, coconut, or chocolate)
Brownies
Cakes (all kinds except angel)
Cookies
Custards
Eclairs
Ice cream
Pies
Puddings (bread, tapioca, rice, with whole milk, whole eggs)
Sherbets, milk

Fats and Oils
Bacon
Butter
Chicken
Coconut oil
Cooking fats (hydrogenated)
Lard
Margarine
Mayonnaise or salad dressing with coconut oil

Fish
Creamed with whole milk, butter, margarine
Fried in saturated fats
Soups and chowders with whole milk, salt pork, butter, margarine

Flours and Flour Products
Bisquick
Cake mixes
Cookie mixes
Muffin mixes

Pancake mixes
Pie crust mixes

Meats
Bacon
Beef
Chicken
Cold cuts
Duck
Frankfurter
Goose
Ham
Heart
Kidney
Lamb
Liver
Pork
Rabbit
Sausage
Tongue
Turkey
Veal

Nuts
Chocolate coated nuts
Coconut
Peanut butter (hydrogenated)

Sauces
Commercial and homemade with whole milk, whole egg, butter, margarine
Gravies

Soups (see page 67)
Commercial or homemade with whole milk, meats, salt pork, lard, hydrogenated shortenings, butter, margarine

Sweets (candies)
Commercial or homemade with chocolate, coconut, whole egg, whole milk, butter, margarine

Vegetables
Canned, fresh, or frozen prepared with added butter, margarine, salt pork, whole egg, whole milk such as fried or creamed
Potato chips

5. FATTY ACID CONTENT OF FOOD FATS, UNSAPONIFIABLE MATTER, AND IODINE VALUE*

(Grams per 100 grams ether extract or crude fat) †

Food fat or oil	Saturated fatty acids			Unsaturated fatty acids				Other	Unsaponifiable matter	Iodine value
	Total‡	Palmitic C_{16}	Stearic C_{18}	Total	Oleic $C_{18}(-2H)$	Linoleic $C_{18}(-4H)$	Linolenic $C_{18}(-6H)$			
ANIMAL PRODUCTS										
Meats:										
1. Beef	48	28	19	47	44	2	§Trace	1	—	47
2. Buffalo	66	34	28	30	24	1	—	5	Trace	31
3. Deer	63	24	34	32	24	3	2	3	Trace	36
4. Goat	57	26	24	37	33	2	—	2	2	33
5. Horse	30	24	5	60	30	6	13	11	6	75
6. Lamb	56	29	25	40	36	3	1	Trace	—	40
7. Luncheon meats	36	24	11	59	45	7	Trace	7	—	61
8. Pork:										
a. Back, outer layer	38	26	12	58	46	6	—	6	—	64
b. Bacon	32	21	9	63	48	9	Trace	6	—	67

* Fatty Acids in Food Fats, *Home Economics Research Report No. 7*, prepared by Verz R. Goddard, Nutrition Specialist, Louise Goodall, Statistical Assistant, Human Nutrition Research Division, Agricultural Research Service, Washington, D. C. (Issued March 1959).

† The figures for fatty acids per 100 grams of ether extract (crude fat) shown in this table, have been computed from the data on fatty acids as per cent of total fatty acids by correcting for glycerol in the fat and for the content of unsaponifiable matter reported in the ether extract of each food fat. Glycerol values are not shown in the table. To calculate fatty acids in foods, it is necessary only to multiply the amount (grams) of fat in a food portion by the value of each fatty acid.

‡ Includes other saturated fatty acids in addition to palmitic and stearic.

§ Trace is used to indicate values of 0.5 or less.

Food	(1)	(2)	(3)	(4)	(5)	(6)	(7)	(8)	(9)	(10)
c. Liver	34	18	18	61	27	5	—	29	—	—
d. Other cuts	36	21	13	59	42	9	Trace	8	—	64
9. Rabbit, domesticated	38	28	4	58	35	11	2	10	—	66
Milk Fat:										
10. Buffalo, Indian	62	29	15	33	26	1	—	6	Trace	30
11. Cow	55	25	12	39	33	3	1	2	Trace	33
12. Goat	62	27	8	33	25	5	—	3	Trace	37
13. Human	46	22	7	*48	34	7	Trace	7	—	—
Poultry and Eggs:										
14. Chicken	32	24	7	*64	38	20	2	4	—	92
15. Turkey	29	22	6	*67	43	21	1	2	3	84
16. Chicken eggs	32	25	7	61	44	7	1	9	—	84
Fish and Shellfish:										
17. Eel, body	23	17	2	73		36 (—2.6H)		37		119
18. Herring, body	19	11	1	77		19 (—3.5H)		58		140
19. Menhaden, body	24	15	3	71	15	3	2	51	1	
20. Salmon, body	15	12	3	79		26 (—2.8H)		53	1	151
21. Tuna, body	25	18	3	70		25 (—3.2H)		45		
22. Turtle	44	16	7	51		31 (—2.6H)		20		74
Separated Fats and Oils:										
23. Butter	55	25	12	39	33	8	1	2	Trace	33
24. Lard	38	31	7	57	46	10	1	Trace	Trace	64
25. Shortening, See item 69										
26. Codfish liver	15	12	1	81		25 (—3.3H)		56		178
27. Halibut liver	17	13	Trace	72	31			41	7	120
Whale blubber	15	9	1	41		21 (—2.4H)		20	40	87
PLANT PRODUCTS										
Cereals and Grains:										
28. Cornmeal, white	11	8	1	82	34	44	1	3	3	123
29. Millet (Foxtail)	31	10	14	61	20	35	6	—	3	120
30. Oats, rolled	22	13	4	74	32	41	1	Trace	—	
31. Rice	17	12	2	74	39	35	—	—	5	100

* Includes 1 gram arachidonic acid.

| Food fat or oil | Saturated fatty acids | | | Unsaturated fatty acids | | | | | Unsaponifiable matter | Iodine value |
	Total*	Palmitic C16	Stearic C18	Total	Oleic C18(−2H)	Linoleic C18(−4H)	Linolenic C18(−6H)	Other		
82. Sorghum	12	7	5	81	37	44	—	—	3	120
83. Wheat flour, white	14	10	4	76	31	42	3	—	6	129
84. Wheat germ	15	11	4	77	23	48	6	—	4	
Fruits and Vegetables including seeds:										
85. Avocado pulp	20	18	2	69	45	13	1	10	6	88
86. Cantaloupe seed	15	10	4	79	26	53	—	—	1	126
87. Chickpea	9	4	2	87	50	36	—	1		114
88. Chocolate	56	23	33	39	37	2	—	1	Trace	37
89. Olives	11	9	2	84	76	7	—	1	1	84
90. Pigeonpea	33	9	—	57	6	46	5	—	6	104
91. Pumpkin seed	17	9	8	78	37	41	—	—	1	119
92. Rape seed	14	2	2	89	16	14	9	50	—	104
93. Sesame seed	20	8	4	80	38	42	—	Trace	2	114
94. Soybeans	18	11	7	75	16	52	7	Trace	—	128
95. Squash seed	18	12	6	77	35	42	—	—	1	121
96. Watermelon seed	17	10	6	78	18	59	—	1	1	128
Nuts and Peanuts:										
97. Almond	8	7	1	87	67	20	—	—	Trace	101
98. Beechnut	8	5	3	87	54	31	2	2	1	112
99. Brazil nut	20	14	6	76	48	26	—	2	—	—
100. Cashew	17	6	11	78	70	7	—	1	Trace	
101. Coconut	86	10	2	8	7	Trace	—	1	1	9
102. Filbert (hazelnut)	5	2	1	91	54	16	—	21	Trace	95
103. Hickory	8	6	1	87	68	18	—	1	1	94
104. Peanut	22	11	4	72	43	29	—	—	1	101

*Includes other saturated fatty acids in addition to palmitic and stearic.

55. Peanut butter	26	11	6	70	45	25	—	—	Trace	100
56. Pecan	7	6	1	84	63	20	1	Trace	5	105
57. Pistachio	10	8	2	85	65	19	—	1	1	95
58. Walnut, black	6	3	2	90	35	48	7	—	Trace	135
59. Walnut, English	7	5	2	89	15	62	8	4	Trace	162
Separated Fats and Oils:										
60. Cacao butter	56	23	33	89	37	2	—	—	Trace	37
61. Corn oil	10	8	2	84	28	53	1	2	2	127
62. Cottonseed oil	25	22	2	71	21	50	Trace	—	—	109
63. Margarine *	26	21	3	70	57	9	—	4	—	72
64. Olive oil	11	9	2	84	76	7	Trace	—	1	84
65. Palm oil	45	39	4	49	40	8	—	1	1	51
66. Peanut oil	18	8	6	76	47	29	—	—	1	101
67. Safflower oil	8	3	4	87	15	72	—	—	1	146
68. Sesame oil	14	8	4	80	38	42	—	Trace	2	114
69. Shortening (animal and vegetable) *	43	27	12	53	41	11	1	Trace	—	59
70. Shortening (vegetable)*	23	14	6	72	65	7	Trace	Trace	—	75
71. Soybean oil	15	9	6	80	20	52	7	1	1	133
72. Sunflower oil	12	6	5	83	20	63	—	—	Trace	134

* Varies widely depending on the fats used.

INDEX

GENERAL INDEX

Effect of cooking on sodium content, 80
for fat restriction, 79-83, 322
Fillings for Sandwiches,286-88
Freezing, 277
Grades to use, 81
Place in diet, 79-80
Restrictions for saturated fat control diet, 79, 81, 84, 86-88, 91-92, 93, 94, 96, 322
Restrictions for sodium-restricted diet, 22, 79, 81
Sandwiches, 286-88
Seasonings to go with, 82-83
Stretchers, 104-05
Tenderizers, 82
Meats, 79-106
Analysis; see Appendix I, 328
Beef, 80, 83, 84, 86-87, 286; see also recipes
Commercial available, 24, 347-48
How to cook, 81-83
for saturated fat control, 82, 86
Koshered, 19, 81
Lamb, 80, 94, 287; see also recipes
Manufacturer of; see Appendix II, 346
Pork, 80, 83, 96-97, 287
Processed, 19, 24
Saturated fat content high, 27-28, 79
Content; see recipes
Selection, importance of, 28, 80
Shrinkage, 36, 80
Sodium content high, 19, 79-80; see also recipes and Appendix I, 328
Veal, 80, 83, 99-100, 287
What to serve with, 105-06
Medications, 23
Menu Patterns, 39-46
Family, 39-40
Restricted saturated fat with added vegetable oil, 43-44
Sodium-restricted, 40-43, 46
Total fat-restricted, 45-46
Menus; see also Menu Patterns
Eating out with saturated fat restrictions, 295-96
Eating out with sodium restrictions, 294-95
Frozen Dinners, 278-82
Lunch Box, 285-92
Special Occasions, 314-18
Birthday Dinners, 315-16
Christmas Dinners, 317-18
Sunday Night Suppers, 314-15
Thanksgiving, 316-17
Milk; see also Low sodium milk
Amount recommended, 34
Analysis, 337
Non-fat, 29, 190
Low sodium, 23
Molded Salads; see Salads
Muffins; see Bread and Breads, Quick
Mushrooms; see Vegetables

NATIONAL CANNERS ASSOCIATION, 23, 33

National Food Guide
Foods and amounts, family use, 34
Restrictions for dieter, 34
Nutritional needs; see National Food Guide
Nuts, 20, 29, 352
Most low in saturated fat, 352

OLEIC ACID; see Appendix V, 356
Oleomargarine; see Fats
Onions; see Vegetables
Ornstein, George, M. D., 80

PALMITIC ACID; see Appendix V, 356
Pancakes and Waffles, 209-13
Parsley; see Herbs
Parsnips; see Vegetables
Peanut butter, hydrogenated, pure, 28
Peanut oil, 56
Peas; see Vegetables
Pectin, 270-71
Analysis, homemade, 271
Pepper; see Seasonings
Peppers; see Vegetables
Pie; see Desserts
Piper, Kathleen, 257
Pork; see Meats
Potatoes; see Vegetables
Pottages; see Soups
Pressure cooking, 82
Processed foods
Allowable, low in saturated fat, 30-31, 67-68, 306
Allowable, sodium-restricted, 23-25; see also Appendix II, 346
Commercial; see Appendix II
Analysis; see Appendix I, 328
Prout, Mrs. Frances, 213
Puddings; see Desserts

RABBIT, 123-24
Recipes
Adapting for saturated fat control, 32, 36, 38, 191
Adapting for sodium restriction, 36, 38, 191
Calculations approximate, 36; see also recipes
Rolls; see Bread and Breads, Quick
Rosemary; see Herbs

SAGE; see Herbs
Salad
Containers for lunch, 290-92
Dressings, 183-87
Restrictions for saturated fat control, 170
Restrictions for sodium restricted diet, 168-69
Salads, 168-82
Appetizer, 169; see also recipes
Dessert, 194; see also recipes
Hints in making, 170-71
How to make Tossed, 171-72; see also recipes

RECIPE INDEX